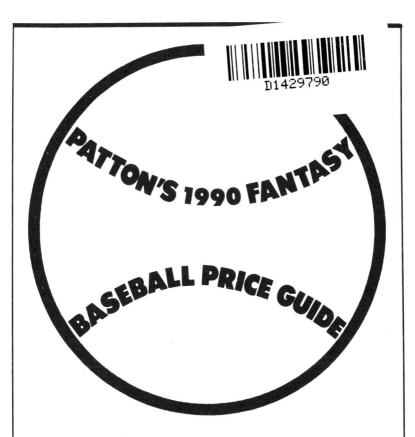

PATTON'S 1990 FANTASY

BASEBALL PRICE GUIDE

ALEX
PATTON

A FIRESIDE BOOK • PUBLISHED BY SIMON & SCHUSTER INC.
NEW YORK • LONDON • TORONTO • SYDNEY • TOKYO • SINGAPORE

FIRESIDE

Simon & Schuster Building
Rockefeller Center
1230 Avenue of the Americas
New York, New York 10020

Manufactured in the United States of America

10 9 8 7 6 5 4 3 2 1

ISBN 0-671-69605-X

"Rotisserie League Baseball" *is a trademark of Rotisserie League Baseball,* *Inc., and is used by permission. For further information about the Rotisserie* *League Baseball Association, which provides position eligibility lists, official* *24-man rosters mailed on Opening Day, a quarterly newsletter, access to a* *National Commissioner to interpret rules and settle disputes, a championship* *certificate for your pennant winner, and a bottle of Yoo-Hoo (if you live outside* *the Yoo-Hoo belt) to pour over your champion's head, write to the Rotisserie* *League Baseball Association, 211 West 92nd Street, Box 9, New York, NY* *10025, or call 212-496-8098.*

CONTENTS

Jerry Heath of Heath Research has once again been the single largest source of information on Rotisserie leagues. Thank you, Jerry; if everyone didn't know who you were already, I'd give the name and address of your stat service. (They're in the first chapter.)

Many individual players of the game have sent me information. I learn much more from this wealth of material than I'm able to show in the text, and at the very least I should be able to name my sources. I can, I hope; however, during the summer, a disaster befell my office. Humpty was finally put back together, but if pieces are missing, no one regrets it more than I do.

My informants were: Michael Belsky, Lloyd Benson, Terry Bucher, Jim Chaffin, Greg Churchill, Jack Cohen, Jack Curtis, Barry Cohen, Dave Disselbrett, Peter Donahoe, Don Egan, Mike Fengler, Ron Fox, Steve Fox, David Gates, Bruce Grabell, Richard Gurnett, Roger Hayes, Steve Hendrick, Joe David Jackson, Adam Jacobs, Karl Junkersfeld, Frank Kastelic, Ted Koch, Tom Leone, John Melting, Russ Miller, Roy Nelson, David Peregrim, Harold Rennett, Stuart Rosen, David Sebastian, Chris Stavros, Bob Vavra, Sam Watson, Kirk Whittaker, and Cary Wolfson.

Two other people were happy to help me with my scientific pursuits, and they did, but they felt that their names here would be counterproductive. This has become a serious business.

Okay. Why should I buy this book?

Because someone else might.

But I think you'll find a lot that's useful here. First, I have to ask you: Are you an old hand at this or is yours a new league?

New league.

Then I know you will. Rotisserie baseball distorts real baseball in two particularly blatant ways, which my prices reflect. Who would you say was the best player in baseball last year if I told you it was not Kevin Mitchell?

Hojo.

How'd you know that? You were supposed to say Will Clark. Second was Rickey Henderson. Who would you say the best pitcher was?

Saberhagen. Not even close.

In real baseball, you're right. In Rotisserie baseball, you're almost right. For the first time in the four years I've been ranking both leagues, a starting pitcher earned the most in one of the leagues, but overall it's again a relief pitcher. I've listed the 10 top Rotisserie MVPs last year— but since you're new to the game, you might want to list your own before you read it.

No, that's all right.

Sure? I mean, they're all good players, but there are some good players missing.
   I guess you're sure.

HOWARD JOHNSON $51	KEVIN MITCHELL $45
RICKEY HENDERSON $48	DENNIS ECKERSLEY $43
MARK DAVIS $48	ERIC DAVIS $43
BRET SABERHAGEN $45	WILL CLARK $40
JEFF RUSSELL $45	DOUG JONES $39

Who are the good players missing?

I don't know—Mike Scott? Wouldn't you expect to see him?

A 3.10 ERA in the National League is nothing to write home about.

You're right. Um . . . Fred McGriff?

Only 92 ribbies. Nine AL hitters had 100 or more.

You're right again. Um . . .
   Well, *normally* there are good players missing. You're at least supposed to be surprised to see Doug Jones in there.

Thirty-three saves, doesn't walk anybody.

Is all this stuff in your head?

I like baseball.

Well, you've come to the right place. Maybe.
   Let me ask you this: Three players on the list are repeats from 1988. One is a three-year repeat; he's also a four-year repeat.

Henderson?

Thank God. No. Eric Davis. The other two-year repeats are Eckersley and good old Doug.

It looks to me like Saberhagen was only tied for the best AL pitcher.

There are no ties. Opening up the spreadsheet, we get Saberhagen $45.36 and Russell $45.31.

2

So that's my price guide for this year? $45.36 for Bret Saberhagen?

It's what he earned last year. My prices are not projections and they're not predictions. Occasionally someone misses that point and goes into a draft bidding last year's values; the results are often embarrassing. All this book does is calculate the value of players' performances in the past.

The biggest shock you're going to have is that perfectly respectable starting pitchers in real baseball aren't worth ten cents in this game.

How?

How?

Calculate how?

Oh. For the technical explanation you're welcome to the chapter called "Notes for Masochists," but the theory is quite simple. When the season's over, I know the statistics of the average hitter and pitcher, and I can determine how much those statistics helped the typical Rotisserie team. With the standard salary cap of $260, I know what the average player was worth. All what's left is to compare the statistics of actual players to the average player to figure out what they were worth.

I don't ignore batting average, ERA, and ratio. If a player helps a team in these categories, he gains points as surely as he does with a home run or a win. However, in these qualitative categories, players can also lose points for a team. Hitters can lose in one category, pitchers in two. They can and they do and they must. By definition, the average hitter only contributes in three categories. The average pitcher contributes in even fewer, two. That hitter is bringing in three "good things," that pitcher two, so I make the average hitter worth 50 percent more than the average pitcher.

Even though pitchers still account for half the standings?

Yes.

Even though there are fewer pitchers than hitters?

Yes. I know it's a radical theory, but it's my theory. And in practice, it's not radical at all.

There are two "salaries" to consider, of course. Mine is the retrospective one, what players end up earning, the salary that Karl Marx would award them in October. The other is what we have to pay to own them. This is determined at auction in April. It's their market price, and believe me, people spend more on hitters than they do on pitchers.

More on each hitter?

Absolutely. Thanks to Jerry Heath of Heath Research, a stat service with dozens of leagues (3841 Croonenberg Way, Dept. P, Virginia Beach, VA), I've got the market prices from all over the country, and the rule of thumb is, the older the league, the more it spends on hitters.

All because of the pitchers' two bad things?

Essentially, yes, although there are other factors, which I'll get to.

The average price per player theoretically is $11.3 ($260 divided by 23). The Dirty Dozen, formed in 1988, spent $11.5 per hitter; South Main Street (1987) spent $11.8 per hitter; the Crabhouse League (1986), $12.2. On and on like that, until you get to the American Dreams, formed in 1981, spending $12.8 on each hitter. It's fascinating stuff. If you want the complete details, you should give Jerry a call at (804) 498-8197.

Hey, I'm surprised he doesn't have a 900 number.

Don't underestimate the difference between 12.8 and 11.5. On a per-player basis it's hard to see, although it is visible. For teams as a whole, it's more apparent, and for entire leagues it's obvious: Leagues that spend much less than $13 per hitter are spending much more than $8.67 per pitcher, and in the process are burning their money up, buying things that aren't there.

Like Danny Jackson, for instance?

Exhibit A. But you'll see much more sneaky exhibits at the end of this chapter—Fernando, Charlie Hough, people who got the job done in real baseball. It might be a good idea to take an inventory of a league first, however, to see how it's a closed system.

Jerry Heath runs up what he calls hypothetical final standings for his customers after the season: standings based on draft rosters with no changes. No trades, no activation of reserves, no waiver claims. From these standings of his it's easy to see exactly what each team bought in the draft. Here's the analysis of the PTL Clubs, a National League Rotisserie formed in Virginia in 1988:

4

PTL CLUBS
STATISTICS BOUGHT IN THE DRAFT

PITCHING	IP	W	S	ERA	RTO	SPENT	EARNED	+/−
COCKROACHES	1219	74	56	3.10	10.89	77	107	30
LOUNGE YANKS	1065	73	70	3.11	10.63	106	120	14
MUFFINS	1058	57	43	3.41	11.44	76	71	−5
CEPEDAS	1104	66	54	3.60	11.72	97	79	−18
LAST TRAIN	1114	59	9	3.34	11.00	42	52	10
CONSTRUCTION	1198	65	55	3.39	11.85	81	81	0
CLUB MED	1371	81	7	3.34	11.49	72	58	−14
ALWAYS 2ND	1483	78	25	3.27	11.04	82	79	−3
MEADOWS	1389	84	42	3.49	11.10	109	90	−19
SLUGS	1047	64	7	3.78	11.87	88	33	−55
LEAGUE	12049	700	370	3.38	11.29	830	772	−58

HITTING	AB	HR	RBI	SB	BA	SPENT	EARNED	+/−
COCKROACHES	5774	128	650	155	.263	174	209	35
LOUNGE YANKS	5162	142	662	144	.261	152	212	60
MUFFINS	5205	131	599	170	.266	182	211	29
CEPEDAS	5660	114	646	146	.262	160	198	38
LAST TRAIN	5728	128	610	138	.254	211	191	−20
CONSTRUCTION	5442	111	643	134	.275	175	201	26
CLUB MED	4328	125	547	137	.261	188	185	−3
ALWAYS 2ND	4779	120	510	62	.228	174	130	−44
MEADOWS	4281	52	406	107	.249	145	112	−33
SLUGS	4791	101	576	139	.247	172	168	−4
LEAGUE	51150	1152	5849	1332	.257	1733	1817	84

OVERALL	SPENT	EARNED	+/−	H.F.S.* PTS	FINAL STANDINGS	PTS
COCKROACHES	251	316	65	68.5	LOUNGE YANKS	70.0
LOUNGE YANKS	258	332	74	68.0	COCKROACHES	69.0
MUFFINS	258	282	24	49.0	CEPEDAS	48.5
CEPEDAS	257	276	19	44.0	LAST TRAIN	44.5
LAST TRAIN	253	243	−10	42.5	CONSTRUCTION	41.0
CONSTRUCTION	256	282	26	42.0	MUFFINS	41.0
CLUB MED	260	244	−16	38.5	ALWAYS 2ND	34.0
ALWAYS 2ND	256	209	−47	36.0	CLUB MED	32.5
MEADOWS	254	203	−51	31.0	MEADOWS	31.0
SLUGS	260	202	−58	20.5	SLUGS	28.5
LEAGUE	2563	2589	26			

*hypothetical final standings

Under "spent" we have the total of actual salaries, or market prices, for each team's pitchers and hitters. Notice the wide variation: from $42 to $109 on pitching.

Under "earned" is the Patton $ value of the statistics the players produced. Even wider fluctuations: from $33 all the way to $120 in pitching. Far and away the best staff belongs to the Lounge Yanks, who spent the second highest amount on pitching. However, between the Meadows and the Last Train, who did a better job?

Last Train, I say. The Meadows' pitchers weren't bad, but they sure didn't deliver as they were supposed to.

Name a few of their stiffs.

Bruce Hurst $25, Pascual Perez $15, Bob Ojeda $12—they weren't stiffs at all, just not worth those prices.

The 10 teams combined spent $830, or $9.22 per pitcher, for a total loss of $58.

The hitters get it back.

No they don't. They more than get it back. How's that? How can a whole league turn a profit?

Good question.

I mean, is this a closed system or not?

How did you spot that? Are you an accountant?

But you're right; the books have to balance—the players earn exactly what you spend on them—so if the pitchers lose a certain amount, the hitters gain it. There are two reasons why they don't for the PTL Clubs. The formulas I use are based on a composite of draft rosters; they will be accurate to the extent that a given league conforms to that profile. In essence, if your league has a sharper draft than the average league, it will turn a slight profit, but it's extremely slight. A formula tailored specifically to the PTL Clubs would change a few decimals and not a single player value would change.

The second variable is how much money leagues actually spend. I base my prices on $2600 for NLRs (National League Rotisseries) and $3120 for ALRs. The PTL Clubs didn't use $37 of their budget. By underspending it looks like they turned a profit, whereas in fact they were $11 short of the average league. The important thing, though, is that prices for them will be 99.5% (2589/2600) accurate.

How could the Cockroaches only spend $251?

I really don't know. As you can see, Heath has them ahead of the Lounge Yanks by half a point if no changes occur after the draft, and

6

then virtually no changes occur. Neither team, I know from the Heath rosters, made a trade all year. The Lounge Yanks picked up a little offense from a few stabs at its reserve list or waivers and gained two points. The Cockroaches gained half a point in the same halfhearted way, to come in second by one point.

Me, I'd go—I will go crazy if that happens. I'd pound the waivers every week.

Me, too. The only team that was at all aggressive in this league was the Slugs, with four trades, and it didn't quite get them out of last. But the team that I feel for is the Muffins. They had a good draft, both by Heath's reckoning and Patton $. Their long suit was stolen bases: 15 more than the second-best team, a nice surplus. So they did the right thing, they dealt it, and here's how it looked in stolen bases at the end:

COCKROACHES	163
LOUNGE YANKS	161
SLUGS	159
MUFFINS	157

The next team had 141.

And I see the Muffins ended up tied for fifth, instead of third.

Yes. If you can buy over $275 in the draft, you've got a good shot at finishing in the money. If you can buy over $300, you're a contender for first.

Unless someone else buys $400.

I've never seen that happen. You'd need a lot of cooperation from the bottom. Here you see three teams—Always 2nd, the Meadows, and the Slugs—that are hopelessly out of it after the draft, but five teams are in a scuffle for third and fourth.

They can't trade their way into contention with the two big guys?

No harm in trying—in fact, the whole fun is to try; I don't know why you would just sit there—but it seldom works. Luckily, we can't know it at the time, but our fates are pretty well sealed at the draft.

What was your draft team worth?

$284.

Where'd you finish?

Third.

How much you make?

We don't play for money.

Who are you kidding?

You. I don't know you.

Well, did you make any trades?

Four, ranging from neutral to terrible. I had a fortunate reserve list and picked up some good scrubs on waivers. I basically finished where I belonged, and even so missed second on the last day because Mike Heath broke early for third in a bunt situation, a rookie pitcher threw the ball away, and Heath was credited with a steal. I was sitting there in Yankee Stadium with the fellow who owned Heath—his team was the second-place team—and he hooted and I hollered. It was a great season.

Let's just hope the idiots don't screw up this one.

Do you mind if we don't talk about that?

In the player charts you'll find everyone that anyone spent a nickel on, right down to Willie Upshaw. Asterisks indicate players who were not available at the start of the season.

The first number in boldface is what the player earned last year in Patton $. The next five columns are the market prices for five different start-up leagues, designated by their initials. The "average salary" is obviously the average of these five, and the "profit or loss" is determined by subtracting the average salary from the player's earnings—that is, market prices from Patton $.

The advantage of using start-up leagues only is that almost all established leagues allow owners to freeze at least a few underpriced players, which affects all prices, as I'll discuss. The disadvantage would seem to be that start-up leagues—no offense—don't know what they're doing.

No problem.

I picked the five leagues carefully from the possibilities supplied by Jerry Heath, and as veteran owners look over the prices, I think they'll agree that these rookie owners knew more than we did when we were rookies. I was impressed.

There are two advantages, it seems to me, of listing specific market prices instead of just the average, or the average and the high and low. Number one, you see the evidence. I always like to see it.

Number two, the five prices contain their own drama—I almost said music: the strange harmony on the subject of Canseco, the wild adulation of Clemens, the foreboding gloom about Dale Murphy, the disarray caused by Mitch Williams. There are all sorts of patterns here, or not here; road signs telling us, if we can read them, who might be available this year at a good price.

I see you glancing ahead—what do you think?

Huh? Holy mother of God, look what one team spent on Rickey! What did you say?

EARNINGS AND MARKET PRICES FOR NL HITTERS

	EARNED 1989	MARKET PRICES					AVG. SAL.	PROFIT OR LOSS
		PEW	FAI	CFL	PNC	LGV		
ALDRETE, MIKE	1	4	9	1	3	4	4	−3
ALOMAR, ROBERTO	33	17	11	14	26	11	16	17
ANDERSON, DAVE	2	1			1	1	1	1
ASHBY, ALAN	−1	3	5	1	5	2	3	−4
BASS, KEVIN	16	21	25	22	27	16	22	−6
BELL, JAY	6				5	2	4	3
BELLIARD, RAFAEL	1							
BENEDICT, BRUCE	−2	1					1	−3
BENZINGER, TODD	17	6	14	12	10	5	9	8
BERROA, GERONIMO	2	2		1		1	1	1
BERRYHILL, DAMON	8	12	25	6	4	7	11	−3
BIGGIO, CRAIG	22	1	5	4	1	2	3	19
BLAUSER, JEFF	15	15	8		7	2	8	7
BONDS, BARRY	28	36	24	22	36	31	30	−2
BONILLA, BOBBY	30	33	30	20	41	24	30	0
BREAM, SID	0	12	13	8	8	10	10	−10
BROOKS, HUBIE	20	25	17	22	27	21	22	−2
BRUNANSKY, TOM	20	27	22	22	9	26	21	−1
BUTLER, BRETT	21	27	22	17	7	15	18	3
CAMINITI, KEN	15	3	1	3	10	1	4	11

	EARNED 1989	MARKET PRICES					AVG. SAL.	PROFIT OR LOSS
		PEW	FAI	CFL	PNC	LGV		
CANGELOSI, JOHN	4		1				1	3
CARREON, MARK	8					1	1	7
CARTER, GARY	0	15	13	12	8	11	12	−12
CLARK, JACK	25	30	15	27	36	14	24	1
CLARK, WILL	40	42	38	45	36	37	40	0
COLEMAN, VINCE	29	39	31	39	40	27	35	−6
COLLINS, DAVE	1				1		1	0
DANIELS, KAL	7	32	29	36	38	27	32	−25
DAULTON, DARREN	5	1		1	1	1	1	4
DAVIS, ERIC	40	46	38	43	47	39	43	−3
DAVIS, GLENN	31	36	30	31	27	30	31	0
DAVIS, JODY	−1	25	9	13	10	7	13	−14
DAVIS, MIKE	7	1	4	1		1	2	5
DAWSON, ANDRE	23	31	24	31	32	30	30	−7
DEMPSEY, RICK	1	1	4		1	2	2	−1
DERNIER, BOB	−1	3	4	1	8	2	4	−5
DIAZ, BO	0	3	7	5		5	5	−5
DISTEFANO, BENNY	3				1	1	1	2
DORAN, BILL	15	15	15	20	8	18	15	0
DUNCAN, MARIO	7	2	1			1	1	6
DUNSTON, SHAWON	22	26	19	19	18	24	21	1
DYKSTRA, LENNY	16	9	14	16	5	17	12	4
ELSTER, KEVIN	10	6	14	8	20	11	12	−2
EVANS, DARRELL	7	3	3	1			2	5
FITZGERALD, MIKE	8	1	2	1	1		1	7
FLANNERY, TIM	1	1	2	1	2	2	2	−1
FOLEY, TOM	6	1	11	1	4	8	5	1
FORD, CURT	3			1			1	2
GALARRAGA, ANDRES	27	34	32	45	40	37	38	−11
GANT, RON	5	23	21	19	30	21	23	−18
GARCIA, DAMASO	6		3		2		3	4
GIBSON, KIRK	9	28	24	26	29	22	26	−17
GIRARDI, JOE	3		1	1	1		1	2
GONZALES, JOSE*	8							
GRACE, MARK	29	12	23	22	15	16	18	11
GREGG, TOMMY	6	6		3	1	1	3	3
GRIFFEY, KEN SR.	10		1	1	2	1	1	9
GRIFFIN, ALFREDO	6	3	8	3	1	2	3	3
GRISSOM, MARQUIS	1							
GROSS, GREG	−1			3			3	−4

	EARNED 1989	MARKET PRICES					AVG. SAL.	PROFIT OR LOSS
		PEW	FAI	CFL	PNC	LGV		
GUERRERO, PEDRO	32	19	30	21	20	12	20	12
GWYNN, CHRIS	1					1	1	0
GWYNN, TONY	37	42	31	33	40	24	34	3
HALL, ALBERT	1		1				1	0
HAMILTON, JEFF	11	1	1		1	2	1	10
HARRIS, LENNY	8	1			1		1	7
HATCHER, BILLY	14	12	9	17	22	15	15	−1
HATCHER, MICKEY	7	1	3	1	1	1	1	6
HAYES, CHARLIE*	11							
HAYES, VON	34	20	24	27	8	24	21	13
HERNANDEZ, KEITH	3	16	16	10	10	17	14	−11
HERR, TOM	14	13	5	1	5	6	6	8
HUDLER, REX	10	2	11	11	5	10	8	2
JACKSON, DARRIN	3	1	7	1	1	1	2	1
JAMES, CHRIS	15	10	20	16	23	6	15	0
JAMES, DION	2		5	4	2	1	3	−1
JEFFERIES, GREGG	21	20	25	17	31	25	24	−3
JELTZ, STEVE	6							
JOHNSON, HOWARD	51	13	22	28	22	25	22	29
JOHNSON, WALLACE	4					1	1	3
JONES, RON	2	4	14	1	5	3	5	−3
JONES, TIM	2	1					1	1
JONES, TRACY	0	3	5	5	5	5	5	−5
JORDAN, RICKY	21	18	15	11	3	15	12	9
KENNEDY, TERRY	6	5	2	1	3	2	3	3
KING, JEFF*	3							
KRUK, JOHN	15	7	18	22	8	2	11	4
LAKE, STEVE	3	1		7		1	3	0
LARKIN, BARRY	18	31	28	31	32	25	29	−11
LAVALLIERE, MIKE	7	4	12	6	3	10	7	0
LAW, VANCE	7	10	11	4	33	25	17	−10
LIND, JOSE	9	9	7	12	13	12	11	−2
LINDEMAN, JIM	−2		1				1	−3
LITTON, GREG*	4							
LOMBARDOZZI, STEVE	0					3	3	−3
LYONS, BARRY	4		4	2		1	2	2
MCCLENDON, LLOYD	15							
MCDOWELL, ODDIBE*	16							
MCGEE, WILLIE	6	25	20	21	37	31	27	−21
MCGRIFF, TERRY	0				2		2	−2

	EARNED 1989	MARKET PRICES					AVG. SAL.	PROFIT OR LOSS
		PEW	FAI	CFL	PNC	LGV		
MCREYNOLDS, KEVIN	29	39	34	40	34	36	37	−8
MAGADAN, DAVE	11	8	8	1		2	5	6
MALDONADO, CANDY	7	11	9	14	13	14	12	−5
MANWARING, KIRT	0	1	5	2		5	3	−3
MARSHALL, MIKE	12	25	24	23	15	25	22	−10
MARTINEZ, CARMELO	5	4	9	3	2	6	5	0
MARTINEZ, DAVE	15	4	6	1	1	1	3	12
MAZZILLI, LEE	2	2	1		1		1	1
MITCHELL, KEVIN	45	21	34	28	13	30	25	20
MORRIS, JOHN	3	1		4			3	1
MURPHY, DALE	17	30	17	25	16	18	21	−4
MURPHY, DWAYNE	6			3			3	3
MURRAY, EDDIE	22	24	26	28	30	8	23	−1
NIXON, DONNELL	7		3	1	1		2	5
NIXON, OTIS	14	10	5	9	17	8	10	4
OBERKFELL, KEN	4	3		2	1	1	2	2
OESTER, RON	2	2	12	1	2	1	4	−2
O'NEILL, PAUL	27	23	14	25	5	20	17	10
OQUENDO, JOSE	13	6	8	17	4	12	9	4
ORTIZ, JUNIOR	2	3	1	1		4	2	0
OWEN, SPIKE	7	1	5	4	7	7	5	2
PAGLIARULO, MIKE*	1							
PAGNOZZI, TOM	−2		3		2		3	−5
PARENT, MARK	4							
PENA, TONY	9	12	13	9	2	11	9	0
PENDLETON, TERRY	20	9	10	7	25	4	11	9
PERRY, GERALD	8	36	25	20	35	31	29	−21
PUHL, TERRY	8	12	7	5	1	5	6	2
QUINONES, LUIS*	10							
QUINONES, REY*	2							
RAINES, TIM	32	35	25	30	41	40	34	−2
RAMIREZ, RAFAEL	9	9	8	1	8	7	7	2
RAMOS, DOMINGO	4							
RANDOLPH, WILLIE	12	11	8	8	2	13	8	4
READY, RANDY	9	4	6	17	1	3	6	3
REDUS, GARY	19	3	6	1	1	3	3	16
REED, JEFF	2			1		3	2	0
REYNOLDS, CRAIG	0	1		1	5		2	−2
REYNOLDS, RJ	19	4	16	1	9	3	7	12
RILES, ERNEST	10	1	3	3	2	4	3	7

	EARNED 1989	PEW	FAI	CFL	PNC	LGV	AVG. SAL.	PROFIT OR LOSS
ROBERTS, BIP	17							
ROOMES, ROLANDO*	13							
RUSSELL, JOHN	−1	1		1	1		1	−2
SABO, CHRIS	12	21	17	19	27	23	21	−9
SALAZAR, LUIS	11	3	5	7	1	3	4	7
SAMUEL, JUAN	24	21	17	19		22	20	4
SANDBERG, RYNE	35	39	26	21	29	23	28	7
SANTIAGO, BENITO	17	25	29	26	24	17	24	−7
SANTOVENIA, NELSON	7	3	9	3	1	11	5	2
SASSER, MACKEY	5	1	1	2	1	3	2	3
SCHMIDT, MIKE	4	18	17	24	35	17	22	−18
SCIOSCIA, MIKE	10	6	7	9	5	4	6	4
SHELBY, JOHN	−1	7	8	9	5	8	7	−8
SMITH, DWIGHT*	21							
SMITH, LONNIE	37	15	3	1	2	4	5	32
SMITH, OZZIE	21	19	13	22	20	14	18	3
SPEIER, CHRIS	0	1		1		1	1	−1
STRAWBERRY, DARRYL	24	45	41	39	49	40	43	−19
STUBBS, FRANKLIN	6	3	6	1	1	2	3	3
TEMPLETON, GARRY	8	4	1	1	3	8	3	5
TEUFEL, TIM	3	2	3	4	1	4	3	0
THOMAS, ANDRES	8	13	14	17	8	4	11	−3
THOMPSON, MILT	26	3	4	1	1	2	2	24
THOMPSON, ROBBY	15	11	11	7	3	2	7	8
THON, DICKIE	19	10	3	6	8	2	6	13
TREADWAY, JEFF	13		1	1	1		1	12
TREVINO, ALEX	4	1			2	1	1	3
TRILLO, MANNY	−1		1		1		1	−2
URIBE, JOSE	2	2	5	10	7	4	6	−4
VAN SLYKE, ANDY	15	46	34	39	44	37	40	−25
VARSHO, GARY	0		1		1		1	−1
WALLACH, TIM	20	14	15	14	21	13	15	5
WALLING, DENNY	3	1	2		1		1	2
WALTON, JEROME	22	11	1	12	1	3	6	16
WEBSTER, MITCH	9	9	8	14	3	5	8	1
WILKERSON, CURTIS	3	3	5	1	3	1	3	0
WILLIAMS, MATT	11	2	6	2	3	14	5	6
WILSON, GLENN	15	3	10	12	3	2	6	9
WILSON, MOOKIE	3	14	9	15	14	16	14	−11
WINNINGHAM, HERM	8	1	1	1	1	1	1	7

	EARNED 1989	MARKET PRICES					AVG. SAL.	PROFIT OR LOSS
		PEW	FAI	CFL	PNC	LGV		
WYNNE, MARVELL	9	5	8	5	1	3	4	5
YELDING, ERIC	5				2		2	3
YOUNG, GERALD	14	26	16	30	10	21	21	−7
YOUNGBLOOD, JOEL	2		1				1	1
ZEILE, TODD*	1							

EARNINGS AND MARKET PRICES FOR NL PITCHERS

	EARNED 1989	MARKET PRICES					AVG. SAL.	PROFIT OR LOSS
		PEW	FAI	CFL	PNC	LGV		
AASE, DON	0	2	6	5	2	9	5	−5
ACKER, JIM	8	1					1	7
AGOSTO, JUAN	3	5	7	14	9	4	8	−5
AGUILERA, RICK	14		4	1	5	2	3	11
ALVAREZ, JOSE	4	3			1		2	2
ANDERSEN, LARRY	16			1	1		1	15
ASSENMACHER, PAUL	−1	1	5	1	1	2	2	−3
BAIR, DOUG*	6							
BEDROSIAN, STEVE	25	22	13	9	26	31	20	5
BELCHER, TIM	20	21	7	5	10	16	12	8
BENES, ANDY*	4							
BIELECKI, MIKE	14			1			1	13
BOEVER, JOE	17	18	14	14	13	4	13	4
BOOKER, GREG	−1				1		1	−2
BROWNING, TOM	12	19	15	11	17	28	18	−6
BURKE, TIM	35	6	12	3	24	15	12	23
CARMAN, DON	−16	1	5	1	1	4	2	−18
CARPENTER, CRIS	1	1	1	1		10	3	−2
CHARLTON, NORM	10							
CLANCY, JIM	−11	2	7	12	1	2	5	−16
CLARY, MARTY*	4							
COMBS, PAT*	6							
CONE, DAVID	12	28	25	29	37	16	27	−15

| | EARNED 1989 | MARKET PRICES | | | | | AVG. SAL. | PROFIT OR LOSS |
		PEW	FAI	CFL	PNC	LGV		
COOK, DENNIS*	4							
COSTELLO, JOHN	8		1		1		1	7
CREWS, TIM	-2		1	1	1	1	1	-3
DARLING, RON	6	26	16	24	29	27	24	-18
DARWIN, DANNY	23	1	2			10	4	19
DAVIS, MARK	48	30	26	21	31	19	25	23
DAYLEY, KEN	14	2	3	1	2	12	4	10
DELEON, JOSE	23	6	12	3	7	13	8	15
DESHAIES, JIM	18	7	8	2	4	19	8	10
DIBBLE, ROB	18	1	2	6	1	3	3	15
DIPINO, FRANK	13	3				1	2	11
DOWNS, KELLY	-2	5	15	18	8	14	12	-14
DRABEK, DOUG	18	13	12	24	3	23	15	3
DRAVECKY, DOUG*	2							
DUNNE, MIKE	-4	3	13	1		12	7	-11
EAVE, GARY*	3							
FERNANDEZ, SID	21	10	15	19	5	16	13	8
FISHER, BRIAN	-5		3				3	-8
FORSCH, BOB	-13	2	1	6	1		3	-16
FRANCO, JOHN	27	35	33	45	45	43	40	-13
GARDNER, MARK*	-2							
GARRELTS, SCOTT	25	7	9	9	1	5	6	19
GLAVINE, TOM	12	14	6	3	3		7	6
GOODEN, DWIGHT	11	37	25	38	38	31	34	-23
GOSSAGE, GOOSE	5							
GOTT, JIM	0	13	1	1	32	17	13	-13
GRANT, MARK	9	1		11		1	4	5
GRIMSLEY, JASON*	-4							
GROSS, KEVIN	-3	5	16	11	1	16	10	-13
HAMMAKER, ATLEE	2	2	5	1		13	5	-3
HARRIS, GENE	-1				1		1	-2
HARRIS, GREG A.	-1			3			3	-4
HARRIS, GREG W.	16	1	8		1	1	3	13
HEATON, NEAL	6	1	3				2	4
HEINKEL, DON*	-5							
HERSHISER, OREL	22	33	32	36	44	32	35	-13
HESKETH, JOE	-2	5	7	8	4	7	6	-8
HILL, KEN*	-5							
HOLMAN, BRIAN	-3	1	4	1	1		2	-5
HORTON, RICKEY	-7	2	1	4		2	2	-9

	EARNED 1989	MARKET PRICES					AVG. SAL.	PROFIT OR LOSS
		PEW	FAI	CFL	PNC	LGV		
HOWELL, JAY	35		10	10	10	15	11	24
HOWELL, KEN	10	16			1	2	6	4
HURST, BRUCE	20	16	12	30	24	22	21	−1
JACKSON, DANNY	−12	32	25	22	36	27	28	−40
JOHNSON, RANDY	−7	3	5	15	3	15	8	−15
KILGUS, PAUL	−5		5	1	1	2	2	−7
KIPPER, BOB	10				1		1	9
KNEPPER, BOB	−16	10	6	4	3	12	7	−23
KRUKOW, MIKE	2	5		1			3	−1
LACOSS, MIKE	9	1	7	1	10	13	6	3
LANCASTER, LES*	18							
LANDRUM, BILL	31			1			1	30
LANGSTON, MARK*	12							
LEACH, TERRY	0	5	3	1	2	11	4	−4
LEARY, TIM	2	18	19	19	9	15	16	−14
LEFFERTS, CRAIG	24	4	8	1	2	14	6	18
LEIPER, DAVE	−7		6		1		4	−11
LILLIQUIST, DEREK	−3	4				1	3	−6
MCDOWELL, ROGER	26	5	12	14	7	16	11	15
MCGAFFIGAN, ANDY	−4	3	8	3	6	3	5	−9
MCWILLIAMS, LARRY	−6							
MADDUX, GREG	15	11	16	18	7	12	13	2
MADDUX, MIKE	−4			1	1		1	−5
MADRID, ALEX*	−4							
MAGRANE, JOE	16	12	8	3	4	10	7	9
MAHLER, RICK	0	4	10	1		2	4	−4
MARTINEZ, DENNIS	15	9	14	3	14	9	10	5
MARTINEZ, RAMON*	6							
MATHEWS, GREG	−	1					1	−1
MORGAN, MIKE	15							
MULHOLLAND, TERRY	−9							
MUSSELMAN, JEFF*	1							
MYERS, RANDY	28	27	18	40	45	42	34	−6
OJEDA, BOB	5	7	12	12	21	18	14	−9
ONTIVEROS, STEVE	−1	1	3	1			2	−3
PARRETT, JEFF	14	6	6	7	1	3	5	9
PATTERSON, KEN*	4							
PENA, ALEJANDRO	13	5	12	2	1	15	7	6
PEREZ, PASCUAL	11	14	14	14	8	19	14	−3
PERRY, PAT	4							

	EARNED 1989	MARKET PRICES					AVG. SAL.	PROFIT OR LOSS
		PEW	FAI	CFL	PNC	LGV		
PICO, JEFF	−1							
PORTUGAL, MARK*	9							
POWER, TED*	5							
PRICE, JOE	−3				1	1	1	−4
PULEO, CHARLIE	−2					1	1	−3
QUISENBERRY, DAN	10		2		4		3	7
RASMUSSEN, DENNIS	−5	8	11	19	7	15	12	−17
REUSCHEL, RICK	17	12	8	15	6	10	10	7
RHODEN, RICK	−7	2		5	3	3	3	−10
RIJO, JOSE	5	11	10	12	9	21	13	−8
ROBINSON, DON	13	5	11	2	5	7	6	7
ROBINSON, JEFF	−6	7	11	7	10	5	8	−14
ROBINSON, RON*	3							
RUFFIN, BRUCE	−12		1		1		1	−13
SANDERSON, SCOTT	4				1	1	1	3
SCHIRALDI, CALVIN	5	2	2	5	1	3	3	2
SCOTT, MIKE	24	23	20	32	28	23	25	−1
SCUDDER, SCOTT*	−6							
SEBRA, BOB*	−6							
SHOW, ERIC	−1	13	9	18	15	4	12	−13
SMILEY, JOHN	18	7	7	16	4	16	10	8
SMITH, BRYN	18	10	7	3	4	5	6	12
SMITH, DAVE	25	7	15	11	38	13	17	8
SMITH, PETE	−8	3	6	1	1	1	2	−10
SMITH, ZANE	0	3	5	6	2	10	5	−5
SMOLTZ, JOHN	16	8	1	1	5	1	3	13
STANTON, MIKE*	9							
SUTCLIFFE, RICK	12	6	11	11	20	4	10	2
TEKULVE, KENT	−5			1	1	1	1	−6
TERRELL, WALT	0	2	7	2		2	3	−3
TERRY, SCOTT	6	7	8	1	2	17	7	−1
TUDOR, JOHN	−1	11	5	2		1	5	−6
VALENZUELA, F.	0	7	2	1	6	3	4	−4
VIOLA, FRANK*	5							
WALK, BOB	−3	5	6	4	8	15	8	−11
WEST, DAVID*	−5							
WETTELAND, JOHN*	6							
WHITSON, ED	23	2	9	10	11	5	7	16
WILLIAMS, MITCH	30	6	9	28	18	25	17	13
WILSON, STEVE*	2							

	EARNED	MARKET PRICES					AVG.	PROFIT
	1989	PEW	FAI	CFL	PNC	LGV	SAL.	OR LOSS
WORRELL, TODD	**19**	36	19	17	39	29	28	**−9**
YOUMANS, FLOYD	**−7**	1	11	7	3	3	5	**−12**

EARNINGS AND MARKET PRICES FOR AL HITTERS

	EARNED	MARKET PRICES					AVG.	PROFIT
	1989	GOL	HQL	MLB	WEB	SCR	SAL.	OR LOSS
AGUAYO, LUIS	**−1**	1	1			2	1	**−2**
ALLANSON, ANDY	**2**	4	13	4	16	5	8	**−6**
ANDERSON, BRADY	**6**	6	4	2	5	5	4	**2**
ARMAS, TONY	**8**		5	3	1	1	3	**6**
BACKMAN, WALLY	**1**	9	15	24	6	7	12	**−11**
BAINES, HAROLD	**21**	20	10	4	9	10	11	**10**
BALBONI, STEVE	**13**	11	5	3	10	9	8	**5**
BARFIELD, JESSE	**17**	20	18	11	23	24	19	**−2**
BARRETT, MARTY	**5**	10	14	9	9	11	11	**−6**
BEAN, BILLY	**−1**		1	1			1	**−2**
BELL, BUDDY	**−1**	1			2	1	1	**−2**
BELL, GEORGE	**27**	31	33	32	30	33	32	**−5**
BELLE, JOEY*	**6**							
BERGMAN, DAVE	**8**	6	1	1	4	3	3	**5**
BICHETTE, DANTE	**2**	2		2	1		2	**0**
BLANKENSHIP, LANCE*	**2**							
BOGGS, WADE	**19**	33	33	42	32	33	35	**−16**
BOONE, BOB	**8**	6	5	6	3	8	6	**2**
BORDERS, PAT	**5**	1	1	1	2	2	1	**4**
BOSTON, DARYL	**7**	3	6	1		1	3	**4**
BRADLEY, PHIL	**22**	8	16	10	13	11	12	**10**
BRADLEY, SCOTT	**7**	4	4	2	2	1	3	**4**
BRAGGS, GLENN	**20**	14	16	14	11	8	13	**7**
BRANTLEY, MICKEY	**2**	10	8	3	10	11	8	**−6**
BRENLY, BOB	**−1**		1	3	2		2	**−3**

	EARNED 1989	MARKET PRICES					AVG. SAL.	PROFIT OR LOSS
		GOL	HQL	MLB	WEB	SCR		
BRETT, GEORGE	23	33	34	38	33	30	34	−11
BRILEY, GREG	17							
BROCK, GREG	14	1	1	5	6	3	3	11
BROOKENS, TOM	2	1	6	1	3	5	3	−1
BROWER, BOB	2							
BROWN, CHRIS	−1	2	10	2	5	8	5	−6
BROWNE, JERRY	19	1	6	10	4	2	5	14
BRUMLEY, MIKE	2		2	1			2	1
BUCKNER, BILL	1			1	1	3	2	−1
BUECHELE, STEVE	11	9	8	22	14	9	12	−1
BUHNER, JAY	9			1			1	8
BURKS, ELLIS	26	38	32	38	37	34	36	−10
BUSH, RANDY	15	4	7	2	13		7	9
CALDERON, IVAN	23	13	7	3	7	5	7	16
CANSECO, JOSE	17	45	46	42	46	43	44	−27
CARTER, JOE	31	36	40	49	39	37	40	−9
CASTILLO, CARMEN	9	3	4	1		2	3	7
CERONE, RICK	6	1	1	4		1	2	4
CLARK, DAVE	5	3	1	1		1	2	4
COLES, DARNELL	12	11	13	4	5	5	8	4
COTTO, HENRY	13	1	3	2	4	3	3	10
DAVIS, ALVIN	26	22	24	12	30	16	21	5
DAVIS, CHILI	23	18	19	12	12	18	16	7
DEER, ROB	14	23	22	6	20	16	17	−3
DEVEREAUX, MIKE	19	1	3		1		2	17
DIAZ, MARIO	1	5	1		2	3	3	−2
DOWNING, BRIAN	16	11	13	5	7	8	9	7
DUCEY, ROB	1			15	7	1	8	−7
DWYER, JIM	8			2		1	2	7
EISENREICH, JIM	27		1		4	3	3	24
ENGLE, DAVE	1	1			2		2	−1
ESASKY, NICK	29	15	11	3	11	15	11	18
ESPINOZA, ALVARO	8	2			1		2	7
ESPY, CECIL	25	12	13	4	10	10	10	15
EVANS, DWIGHT	25	27	22	17	20	19	21	4
FELDER, MIKE	14					2	2	12
FELIX, JUNIOR*	17							
FERMIN, FELIX	2		7	1	2		3	−1
FERNANDEZ, TONY	21	5	19	31	10	24	18	3
FINLEY, STEVE	11	1		1	2	1	1	10

	EARNED 1989	MARKET PRICES					AVG. SAL.	PROFIT OR LOSS
		GOL	HQL	MLB	WEB	SCR		
FISK, CARLTON	17	20	15	11	14	14	15	2
FLETCHER, SCOTT	5	3	11	4	9	10	7	-2
FRANCO, JULIO	33	27	24	32	21	23	25	8
FRANCONA, TERRY	3	1	3	3			2	1
GAETTI, GARY	19	37	31	40	28	31	33	-14
GAGNE, GREG	16	15	5	10	13	16	12	4
GALLAGHER, DAVE	8	4	3	1	8	2	4	4
GALLEGO, MIKE	7				1	1	1	6
GANTNER, JIM	14	10	13	8	6	6	9	5
GEDMAN, RICH	0	8	10	2	5	14	8	-8
GEREN, BOB*	9							
GLADDEN, DAN	23	19	21	12	16	12	16	7
GONZALES, RENE	3		1				1	2
GREENWELL, MIKE	30	36	36	42	45	36	39	-9
GRIFFEY, KEN JR.	22	10	18	9	21	16	15	7
GRUBER, KELLY	25	29	16	31	30	11	23	2
GUILLEN, OZZIE	22	14	13	7	8	11	11	11
HALL, MEL	14	6	9	8	8	7	8	6
HARPER, BRIAN	17	2	3	1	1	1	2	15
HASSEY, RON	3	7	16	2	5	4	7	-4
HEATH, MIKE	13	1	2	1	1	2	1	12
HEEP, DANNY	11	3					3	8
HENDERSON, DAVE	18	24	19	27	16	13	20	-2
HENDERSON, RICKEY	48	42	50	70	56	51	54	-6
HILL, DONNIE	-				5		5	-5
HILL, GLENALLEN*	3							
HOFFMAN, GLENN	-1		2				2	-3
HORN, SAM	-1	1		1	1	1	1	-2
HOWELL, JACK	11	9	14	21	7	10	12	-1
HRBEK, KENT	23	39	28	47	41	34	38	-15
HUBBARD, GLENN	1	4	3	3	3	5	4	-3
HULETT, TIM*	4							
INCAVIGLIA, PETE	18	16	16	7	10	13	12	6
JACKSON, BO	38	34	31	25	30	22	28	10
JACOBY, BROOK	15	11	19	5	13	7	11	4
JAMES, DION*	8							
JAVIER, STAN	8	5	7	3	11	2	6	2
JEFFERSON, STANLEY	8	1	1	1		1	1	7
JOHNSON, LANCE*	11							
JONES, TRACY*	5							

| | EARNED 1989 | MARKET PRICES | | | | | AVG. SAL. | PROFIT OR LOSS |
		GOL	HQL	MLB	WEB	SCR		
JOSE, FELIX	−1		1	3			2	−3
JOYNER, WALLY	21	22	28	30	20	24	25	−4
KARKOVICE, RON	4							
KELLY, ROBERTO	30	11	10		4	1	7	24
KINGERY, MIKE	1			1			1	0
KITTLE, RON	11	5	4	2	3	5	4	7
KOMMINSK, BRAD*	10							
KREUTER, CHAD	−1	6	2	3	1	3	3	−4
KUNKEL, JEFF	9			1			1	8
KUTCHER, RANDY*	3							
LANSFORD, CARNEY	34	13	13	26	15	18	17	17
LARKIN, GENE	11	15	7	1	7	5	7	4
LAUDNER, TIM	4	12	17	6	5	12	10	−6
LAWLESS, TIM	5	1					1	4
LEACH, RICK	5	3		1	1	2	2	3
LEE, MANNY	7	12	12	7	10	6	9	−2
LEMON, CHET	6	7	8	4	6	9	7	−1
LEONARD, JEFFREY	23	12	17	12	5	6	10	13
LIRIANO, NELSON	16	3	6	3	3	3	4	12
LOVULLO, TOREY	−3	9	5	1	10	6	6	−9
LYNN, FRED	9	11	11	7	8	12	10	−1
LYONS, STEVE	11	4	3	1	5	1	3	8
MCDOWELL, ODDIBE	7	11	17	25	10	11	15	−8
MACFARLANE, MIKE	1				1		1	0
MCGRIFF, FRED	31	33	30	41	41	39	37	−6
MCGWIRE, MARK	22	35	34	52	43	36	40	−18
MCLEMORE, MARK	4	1		2			2	3
MANRIQUE, FRED	13	1	1	1	6	2	2	11
MARTINEZ, CARLOS	11				1		1	10
MARTINEZ, EDGAR	3		3				3	0
MATTINGLY, DON	31	33	39	45	41	39	39	−8
MAZZILLI, LEE*	3							
MEDINA, LUIS	1	6	10	4	5	5	6	−5
MELVIN, BOB	3	3					3	0
MEYER, JOEY	5	12	3	3	4	4	5	0
MILLIGAN, RANDY	15			1	2	1	1	14
MOLITOR, PAUL	32	31	21	27	22	21	24	8
MORELAND, KEITH	11	7	1	1		7	4	7
MOSEBY, LLOYD	16	22	14	10	20	11	15	1
MOSES, JOHN	12	3	2		1	1	2	10

	EARNED 1989	MARKET PRICES					AVG. SAL.	PROFIT OR LOSS
		GOL	HQL	MLB	WEB	SCR		
MULLINIKS, RANCE	3	12	10	3	6	6	7	−4
NEWMAN, AL	15	3	1		4	1	2	13
NOKES, MATT	8	23	25	27	15	23	23	−15
O'BRIEN, PETE	13	16	15	7	11	16	13	0
ORSULAK, JOE	14	3	5		8	1	4	10
PAGLIARULO, MIKE	0	4	9	5	8	13	8	−8
PALMEIRO, RAFAEL	15	15	20	21	13	22	18	−3
PARKER, DAVE	21	13	8	9	8	8	9	12
PARRISH, LANCE	11	16	15	10	7	14	12	−1
PASQUA, DAN	10	3	2	3	4	4	3	7
PECOTA, BILL	3							
PETRALLI, GENO	7	9	4	3	5	4	5	2
PETTIS, GARY	21	4		5		10	6	15
PHELPS, KEN	5	12	13	6	9	8	10	−5
PHILLIPS, TONY	8	1	5	2	8	2	4	4
POLIDOR, GUS	0		1	1		2	1	−1
POLONIA, LUIS	21	7	4	4	9	6	6	15
PRESLEY, JIM	7	5	7	5	9	10	7	0
PUCKETT, KIRBY	31	39	39	55	39	41	43	−12
QUINONES, REY	−1	8	1	8	4	10	6	−7
QUIRK, JAMIE	−1		3	1			2	−3
RAY, JOHNNY	16	18	9	6	10	17	12	4
REED, JODY	11	9	7	4	6	9	7	4
REYNOLDS, HAROLD	22	24	25	10	11	24	19	3
RICE, JIM	3	15	13	25	14	14	16	−13
RIPKEN, BILLY	2	1	1	1	6		2	0
RIPKEN, CAL	21	26	24	37	28	30	29	−8
ROBIDOUX, BILLY JO	−1	5					5	−6
ROMERO, ED	−1				3	1	2	−3
ROMINE, KEVIN*	4							
SANTANA, RAFAEL	-					3	3	−3
SAX, STEVE	37	26	25	19	21	22	23	14
SCHOFIELD, DICK	6	8	12	8	7	13	10	−4
SCHROEDER, BILL	2				2	2	2	0
SCHU, RICK	3	5		2		3	3	0
SEITZER, KEVIN	18	23	14	26	31	21	23	−5
SHEETS, LARRY	6	3	6	16	1	6	6	0
SHEFFIELD, GARY	9	19	15	13	20	19	17	−8
SHERIDAN, PAT	4	5	6	4	4	1	4	0
SIERRA, RUBEN	37	31	29	40	24	26	30	7

	EARNED 1989	GOL	HQL	MLB	WEB	SCR	AVG. SAL.	PROFIT OR LOSS
SKINNER, JOEL	1		1	1		2	1	0
SLAUGHT, DON	6	9	9	7	6	10	8	−2
SNYDER, CORY	12	23	22	33	19	22	24	−12
SOSA, SAMMY*	6							
SPIERS, BILL	9							
STANICEK, PETE	-			1	1		1	−1
STANLEY, MIKE	2	1	1				1	1
STEINBACH, TERRY	10	12	16	15	8	12	13	−3
STILLWELL, KURT	13	12	5	5	5	12	8	5
SUNDBERG, JIM	−1	1			1	1	1	−2
SURHOFF, B.J.	13	19	17	17	14	15	16	−3
SVEUM, DALE	-	1	1	20	2	4	6	−6
TABLER, PAT	5	9	6	2	11	3	6	−1
TARTABULL, DANNY	18	33	24	37	23	26	29	−11
TETTLETON, MICKEY	20	3	3	3	2	2	3	17
THURMAN, GARY	6		1				1	5
TRABER, JIM	3	4	3	1	4	3	3	0
TRAMMELL, ALAN	9	24	29	37	15	31	27	−18
UPSHAW, WILLIE	-			1			1	−1
VALLE, DAVE	5	4	11	4	4	7	6	−1
VAUGHAN, GREG*	7							
VELARDE, RANDY*	4							
VIZQUEL, OMAR	−1			1	1		1	−2
WALKER, GREG	2	20	10	13	9	9	12	−10
WARD, GARY	7	1	3		3		2	5
WASHINGTON, CLAUDELL	18	21	9	5	9	11	11	7
WEISS, WALT	5	8	13	3	12	4	8	−3
WELLMAN, BRAD	3				1		1	2
WHITAKER, LOU	24	17	20	13	7	16	15	9
WHITE, DEVON	29	20	23	20	12	14	18	11
WHITE, FRANK	6	9	10	3	7	8	7	−1
WHITT, ERNIE	13	21	17	13	15	15	16	−3
WILLIAMS, EDDIE	4		5				5	−1
WILLIAMS, KEN	6	9	6		8	1	6	0
WILSON, MOOKIE*	11							
WILSON, WILLIE	16	16	5	5	15	13	11	5
WINFIELD, DAVE	-	1	5	3	25	21	11	−11
WORTHINGTON, CRAIG	13	5	7		4	7	6	7
YOUNT, ROBIN	38	29	26	18	33	19	25	13

EARNINGS AND MARKET PRICES FOR AL PITCHERS

	EARNED 1989	MARKET PRICES					AVG. SAL.	PROFIT OR LOSS
		GOL	HQL	MLB	WEB	SCR		
ABBOTT, JIM	3	15	12	4	10	10	10	−7
ACKER, JIM*	4							
AGUILERA, RICK*	6							
ALEXANDER, DOYLE	−6	9	8	4	12	7	8	−14
ANDERSON, ALLAN	10	15	26	10	30	21	20	−10
APPIER, KEVIN	−8			1			1	−9
AQUINO, LUIS	6	1			1	2	1	5
ARNSBERG, BRAD	1				1		1	0
ATHERTON, KEITH	−1				2		2	−3
AUGUST, DON	−8	12	7	4	11	16	10	−18
BAILES, SCOTT	3		4			2	3	0
BALLARD, JEFF	12							
BANKHEAD, SCOTT	17	7	4	1	7	10	6	11
BANNISTER, FLOYD	−1	10	9	6	4	7	7	−8
BAUTISTA, JOSE	−2	3	1	3	12	3	4	−6
BERENGUER, JUAN	9	3	5		5	1	4	6
BIRKBECK, MIKE	−7	1		12			7	−14
BLACK, BUD	16	2	5	4	8	1	4	12
BLYLEVEN, BERT	28	3	8	15	9	5	8	20
BODDICKER, MIKE	7	14	16	6	17	15	14	−7
BOSIO, CHRIS	23	2	9	4	8	13	7	16
BOYD, OIL CAN	1	5	8	13	11	8	9	−8
BROWN, KEVIN	14							
BURNS, TODD	22	7	2	3		5	4	18
CADARET, CHRIS	−3	3	5		5	2	4	−7
CAMPBELL, MIKE	−5							
CANDELARIA, JOHN	0	11	12	14	10	12	12	−12
CANDIOTTI, TOM	19	14	4	7	10	8	9	10
CARY, CHUCK*	9							
CASTILLO, TONY	−2	1	2	1	6	1	2	−4
CERUTTI, JOHN	13	1	2	1	6	4	3	10
CLEMENS, ROGER	21	33	31	50	41	36	38	−17
COOK, MIKE	−4				1		1	−5
CORSI, JIM*	6							
CRIM, CHUCK	17	8	3	4	10	11	7	10

	EARNED 1989	MARKET PRICES					AVG. SAL.	PROFIT OR LOSS
		GOL	HQL	MLB	WEB	SCR		
DAVIS, STORM	4	12	13	6	17	21	14	−10
DOPSON, JOHN	5		9	2	5	3	5	0
DOTSON, RICHARD	−8	1		4		2	2	−10
DUNNE, MIKE*	−9							
DYER, MIKE*	−4							
ECKERSLEY, DENNIS	43	31	40	50	46	41	42	1
FARR, STEVE	12	21	15	15	9	9	14	−2
FARRELL, JOHN	8		2	3	8	1	4	5
FINLEY, CHUCK	21	1	1	2			1	20
FLANAGAN, MIKE	3	4	7	2	5	6	5	−2
FOSSAS, TONY*	3							
FRASER, WILLIE	10	2	2	1	4	2	2	8
GARDNER, WES	−11	7	11	2	5	3	6	−17
GIBSON, PAUL	−4							
GLEATON, JERRY DON	−3		1			2	2	−5
GONZALES, GERMAN	0		3	1	2	1	2	−2
GORDON, TOM	14	12	1	1	11	6	6	8
GOSSAGE, GOOSE*	2							
GUANTE, CECILIO	3	10	2	2	5	4	5	−2
GUBICZA, MARK	20	24	26	39	35	23	29	−9
GUETTERMAN, LEE	21							
GUZMAN, JOSE	0	3	2	5	9	6	5	−5
HANSON, ERIK	11		1	1	3	5	3	9
HARNISCH, PETE	−5	3			4	3	3	−8
HARRIS, GENE*	−6							
HARVEY, BRYAN	22	21	18	37	19	16	22	0
HAVENS, BRAD	−5		2				2	−7
HAWKINS, ANDY	−4	9	12	3	8	15	9	−13
HENKE, TOM	33	27	29	32	22	34	29	4
HENNEMAN, MIKE	11	28	30	20	20	21	24	−13
HERNANDEZ, GUILLERMO	9	1	1	2	6	5	3	6
HETZEL, ERIC*	−8							
HIBBARD, GREG*	6							
HICKEY, KEVIN	5							
HIGUERA, TEDDY	9	12	26	31	22	29	24	−15
HILLEGAS, SHAWN	−2	5	2	11	4	2	5	−7
HOLMAN, BRIAN	5							
HOLTON, BRIAN	−3	4			4	3	4	−7
HONEYCUTT, RICK	19	1	5	1	5	2	3	16

	EARNED 1989	MARKET PRICES					AVG. SAL.	PROFIT OR LOSS
		GOL	HQL	MLB	WEB	SCR		
HOUGH, CHARLIE	−1	14	14	19	10	19	15	−16
HUDSON, CHARLES	−9	4		1	4	1	3	−12
JACKSON, MIKE	10	2	1	3	3	1	2	8
JEFFCOAT, MIKE*	7							
JOHN, TOMMY	−9	9	8	4	7	5	7	−16
JOHNSON, DAVE	1							
JOHNSON, RANDY	−1							
JONES, BARRY	6		1	1			1	5
JONES, DOUG	39	33	29	16	41	33	30	9
KEY, JIMMY	14	19	29	40	31	27	29	−15
KING, ERIC	9		3		4		4	6
KNUDSON, MARK	12	1	1	1			1	11
KRUEGER, BILL*	3							
LAMP, DENNIS	15	1	2				2	14
LANGSTON, MARK	7	17	17	38	16	21	22	−15
LAPOINT, DAVE	−12	7	14	2	2	12	7	−19
LEIBRANDT, CHARLIE	−11	14	17	25	12	15	17	−28
LEITER, AL	−4	6	2	5	4	7	5	−9
LONG, BILL	2	2					2	0
MCCASKILL, KIRK	19	4	9	3	4	13	7	12
MCCLURE, BOB*	14							
MCCULLERS, LANCE	1	11	3	16	9	5	9	−8
MCDOWELL, JACK	-		3				3	−3
MCMURTRY, CRAIG	−6				1	1	1	−7
MCWILLIAMS, LARRY*	2							
MILACKI, BOB	10	7	1	3	10	6	5	5
MINTON, GREG	15	1	1		6	3	3	12
MIRABELLA, PAUL	−3	2		2	1	3	2	−5
MMAHAT, KEVIN*	−5							
MOHORCIC, DALE	−1	2	6	3	3	5	4	−5
MONTGOMERY, JEFF	33	1	2				2	32
MOORE, MIKE	29	11	16	36	27	20	22	7
MORRIS, JACK	−7	15	17	40	15	16	21	−28
MOYER, JAMIE	−4	8	1	4	6	9	6	−10
MURPHY, ROB	15	9	8	5	3	1	5	10
MUSSELMAN, JEFF	−6	2	1	3	8	3	3	−9
NAVARRO, JAMIE*	6							
NELSON, GENE	9	6	12	1	10	1	6	3
NIEDENFUER, TOM	−7	8	17	3	10	10	10	−17
NIEVES, JUAN	-	1		2	1		1	−1

	EARNED 1989	MARKET PRICES					AVG. SAL.	PROFIT OR LOSS
		GOL	HQL	MLB	WEB	SCR		
OLSON, GREGG	34	1	2	11	2	4	4	30
OROSCO, JESSE	14	6	2	5	3	7	5	9
PALL, DON	10	7	3		4	3	4	6
PALMER, DAVID*	−6							
PARKER, CLAY*	4							
PATTERSON, KEN	1	5					5	−4
PEREZ, MELIDO	−7	5	3	6	5	9	6	−13
PETRY, DAN	−3	1					1	−4
PLESAC, DAN	36	33	40	30	37	35	35	1
PLUNK, ERIC	6	6	8	3	6	4	5	1
PRICE, JOE*	−2							
RAWLEY, SHANE	−10	7	12	1	9	8	7	−17
REARDON, JEFF	31	44	31	26	39	39	36	−5
REED, JERRY	7							
REUSS, JERRY	−4	5	1	3	3	2	3	−7
RIGHETTI, DAVE	22	16	17	29	13	22	19	3
RITZ, KEVIN*	−3							
ROBINSON, JEFF	−4	14	3	14	11	8	10	−14
ROGERS, KENNY	5							
ROSENBERG, STEVE	−7					3	3	−10
RUSSELL, JEFF	45	5	7	23	10	14	12	33
RYAN, NOLAN	25	15	10	9	16	20	14	11
SABERHAGEN, BRET	45	17	24	10	23	17	18	27
SANCHEZ, ALEX*	−6							
SCHMIDT, DAVE	−8		1	1	3	3	2	−10
SCHOOLER, MIKE	31	8	4	25	10	5	10	21
SEARCY, STEVE*	−3							
SHIELDS, STEVE	−5			2			2	−7
SMITH, LEE	26	30	20	31	25	25	26	0
SMITH, ROY	6	2	1		3		2	4
SMITHSON, MIKE	−2					3	3	−5
STANLEY, BOB	−1	2	1	1	4	1	2	−3
STEWART, DAVE	20	23	30	25	16	25	24	−4
STIEB, DAVE	20	20	21	16	16	17	18	2
STOTTLEMYRE, TODD	2			1	3		2	0
STRAKER, LES	−			1			1	−1
SWIFT, BILLY	1			1			1	0
SWINDELL, GREG	15	23	30	30	22	25	26	−11
TANANA, FRANK	7	4	2	1	8	7	4	3
THIGPEN, BOBBY	30	14	23	31	26	31	25	5

	EARNED 1989	MARKET PRICES					AVG. SAL.	PROFIT OR LOSS
		GOL	HQL	MLB	WEB	SCR		
THURMOND, MARK	4					1	1	3
TIBBS, JAY*	3							
TOLIVER, FRED	-7	1	4	4		1	3	-10
TROUT, STEVE	-5					4	4	-9
TRUJILLO, MIKE*	-5							
VIOLA, FRANK	8	31	40	53	32	30	37	-29
WARD, DUANE	15	17	6	8	8	11	10	5
WAYNE, GARY	5			4			4	1
WEGMAN, BILL	-9	3	9	2	8	7	6	-15
WELCH, BOB	18	20	17	18	15	23	19	-1
WELLS, DAVID	15	1	1		4		2	13
WEST, DAVID*	-5							
WILLIAMS, FRANK	-1			3			3	-4
WILLIAMSON, MARK	19		1		1		1	18
WITT, BOBBY	-8	4	4	4	1	12	5	-13
WITT, MIKE	-1	8	10	6	12	13	10	-11
YETT, RICH	-7	3	1	1		2	2	-9
YOUNG, CURT	0	6	7	5	7	10	7	-7
YOUNG, MATT*	-9							
ZAVARAS, CLINT*	-4							

Did all these leagues have their drafts before the start of the season?

Either before, or after the first week.

I'm trying to figure out why anyone would spend $20 on Dale Sveum.

Probably a frustration bid, someone with too much money at the end. Judging by Dave Winfield, the WEB and SCR leagues held their drafts more than a week early, before his surgery. There are a few other glitches, but not many. Certainly these prices are more valid than, say, the following for Doug Jones in Heath's veteran leagues: $1, $5, $4, $9, $4, $2, $2 . . .

I agree. Look at the swing on John Kruk, from $2 to $22.

And he came out right about in the middle. Which league are you going to be in, anyway?

Both.

Uh-oh, not a *mixed* league?

No, one National and one American.

My, that is ambitious.

You only live once, right?

I just hope you don't live *with* anybody.

Did you say all this stuff was on a spreadsheet?

Yes.

Mind running some sorts for me? I'd sort of like to see the top 10 salaries in each league matched against what they earned.

NL	COST	EARNED	NET	AL	COST	EARNED	NET
STRAWBERRY	43	24	−19	HENDERSON	54	48	−6
DAVIS, E	43	40	−3	CANSECO	44	17	−27
FRANCO	40	27	−13	PUCKETT	43	31	−12
VAN SLYKE	40	15	−25	ECKERSLEY	42	43	1
CLARK, W	40	40	0	CARTER	40	31	−9
GALARRAGA	38	27	−11	MCGWIRE	40	22	−18
MCREYNOLDS	37	29	−8	MATTINGLY	39	31	−8
HERSHISER	35	22	−13	GREENWELL	39	30	−9
COLEMAN	35	29	−6	CLEMENS	38	21	−17
MYERS	34	28	−6	HRBEK	38	23	−15
AVERAGE	39	28	−10	AVERAGE	42	30	−12

Eighteen out of 20 are losers.

Well, they're going to be. What we have is a pretty good sampling of' the 1988 all-star teams—not just all-stars, but career years in most cases. Here's where the specific market prices provide useful cautions. For example, you know Kirby Puckett is going to fetch some money, but $55? That's two owners, or more, getting completely carried away. It's such a shame Canseco was hurt. As it is, he's still the second most expensive player in both drafts. The average market price for him would have been somewhere in the mid-60s, don't you think?

I've heard this career-year business before, but Puckett had just followed a career year with a career year. How do you know he's not going to have a third one?

You don't. I don't see anything wrong with his average market price. He's an excellent place to safekeep $43—you might get it all back and you shouldn't lose much. The prices on McGwire and Mattingly, on the other hand, are almost certain losses, since they have no speed.

Will Clark has no speed.

True. And I probably would have stopped bidding on him around $35, and I would have been sorry.

The big-ticket items are going to lose money on the whole; all you want to do is break even.

Not avoid them altogether?

No, not if you think you'll break even or come close, because you've got to spend your money somewhere. It's just that the more you spend, the less risk you like to assume. That's why I could have easily paid the average market price for Galarraga but not for Hershiser, even though Hershiser had a better year than Galarraga and they lost basically the same.

If he had a better year, why isn't he worth more?

I meant in real baseball.

Hershiser would be worth more than a buck more than Clemens in the AL, I take it?

If he had the same stats he would. The way players are listed in the appendix shows this more clearly. Jose DeLeon and Nolan Ryan, for instance, both won 16 games. DeLeon had a better ERA and ratio. But Ryan's ERA and ratio are worth more in his league context, and he outearns DeLeon.

That's why you don't like mixed leagues?

That and the fact that, unless you have a league the size of the NFL, you end up with all-star teams.

So your prices don't work for them?

Good Lord, no. Oh, I suppose the order of players (another feature of the appendix) is useful, but that's about it. You sure you're not in a mixed league?

Just wondering. The way you have them listed in the first chapter, though, and this chart here—it makes me wonder about all the money that hitters are losing.

In the alphabetical listing, what catches my eye is that there are just as many losses for hitters in the right-hand column but not nearly as many in the left.

What I see in the chart above is that people spend money first of all on players who have power and speed; second, on relievers; third, on power hitters; fourth, on starters.

Let's do a sort by what players earned.

NL	EARNED	COST	NET	AL	EARNED	COST	NET
JOHNSON, H	51	22	29	HENDERSON	48	54	−6
DAVIS, M	48	25	23	RUSSELL	45	12	33
MITCHELL	45	25	20	SABERHAGEN	45	18	27
CLARK, W	40	40	0	ECKERSLEY	43	42	1
DAVIS, E	40	43	−3	JONES, D	39	30	9
GWYNN	37	34	3	JACKSON, B	38	28	10
SMITH, L	37	5	32	YOUNT	38	25	13
HOWELL	35	11	24	SAX	37	23	14
BURKE	35	12	23	SIERRA	37	30	7
SANDBERG	35	28	7	PLESAC	36	35	1
AVERAGE	40	25	15	AVERAGE	41	30	11

Now we're seeing some profits.

Naturally. These are last year's all-stars. The repeats from the previous chart are Eckersley, Rickey, Eric Davis, and Will Clark. Saberhagen is the only starter among new arrivals, while there are six relievers joining up, some of them pretty obscure.

And the speedy Kevin Mitchell.

The rather well-paid Kevin Mitchell. He hit .251 the year before, with 19 home runs; $25 was about right for him. Hojo, meanwhile, had 24 home runs and 23 stolen bases; $22 was low, although there was trade talk hanging over Hojo.

Eleven dollars for Jay Howell?

I don't get that, either. One league, PEW, didn't pick him up at all.

So the thing to look for is obscure relievers?

In start-up leagues, definitely. They'll be famous about 15 minutes into the season.

If you find they're going cheap, by the way, keep buying them. Too much is never enough.

What's that mean?

Don't stop just because you think you've got the saves category taken care of. Build a surplus of scarcity.

What's that mean?

Scarce items like saves and steals are the hardest to trade for when you don't have them, and so the easiest to trade when you do. As long as you're in a league that *will* trade, it doesn't matter if you're out of balance coming out of the draft. Having a surplus as the trade deadline approaches is kind of fun. Surplus at the end of the season, though, is excess. You really don't want to finish first in any category.

Unless it's all of them?

Oh, then it's all right.

Would you keep Rickey at $54?

I'd give him a lifetime contract at $54. Just because you see that minus sign next to his name and Eric Davis's doesn't mean they didn't get the job done. They may not have won you the pennant, but they didn't lose it either. Remember, you go into the draft with $260 and you want to come out with $300. You've got to make some profits somewhere, and you try like hell not to take big losses anywhere. Little losses on big investments are no big deal; they mean you got big earnings.

So you'd keep ED at $43?

In a second.

Would you keep Strawberry at $43?

I might. Hard call. He can earn it, and I certainly would if I thought he was going to.

Van Slyke at $40?

Easy call. No. He can earn $40, but I know no one's going to bid him that high, so I drop him. If the market price is sure to be under your expected Patton $ worth, go with the market price, clearly.

McGwire at $40?

Drop him. I don't care what the market thinks, he's not going to earn it.

Mattingly at $39?

I would probably drop him. He might come in close to $39 next year, but I have this sense that something's just a little off with him, and I think others share that sense. I either shave a couple of dollars off his salary by buying him back, or I watch a bidding war between two Yankee fans, if there are any left.

There's another sort we should do. How about the true bargains, the people who really made money—the highest nets?

NL	EARNED	COST	NET	AL	EARNED	COST	NET
SMITH, L	37	5	32	RUSSELL	45	12	33
LANDRUM	31	1	30	MONTGOMERY	33	2	31
JOHNSON, H	51	22	29	OLSON	34	4	30
THOMPSON, M	26	2	24	SABERHAGEN	45	18	27
DAVIS, M	48	25	23	EISENREICH	27	3	24
BURKE	35	12	23	KELLY	30	7	23
HOWELL	35	14	21	SCHOOLER	31	10	21
MITCHELL	45	25	20	GUETTERMAN	21	0	21
DARWIN	23	4	19	BLYLEVEN	28	8	20
BIGGIO	22	3	19	FINLEY, C	21	1	20
AVERAGE	35	11	24	AVERAGE	32	7	25

Bill Landrum, Jeff Montgomery . . . Lee Guetterman? *Son of a bitch. Was Landrum even up in April?*

He made the team, and Gott was hurting, as I recall.

You saying you would have picked him?

No, no, I'm saying he was there to be picked, and out of the five start-up leagues, one did. Nobody took Guetterman. Out of the 25 older leagues that Jerry Heath gave me the prices for, only eight took Guetterman. Four didn't take Montgomery. There are simply too many pitchers to choose from, which is another reason you shouldn't spend too much on them.

An average of $7 spent in the American League for the 10 best profits? It makes it seem like the whole thing's a crapshoot.

It is. Sorry. You fight like hell not to lose money on the expensive players, then pray you hit it big with the scrubs.

At least in the National League there are three people on the list who cost more than $20. The average is $11.

So it would seem the NL was more "rational" or "fair" last year, wouldn't it? Well, there's one more sort that we have to do—the biggest losers.

NL	COST	EARNED	NET	AL	COST	EARNED	NET
JACKSON, D	28	−12	−40	VIOLA	37	8	−29
DANIELS	32	7	−25	LEIBRANDT	17	−11	−28
VAN SLYKE	40	15	−25	MORRIS	21	−7	−28
KNEPPER	7	−16	−23	CANSECO	44	17	−27
GOODEN	34	11	−23	LAPOINT	7	−12	−19
PERRY	29	8	−21	AUGUST	10	−8	−18
MCGEE	27	6	−21	MCGWIRE	40	22	−18
STRAWBERRY	43	24	−19	TRAMMELL	27	9	−18
CARMAN	2	−16	−18	RAWLEY	7	−10	−17
DARLING	24	6	−18	NIEDENFUER	10	−7	−17
AVERAGE	27	3	−23	AVERAGE	22	0	−22

An average of $27 spent on the bombs in the NL last year, substantially more than the AL. Five of the bombs are hitters, where your money is supposed to be safe.

How do you account for that?

It was an incredibly chaotic year in the National League last year. Too bad we're only looking at the top 10, because number 11 was Mike Schmidt, number 12 Ron Gant, number 14 Kirk Gibson. It was so bad that people like McReynolds and Galarraga were good.

It's amazing that Carman's on the list, since nobody believed in him to begin with.

There you have it. If you're in one of those excruciating leagues that don't allow you to drop players, Carman has killed you. People in those leagues tell me they have to pay big money for pitchers, so my prices don't help them, but I'm not convinced. If you were in one of those leagues, why would you spend $7 on Rawley? Whereas if you can ditch him, $7 is a reasonable gamble, considering the up side.

Pitchers are your venture capital. The average price for Leibrandt last year was $17, for Saberhagen $18.

That's ridiculous.

No it's not. Check them out in the Player Profiles. Leibrandt had a much better ERA the year before and earned more. Now he's in disgrace; Saberhagen's a one-man pitching staff that someone will pay $50 for this year. We have short memories.

Van Slyke was kind of a total disaster when you think about it, and he still earned $15.

35

Precisely. Kirk Gibson was very similar to Danny Jackson in real baseball, and Gibson earned $9. If you've invested $28 in Jackson, you don't drop him even if you're allowed to. You sit there and take the full beating. You leave the draft, if everyone else breaks even, a $220 team. It's over.

Jack Morris and Alan Trammell—two more big-name players who had equally poor years.

With more invested on Trammell, and less lost.

So what you're saying is, you never spend this kind of money on a starting pitcher?

On starting *pitchers*, I don't. I'd never spend $62 on Jackson and Gooden. If the average pitcher earns $8.67, then nine average pitchers earn $78. That's my budget. I sure don't want to have to find my relief pitching with $16.

Are you serious? You stick to budgets for pitching and hitting?

No, not really. Actually, $78 is kind of high for me. Last year I spent $69.

And you bought a decent pitching staff with that?

Yes, I did, in my terms. The $69 turned out to earn $70, so I broke even. In fact, in Heath's hypothetical final standings, I got 26 points in pitching; the average team in an American League Rotisserie earns 52 points, so that's really breaking even. I hoped to be a little luckier, but at least I hung in there.

I don't like all this talk about luck.

Then play chess instead. Look, I know I'm not going to luck into a good offense. I know that finding good pitchers is to a great extent just throwing darts, so I'm going to throw a few.

Let's group pitchers in—oh—the National League by salary ranges and see what we get.

	#	COST	AVERAGE EARNED	+/−	TOTAL +/−
above $30	4	36	22	−14	−56
$20–29	8	25	18	−7	−56
$10–19	24	11	13	2	48
$5–9	25	6	6	0	0
$1–4	36	2	2	0	0
under $1	16	0.6	5	4	64

Four pitchers (Franco, Hershiser, Myers, and Gooden) were in the over-$30 bracket last year. They earned an average of $22 for a $14 loss. Eight pitchers cost between $20 and $30, and they lost money. The much larger range between $10 and $19 made money. The $5–$9 range broke even. The $1–$4 range, which is the crapshoot (and also the biggest group), broke even. And the Sixteen Bill Landrums, pitchers who as often as not weren't even selected, turned a huge profit.

Four dollars is huge?

When you spend 60 cents it is. Sixteen times $4 is $64; the $10–$19 range only had a total profit of $48. This chart tells me to pursue a starting pitcher that I like into the teens, then wave good-bye and wait for the next one. It tells me to leave at least a couple of slots open for the crapshoot. It tells me to pick pitchers like crazy in the reserve phase.

What about relievers?

More than half your pitching budget should go to them, either in one big bundle for Eckersley or Mark Davis, or spread among several.

The appendix shows the top 90 pitchers in the NL last year, the top 108 in the AL—the pitchers that "perfect" Rotisserie Leagues would carry. You'll notice the average of these ideal populations ($13.22 and $12.79) is worth considerably more than the average pitcher ($8.67); we pretend no roster was ever graced by Bob Knepper or Dave LaPoint. But let's separate these populations into relievers and starters and see who's doing what. For simplicity, let's call anyone who got a save last year a reliever, the rest starters.

NL	IP	W	S	ERA	RTO	$
STARTERS (49)	160	11	0	3.08	10.59	11.20
RELIEVERS (41)	88	5	11	2.73	10.64	16.00

AL	IP	W	S	ERA	RTO	$
STARTERS (59)	152	10	0	3.35	11.30	11.17
RELIEVERS (49)	82	5	11	3.06	11.17	16.17

You just made Doc Gooden a reliever, you realize that?

To tell you the truth, I didn't, but he's one among 41; we can live with it.

And you made Norm Charlton a starter.

I can live with that also—and then again, we can just stop this. Most of this stuff I already know.

No, go ahead; tell me what the chart shows.

You tell me.

It shows the average relief pitcher was worth a hell of a lot more than the average starter.

Why?

He got some wins and all the saves, and had a better ERA and ratio. Except the National League starter had a better ratio. I wonder if that was all Mitch Williams.
  What else?

You're doing just fine.

Let me see . . . We could multiply the number of starting pitchers, 49, times the average earning. That's $549 . . . The number of relievers, 41, times their average earning. That's $656 . . . So the relievers earn well over half the money, even though there aren't as many of them.

You just do that in your head?

Same thing in the American League.

Well, I guess it's going to come as no surprise to you, is it, that the NL relief pitcher not only has a better ERA than the starter, but it's worth more in the ERA standings?

Eighty-eight innings at 2.73 help your team more than 160 innings at 3.08? Sure, I can see that. I'm all set to buy relief pitchers. I'm thinking of having a whole team of them.

You don't have the thousand-innings rule?

Not in one of the leagues.

Maybe I should warn them.
  But at least I can just zip through this stuff, since it's so obvious. The biggest mistakes people starting out make are (1) spending too much on starting pitching—they should be spending much more on relief pitching; (2) overspending on the great hitters who happen to be lead-legs; and (3) overspending on what I call "position scarcity."
  In 1988, Julio Franco earned $28, Wade Boggs $25. You can see that the average salary for Franco last year was $25, for Boggs $35.

In 1988, Brett Butler earned $28 and Benito Santiago $15, yet the average salary last year for Santiago was $24, for Butler $18. And the funny thing is, a lot of people are going to keep Santiago, who earned $17, and are ticked off at Butler for only earning $21.

Their reasoning seems to be that Santiago hits pretty darn good for a catcher, while Butler is kind of a wimp in the outfield.

No stat service that I know of pays attention to who's hitting the homers or getting the steals. The only one who even pictures what your team "looks" like is you. In real baseball Santiago and Tom Pagnozzi would still be the best catching corps around, because only one of them catches at a time. In Rotisserie baseball, you play Tony Pena and Mike Scioscia—who you bought for $13—side by side, and they earn you $19.

So you want depth on offense, a 14-man lineup every day, piling up the at-bats.

Still, don't you tend to get better production from certain positions? The outfield? The corners?

Do you? The way the game is set up, you actually go deeper into outfielders than middle infielders. There are 12 teams in the National League, so 36 outfielders can start on a given day. We're carrying 50; 14, or 28 percent, don't start. Twenty-four middle infielders start. We're carrying 30—

So only 20 percent don't start. Interesting.

The appendix has pretty much sized up for you the depth and strength at each position. Here it is in condensed form:

	NL			AL	
	AVG	WORST		AVG	WORST
OF	$17.39	$6	OF	$18.53	$6
1B	21.55	3	1B	18.01	7
3B	12.70	4	3B	13.55	3
2B	12.53	3	2B	13.19	3
SS	14.61	6	SS	11.27	3
C	6.64	2	C	8.27	2
			DH	5.77	−1

The average shows the dollar value of the average of the top 50 NL outfielders or top 18 NL first basemen, etc. That's the strength of the position. "Worst" is what the 50th outfielder or 18th first baseman earned. That's the depth. You can see how weak third base was last year in both leagues.

Where'd you put Hojo?

At shortstop, of course. Also Matt Williams. That's where most leagues will put them, until they find out there are no other sticks at third. So they'll move Darrell Evans over there, if he's still playing, which is what I've done.

It basically shows me what you would expect: The hitting is at the corners—at least at first base—and in the outfield.

It shows me you better watch out you don't get Wallace Johnson as your first baseman. There's an abrupt drop-off. You'll be giving poor old Darrell his first baseman's mitt back. You'll end up moving Williams to third and calling up Steve Jeltz.

Like hell.

He was actually a pretty good scrub last year. You never know. This is what the game's all about. If it has any value, it's learning to love and hate Steve Jeltz.

Why wouldn't I move Evans to third, bring McClendon to first from the outfield, and instead love the 51st outfielder, Willie McGee?

At a market price of $27, I don't think he was there with the scrubs. All I'm saying is that in the endgame crapshoot, the pickings on offense are slim throughout. It's been my experience that everyone wants to pack the corners, which makes it hard, whereas people get three good outfielders and figure they've taken care of that. I try to sneak a fourth and fifth good outfielder onto my team early, while they're still around.

If we comb through the charts in the previous chapter for the four cheapest National League scrubs at second base and in the outfield (averaging zero in for the leagues that didn't pick them at all), here's what we get:

SECOND BASEMEN	COST	EARNED	+ / −
LENNY HARRIS	1	8	7
STEVE LOMBARDOZZI	1	0	−1
JEFF TREADWAY	1	13	12
DAMASO GARCIA	1	6	5
TOTAL	4	27	23

OUTFIELDERS	COST	EARNED	+/−
DWAYNE MURPHY	1	6	5
GREG GROSS	1	−1	−2
LEE MAZZILLI	1	2	1
GERONIMO BERROA	1	2	1
TOTAL	4	9	5

Are you telling me you'd spend $8 for Lenny Harris? To tell you the truth, I can't get all that excited over Treadway.

I wouldn't spend $2 for Lenny Harris. I wouldn't spend $5 for Treadway. Let me emphasize right here that just because my prices show some marginal player earning a few bucks is no reason in itself to pay a few bucks. You pay as little as you possibly can. You're trying to win this crazy auction where everyone has the same amount of money. Every dollar counts, and you fight for the best deal you can get 23 times.

As a rule of thumb, I'd say that for any player you feel has little chance of earning more than $5, don't pay more than one or two dollars under any circumstances.

By being chintzy here, can I go higher at the top?

Sure. A lot of people do that. But if they win that way, it's normally not because of who they bought at the top, it's because they got Jeff Treadway instead of Geronimo Berroa—and last April who would you have picked for $1?

Know what? I'd still take Berroa. Lemke's going to be the second baseman. How often did you see Treadway's name in the boxes in September?

You didn't have a Rotisserie team and you noticed that?

I just like to follow baseball.

There were so few people following the Braves in September, we're lucky they published the box scores. What you're saying, though, is worth reiterating.

The $13 you see next to Treadway's name is what his statistics were worth in the National League in 1989. The appendix—while it attempts to be forward-looking, moving people to their probable positions, zapping even significant contributions of people who moved out of the league during the season—is basically retrospective. You'll be zapping many more people; you'll want to change the order at each position;

and you'll certainly want to pencil in your own guesses as to what people will earn this year.

What I think they'll earn or what I'm planning to pay?

That's up to you. Why you would plan to pay more than you think they'll earn—especially in a start-up league—more or less eludes me, however.

What's "especially" about it?

I'll get to that. This is only the beginning.

What's next? The Player Profiles?

Why not? Bill James used to put them last, but I say, let the market decide. Apparently they were a big hit last year.

Anything I should know about them?

Yes. The three-year scans of earnings will throw you for a loss if you don't realize that the formulas for each year are different. Darryl Strawberry's best year was in '87, but he gets a much higher salary in '88; how come?

The rabbit ball in '87?

Exactly. The tendency in the market is to spend more on hitting when the home runs are flying, and trash pitching; the reverse should happen. Jimmy Key in '87 was much more valuable than Mike Moore last year, even though his record on the face of it wasn't as good.

If the league totals change drastically, the profile of the average hitter changes noticeably. But he's still worth $13. The average pitcher fluctuates in ERA and ratio, and remains worth $8.67. These are the figures to keep in mind for the three-year scans:

AVERAGE PLAYERS FOR THE LAST THREE YEARS

NATIONAL LEAGUE	HR	RBI	SB	BA	ERA	RATIO
1987	11	49	11	.273	4.00	12.22
1988	8	41	11	.259	3.31	11.03
1989	8	42	10	.257	3.36	11.27

AMERICAN LEAGUE	HR	RBI	SB	BA	ERA	RATIO
1987	14	53	9	.267	4.31	12.36
1988	10	47	8	.263	3.85	11.87
1989	9	46	8	.264	3.76	11.92

It's even bigger with decimals, yet the home run decline by the American League hitter from 14 to nine in three years is still fairly dramatic.

You keep talking about the different league contexts; last year it doesn't look all that big to me.

It's nice to know one person is going to read the masochist chapter, but briefly, you're right about hitting, wrong about pitching. Saberhagen in the National League would be worth $39. That is, if you just moved his statistics over. If you moved him over—well, I don't think the pitchers would even like to bunt against him. Did you see the way he pitched inside last year?

But hitting prices, they don't change that much?

Why do I keep thinking you're in a mixed league?

They change a little. Vince Coleman in the American League would be worth $32 instead of $29.

How come?

Look, everyone else is already reading the Player Profiles. You're supposed to be standing in for most people, and they don't give a hoot. Okay, steals are more scarce in the American League.

All I wanted to know.

Anyway, it does raise the question of how to show Viola, Langston, Oddibe McDowell, and so forth. Not to cut it too fine, I decided to list their statistics overall, then total what they earned in each league. That's just for 1989; for 1987 and 1988, I apply the formula of the league they spent more time in. The parentheses indicate which league they spent less time in.

The next question is where to place the players who qualify at several positions. Is Hojo a shortstop or is he not? He's not, and yet you'll find him under shortstops. Indeed, if you even look for him under third baseman, it's a sign you're not focused; you're musing dreamily about real baseball.

As far as I'm concerned, the numbers are the essence of the profiles. As enjoyable as they are to write, the comments are almost superfluous.

Many of them are already outdated, or proven flat wrong, by the time the book comes out. My idea is generally to look for things that have to do with our narrow perspective, but occasionally I'll stray off hopelessly. Often I have almost nothing to say, and sometimes far too much.

This is where you make your predictions?

They're implied, I suppose, but it's not my purpose to get into the prediction game. That's your job.

Because a friend of mine who read your book last year, when he heard I was going to be talking to you?

Yes?

He said, if Patton says he won any money, will you ask him if he has separate comments for himself?

I'm sure—wasn't he kidding?

It didn't sound like it.

Well, kindly remind him what I just said. About whose job it is . . . I said it last year . . . That's really great, you know, telling me something like that, just when I'm about to stick my head in a noose again.

I'm sorry.

I feel like not saying anything. Trouble is, the book would be too short.

Hey, the guy's a jerk. I know him well. Gotta place our own bets.

Right on.

I'll tell you what: If I see anything really stupid in your comments, I'll tell you afterwards, okay?

No, not okay.

That's all right, too. Let's see now—how's it organized again?

By position, alphabetically.

But you have to let me talk to you at the end, just in case there's anything else?

I don't have to. But I will.

NATIONAL LEAGUE CATCHERS

DAMON BERRYHILL	AB	HR	RBI	SB	BA	$
1988 CHI N	309	7	38	1	.259	9
1989 CHI N	334	5	41	1	.257	8

A good example of the range of opinions about "position scarcity"—his low market price (in Chapter 1) was $4, his high $25! Yet, even with his injury, he earned his keep in three of the five leagues.

CRAIG BIGGIO	AB	HR	RBI	SB	BA	$
1988 HOU	123	3	5	6	.211	3
1989 HOU	443	13	60	21	.257	22

It's puzzling why Biggio's average salary was so low ($3) last year. He earned that drinking his cup of coffee in '88. In Heath's 25 established leagues, it's higher ($7), but it's obvious his name won't be coming up in many auctions this spring.

GARY CARTER

	AB	HR	RBI	SB	BA	$
1987 NY N	523	20	83	0	.235	11
1988 NY N	455	11	46	0	.242	10
1989 NY N	153	2	15	0	.183	0

Last year, when he played, he had trouble reaching the warning track; his ball just doesn't carry anymore. And he's seven years younger than Carlton Fisk.

DARREN DAULTON

	AB	HR	RBI	SB	BA	$
1987 PHI	129	3	13	0	.194	0
1988 PHI	144	1	12	2	.208	1
1989 PHI	368	8	44	2	.201	5

Had done most of his hitting by May.

JODY DAVIS

	AB	HR	RBI	SB	BA	$
1987 CHI N	428	19	51	1	.248	10
1988 CHI N/ATL	257	7	36	0	.230	6
1989 ATL	231	4	19	0	.194	−1

He would have been zapped in favor of Francisco Cabrera, the way Bo Diaz is for Joe Oliver, if I had faith in Cabrera. The latter can hit, but is no catcher. With all their promising young pitchers, the Braves have an especially pressing problem here.

TERRY KENNEDY

	AB	HR	RBI	SB	BA	$
1987 BAL	512	18	62	1	.250	10
1988 BAL	265	3	16	0	.226	1
1989 SF	355	5	34	0	.239	6

When the camera showed Kennedy raging in the dugout after another punishing half-inning by Oakland, I thought: The Giants are going down, but they're still scuffling; it's hard to tell, yet there's Kennedy, who I always thought was a whiner, exhorting his teammates.

The next day I read in the paper that he was cursing the second base umpire for not giving him the call on a throw.

MIKE LAVALLIERE

	AB	HR	RBI	SB	BA	$
1987 PIT	340	1	36	0	.300	7
1988 PIT	352	2	47	3	.261	9
1989 PIT	190	2	23	0	.316	7

The Pirates can't be as high on him as I am or they wouldn't have picked up Don Slaught.

JOE OLIVER	AB	HR	RBI	SB	BA	$
1989 CIN	151	3	23	0	.272	5

He'll get plenty of playing time, but the fact remains that he didn't hit much better than Scotti Madison on the same team in the minors.

MARK PARENT	AB	HR	RBI	SB	BA	$
1988 SD	118	6	15	0	.195	3
1989 SD	141	7	21	1	.191	1

Gets a home run every 20 at-bats. But very few at bats.

BENITO SANTIAGO	AB	HR	RBI	SB	BA	$
1987 SD	546	18	79	21	.300	26
1988 SD	492	10	46	15	.248	15
1989 SD	462	16	62	11	.236	17

Seventh-best catcher in the league over the last two years.

Who says? Thomas Boswell's Total Average, right? Some such silly rating system.

No, it's the Elias Sports Bureau rating system, used to determine free-agent compensation, agreed to by both management and players. Benito barely ranks as a Type A player, and the ironic thing is, when he becomes a free agent, he'll hope he's not, because teams will be even more eager to sign him.

In the meantime, though, you can rest assured that his agent won't show this baffling rating to the judge who hears his arbitration case. But that's all right; the Padres will.

NELSON SANTOVENIA	AB	HR	RBI	SB	BA	$
1988 MON	309	8	41	2	.236	8
1989 MON	304	5	31	2	.250	7

Santovenia ranks right ahead of Santiago. We have the essences of their two-year offensive contributions staring us in the face. Is it defense? Baffling.

MACKEY SASSER	AB	HR	RBI	SB	BA	$
1988 NY N	123	1	17	0	.285	4
1989 NY N	182	1	22	0	.291	5

Barry Lyons figures, as I write, to get more playing time, but he also figures to be packaged in a deal for another catcher. Sasser has a nice little niche for himself and will keep swinging the good bat.

MIKE SCIOSCIA	AB	HR	RBI	SB	BA	$
1987 LA	461	5	38	7	.265	7
1988 LA	408	3	35	0	.257	6
1989 LA	408	10	44	0	.250	10

Remember Will Clark limping in the World Series? He banged his knee sliding into Scioscia. I happened to see it: throw way late, game not close, why the hell doesn't Scioscia let him have the plate?

Because Scioscia's made of cement. It's no sweat to him, whatever the runner does; you have the choice of breaking your ankle, your knee, your shoulder, or your neck. Clark, as he's chugging home, knows he's in trouble, knows the run's not worth it, but what can he do?

DON SLAUGHT	AB	HR	RBI	SB	BA	$
1987 TEX	237	8	16	0	.224	1
1988 NY A	322	9	43	1	.283	11
1989 NY A	350	5	38	1	.251	6

Trades seemed to have inspired him before, but this one is going to inspire LaValliere.

TODD ZEILE	AB	HR	RBI	SB	BA	$
1989 STL	82	1	8	0	.256	1

Fine-looking hitter. Whitey thought so, batting him behind Guerrero at the end of the season. He'll probably settle in at the five or six slot and drive in a lot of runs. But people who are still kicking themselves over Biggio are going to bid him too high.

Player Z

Player Z is supposed to come last, alphabetically. (Didn't I predict Zeile would cause trouble? You make enough predictions, you'll get some of them right.) Player Z is Junior Ortiz or Joe Girardi. As the season progresses, he's Tom Prince or Todd Hundley. He's Lloyd McClendon as soon as he catches his 20th game. And by September he's . . . well, he's Zeile again. Wil Tejada or Brian Deak. Someday he's Tyler Houston. He's my chance to name names that I haven't named yet and may or may not name later.

Leagues need 20 catchers and they're just not there. I wouldn't even waste many of my reserve picks on catchers, because they're not going to be there. The National League frequently triple-platoons this position. Look in the appendix. Branch out and survey both leagues. The only position that's weaker in all of baseball is the DH.

NATIONAL LEAGUE FIRST BASEMEN

TODD BENZINGER	AB	HR	RBI	SB	BA	$
1987 BOS	223	8	43	5	.278	9
1988 BOS	405	13	70	2	.254	13
1989 CIN	628	17	76	3	.245	17

With over 600 at-bats he didn't do any more than he did with 400; he did about half as much as Esasky.

JACK CLARK	AB	HR	RBI	SB	BA	$
1987 STL	419	35	106	1	.286	26
1988 NY A	490	27	91	2	.245	20
1989 SD	455	26	94	6	.242	25

As a new arrival, Clark's market prices in the 25 established leagues can be compared to those in the start-up leagues, and there is a significant difference.

Which way, do you suppose?

Do the seasoned hands realize that this welcome infusion of power is still something not to go bonkers over (a two-category player at best)?

Not at all. They go bonkers, spending $30 for Clark, $6 more than the new guys.

How come? What are the new guys doing turning a profit on a seasoned player who had a nothing-special year, for him?

The answer lies in the next player.

Will Clark cost $40 in the start-up leagues, because they start out with a lot of money to throw around. The older leagues spent $32 for this Clark, in many cases pre-spending it in freezes, so they had money to throw elsewhere.

For the pair of Clarks, the two types of leagues spent virtually the same total dollars.

WILL CLARK	AB	HR	RBI	SB	BA	$
1987 SF	529	35	91	5	.308	**29**
1988 SF	575	29	109	9	.282	**36**
1989 SF	588	23	111	8	.333	**40**

This Clark fetched more than Mattingly on the open market. Only a dollar more, but it's worth noting that a total of 10 rookie leagues, 100 teams, at least 150 baseball outsiders, wouldn't make the offers that general managers supposedly were lining up with after word spread that Mattingly was available last winter. Will Clark and Hammaker, Fred McGriff and Henke. Offers that Steinbrenner was forced to consider before Mattingly apologized.

Wouldn't you give good money for the tape of Clark's apology to Chris Brown? How about a videotape of Clark's expression while Jeffrey Leonard held him in a headlock, thinking? Clark lost just a whole bunch of Pepsi ads by bringing it up again.

"When Clark goes to the plate," says Bob Kennedy of the Giants, "he becomes deaf and dumb."

Becomes, did he say? People thought he was a stand-up guy after the final blowout, remaining in the locker room while almost everyone else was hiding in the trainer's room. Not me. I know what old Will's all about. He never leaves the plate.

GLENN DAVIS	AB	HR	RBI	SB	BA	$
1987 HOU	578	27	93	4	.251	**18**
1988 HOU	561	30	99	4	.271	**32**
1989 HOU	581	34	89	4	.269	**31**

It's not just his ballpark that's against him, it's his team. With no one to drive in and no one to protect him, he needs some kind of "teammate scarcity" formula to get his due.

NICK ESASKY	AB	HR	RBI	SB	BA	$
1987 CIN	346	22	59	0	.272	**14**
1988 CIN	391	15	62	7	.243	**17**
1989 BOS	564	30	108	1	.277	**29**

"No one foresaw [the escalation in player salaries]," Marty Noble reported in *Newsday* at the end of the winter meetings in December. "No one is quite sure why it occurred."

Talk to us, why don't they?

Baseball has started to hire sabermetricians, but if general managers are still as dazed as Noble indicates they should join a Rotisserie league. We know exactly what happens when there's a lot of money in the room and only a limited number of talented players available.

In the absence of a salary cap, Peter Ueberroth somehow browbeat every last owner into colluding; collusion created excellent "freeze lists"; then, simultaneously, collusion was declared illegal and television dumped armloads of extra money into the owners' laps.

When Esasky signed with the Braves, it's too bad all the baseball executives weren't in the same room, the way we are at an auction. Raucous laughter in the first round: $5.6 million? For Esasky? Hoo-hoo! Ha-ha! In the later rounds: terrible teams like the Phillies and the Tigers, yelling bids two and three times higher for whoever's left.

"No matter who you are and how much you believe in supply and demand," Noble wrote, "these new contracts offend your sensibilities."

I'm more offended by Ted Turner keeping all the loot for himself.

ANDRES GALARRAGA	AB	HR	RBI	SB	BA	$
1987 MON	551	13	90	7	.305	**22**
1988 MON	609	29	92	13	.302	**38**
1989 MON	572	23	85	12	.257	**27**

By now there must be a few people—new readers who skipped right to the good parts—who are puzzled by the 1987 and 1988 earnings of some of these players. You'll understand after you've read the bad parts.

MARK GRACE	AB	HR	RBI	SB	BA	$
1988 CHI N	486	7	57	3	.296	**17**
1989 CHI N	510	13	79	14	.314	**29**

Finishing his second year, he's probably going to be available in many drafts. Nominate him early, because for sure he melted as many hearts as Will Clark turned to stone. Yelling his fool head off with one out left in the season, down two runs, no one on. Not whining, Kennedy; just not going gentle.

PEDRO GUERRERO	AB	HR	RBI	SB	BA	$
1987 LA	545	27	89	9	.338	32
1988 LA/STL	364	10	65	4	.286	18
1989 STL	570	17	117	2	.311	32

Hurt his knee in Florida, scared the wee out of investors (not to mention Herzog), then played in 162 games, fulfilling Herzog's every fantasy of how he should fit into the offense.

VON HAYES	AB	HR	RBI	SB	BA	$
1987 PHI	556	21	84	16	.277	23
1988 PHI	367	6	45	20	.272	17
1989 PHI	540	26	78	28	.259	34

If you're wondering why he's listed here, check the 15th first baseman and 60th outfielder in the appendix. (The appendix is also the source for complete position eligibility, based on the 20-game minimum.)

RICKY JORDAN	AB	HR	RBI	SB	BA	$
1988 PHI	273	11	43	1	.308	15
1989 PHI	523	12	75	4	.285	21

He said an interesting thing during the season. "I know I have to hit better than this if I'm a first baseman." Can you imagine Benzinger saying that? It makes me think he's going to hit better.

DAVE MAGADAN	AB	HR	RBI	SB	BA	$
1987 NY N	192	3	24	0	.318	6
1988 NY N	314	1	35	0	.277	7
1989 NY N	374	4	41	1	.286	11

The Mets can't possibly believe Magadan hits adequately for the position, but as I write, he's got it.

EDDIE MURRAY	AB	HR	RBI	SB	BA	$
1987 BAL	618	30	91	1	.277	20
1988 BAL	603	28	84	5	.284	27
1989 LA	594	20	88	7	.247	22

The five new leagues paid $23 for Murray; the 25 existing leagues, $32. A bigger spread than the one for Jack Clark; too big. In Chapter 4 I discuss what freeze lists do to prices. They definitely raise them, but never nearly as much—overall—as 39 percent.

GERALD PERRY	AB	HR	RBI	SB	BA	$
1987 ATL	533	12	74	42	.270	26
1988 ATL	547	8	74	29	.300	30
1989 ATL	266	4	21	10	.252	8

KC is the last stop before Japan.

GARY REDUS	AB	HR	RBI	SB	BA	$
1987 CHI A	475	12	48	52	.236	25
1988 CHI A/(PIT)	333	8	38	31	.249	21
1989 PIT	279	6	33	25	.283	19

Redus, too. That is, it's easy to picture him in a kimono. It's hard to picture him at first, but he doesn't even qualify in the outfield. Assuming Bonilla moves to the outfield, not first, Redus and Sid Bream will be one of the more bizarre platoons.

Player Z

Phil Stephenson. It beats me why he hasn't gotten discouraged and offed to Japan, but since he hasn't, someone should give him a chance. So he's 29. Maybe he's 30. All the more reason. Since 1982 he's been traded, released, and been his own player to be named later. The last two years he's hit as well as anyone in the American Association, and he can run a bit. When last seen, he was getting into some September games with the Padres and showing some power. He excites me more than Mark Ryal, put it that way.

NATIONAL LEAGUE SECOND BASEMEN

ROBERTO ALOMAR	AB	HR	RBI	SB	BA	$
1988 SD	545	9	41	24	.266	19
1989 SD	623	7	56	42	.295	33

Once again, a great finishing kick.

BILL DORAN	AB	HR	RBI	SB	BA	$
1987 HOU	625	16	79	31	.283	27
1988 HOU	480	7	53	17	.248	15
1989 HOU	507	8	58	22	.219	15

Sad and puzzling decline of a player whom most people two springs ago would have taken over Sandberg.

TOMMY HERR	AB	HR	RBI	SB	BA	$
1987 STL	510	2	83	19	.263	15
1988 (STL)/MINN	354	2	32	13	.263	10
1989 PHI	561	2	37	10	.287	14

Much better season than I thought he'd have, but I'd still keep my bets between cautious and gloomy.

REX HUDLER	AB	HR	RBI	SB	BA	$
1988 MON	216	4	14	29	.273	15
1989 MON	155	6	13	15	.245	10

Tom Foley could have been listed instead. Junior Noboa, Jeff Huson, and Johnny Paredes will be trying their best to be listed next year. Damaso Garcia won't.

GREGG JEFFERIES	AB	HR	RBI	SB	BA	$
1988 NY N	109	6	17	5	.321	9
1989 NY N	508	12	56	21	.258	21

We can see what he did in September two years ago. His stats for the same month last year: 8, 17, 7, .300.

If he could do this all year long, he's a $40 ballplayer. So that's the question then: Can he?

I really think so. For three months he swung at pitches that Frank Howard couldn't have reached. All he's got to do is quit that, which he more or less did. He just had a sophomore slump going for the Rookie of the Year award.

JOSE LIND	AB	HR	RBI	SB	BA	$
1987 PIT	143	0	11	2	.322	4
1988 PIT	611	2	49	15	.262	13
1989 PIT	578	2	48	15	.232	9

Bad year, and yet he only cost $2 more than this. People didn't believe in him when it looked like he was on the way up, so he should be an excellent buy now. As long as you don't think he's on the way down.

JOSE OQUENDO	AB	HR	RBI	SB	BA	$
1987 STL	248	1	24	4	.286	5
1988 STL	451	7	46	4	.277	13
1989 STL	556	1	48	3	.291	13

People paid in 1989 what he earned in 1988, which was the right amount.

LUIS QUINONES	AB	HR	RBI	SB	BA	$
1987 CHI N	101	0	8	0	.218	−1
1988 CIN	52	1	11	1	.231	2
1989 CIN	340	12	34	2	.244	10

Ron Oester instead? Keith Lockhart? One does suspect Luis is going to have a three-year scan for one year only.

WILLIE RANDOLPH	AB	HR	RBI	SB	BA	$
1987 NY A	449	7	67	11	.305	17
1988 NY A	404	2	34	8	.230	5
1989 LA	556	2	36	7	.282	13

Admirable year, and Willie probably has another decent one or two in him.

RYNE SANDBERG	AB	HR	RBI	SB	BA	$
1987 CHI N	523	16	59	21	.294	22
1988 CHI N	618	19	69	25	.264	28
1989 CHI N	606	30	76	15	.290	35

Every time the announcers would say in the playoffs, ''Look at him buckle in front of the curveball,'' I would look, and he would hit another rope to right center.

From all the talk about the changed weather in Wrigley, you would think Ryno got all 30 of his homers on the road. Zimmer's feisty style of play was forced on him by the gale winds blowing in, the way I heard Zimmer explain it.

Well, the Cubs hit more homers last year and scored more runs. Sandberg powered 16 of his dingers through the Wrigley gales. The Cubs did try to steal more, going 17-for-28 in their extra attempts. But I forgot: The wind was blowing in from left.

ROBBIE THOMPSON	AB	HR	RBI	SB	BA	$
1987 SF	420	10	44	16	.262	13
1988 SF	477	7	48	14	.264	15
1989 SF	547	13	50	12	.241	15

The playoffs and World Series were like his season before and after the all-star break.

JEFF TREADWAY	AB	HR	RBI	SB	BA	$
1987 CIN	84	2	4	1	.333	3
1988 CIN	301	2	23	2	.252	4
1989 ATL	473	8	40	3	.277	13

Batted .198 against left-handers, so Lemke's at least got a part-time future.

Player Z

Tim Teufel, Lenny Harris, Keith Miller, Mike Sharperson, in addition to those mentioned in the comments above. You might need to borrow Craig Reynolds, Domingo Ramos, or, yes, even Steve Jeltz from the shortstops.

NATIONAL LEAGUE SHORTSTOPS

JAY BELL

	AB	HR	RBI	SB	BA	$
1987 CLE	125	2	13	2	.216	1
1988 CLE	211	2	21	4	.218	1
1989 PIT	271	2	27	5	.258	6

Four of the columns continuously improving. Not bad.

JEFF BLAUSER

	AB	HR	RBI	SB	BA	$
1987 ATL	165	2	15	7	.242	3
1988 ATL	67	2	7	0	.239	2
1989 ATL	456	12	46	5	.270	15

Solid third baseman who's going to be many Rotisserie teams' superior shortstop.

SHAWON DUNSTON

	AB	HR	RBI	SB	BA	$
1987 CHI N	346	5	22	12	.246	6
1988 CHI N	575	9	56	30	.249	21
1989 CHI N	471	9	60	19	.278	22

Patton $ are very disappointing in this case. A buck improvement? How about 200 percent?

KEVIN ELSTER

	AB	HR	RBI	SB	BA	$
1988 NY N	406	9	37	2	.214	5
1989 NY N	458	10	55	4	.231	10

Davey Johnson finally got over his jealousy of Mark Belanger (for I've decided that's what it was) and played this guy, and he played exceedingly well.

ALFREDO GRIFFIN

	AB	HR	RBI	SB	BA	$
1987 OAK	494	3	60	26	.263	16
1988 LA	316	1	27	7	.199	1
1989 LA	506	0	29	10	.247	6

If you were Alfredo, would you be overjoyed to learn that a team that signs you owes no compensation, or would you be somewhat offended?

Elias ranks Dave Anderson ahead of him as a Type C player.

Well, if the point is to make money, Alfredo's made his point. Tony Fernandez chased him out of Toronto, and now Jose Offerman is going to chase him out of LA.

HOWARD JOHNSON	AB	HR	RBI	SB	BA	$
1987 NY N	554	36	99	32	.265	34
1988 NY N	495	24	68	23	.230	25
1989 NY N	571	36	101	41	.287	51

Jerry Heath should do a sort to see who bought Hojo *and* Mitchell.

The surprise isn't that Hojo ranks as the third biggest "winner"; rather, that five teams who bought him still finished last. Perhaps they did what the Mets so nearly did: panicked when he was making those bad throws in April and traded him. The $13 that you see the Pew and Brew League in Chapter 1 spending on Hojo is indication of the same malaise. Just like the Mets, always better to be lucky.

BARRY LARKIN	AB	HR	RBI	SB	BA	$
1987 CIN	439	12	43	21	.244	13
1988 CIN	588	12	56	40	.296	33
1989 CIN	325	4	36	10	.342	18

When he finally was reactivated by the Reds, it must have been a tough choice for teams that had him on reserve. He was going to bat at most once a game. He wasn't going to steal. But the hit that he had a comparatively huge chance of getting—wasn't that better than Jose Uribe?

SPIKE OWEN	AB	HR	RBI	SB	BA	$
1987 BOS	437	2	48	9	.259	9
1988 BOS	257	5	18	3	.249	3
1989 MON	437	6	41	3	.233	7

Batting right: .275. Batting left: .215. Jeff Huson (.304 at Indianapolis) bats left, as does Delino DeShields.

RAFAEL RAMIREZ	AB	HR	RBI	SB	BA	$
1987 ATL	179	1	21	6	.263	4
1988 HOU	566	6	59	3	.276	14
1989 HOU	537	6	54	3	.246	9

From time to time I'm going to keep trying to make sense of the Elias rankings, because they must make some sense. In fielding percentage over the last two years, Ramirez ranks 21. Twenty-one what, I'm not sure. Seventy-one players are ranked, and the highest number is 23. Nevertheless, 21 out of 23 can't be good. The 23rd player, Sharperson, has a higher fielding percentage than Ramirez, so it's not entirely clear what else besides fielding percentage goes into the fielding percentage rankings. But if Elias is saying Rafael is a bad fielder, I have no quarrel with that.

Eric Yelding didn't play enough to make any errors, so he ranks number one. It would seem he's going to get every opportunity to fall in Elias's esteem this season.

OZZIE SMITH	AB	HR	RBI	SB	BA	$
1987 STL	600	0	75	43	.303	27
1988 STL	575	3	51	57	.270	29
1989 STL	593	2	50	29	.273	21

The who-to-believe department.

The day before the season opens, you hear Ozzie is going on the disabled list. The draft starts in an hour; you run off to the AP office to read the ticker.

". . . lost one of their most indestructible players . . . torn muscle fibers in his rib cage."

Ozzie's no spring chicken, plus he's got a scrawny rib cage; take him down five dollars, minimum.

"Trainer Gieselmann said, 'Our track record on this thing is four to six weeks.' "

Ouch! Six dollars. Seven.

" '. . . Hopefully, we can beat the system . . . But the long-range forecast does not look good at all.' "

Ten dollars. Now let's start chopping some money off each Cardinal pitcher.

". . . Herzog was hopeful Smith could play by May 1, but cautioned Smith needs 'to be careful he doesn't reinjure it.' "

Yes; as usual, Whitey's cutting right to the truth: the kind of injury that could bother him all season.

" 'There's no way I'll be out a month,' said Smith."

Dream on, Ozzie. But make that $8. The guy's got spunk.

" 'I can get this out of the way and I'll be fresh the rest of the season,' said Smith, who will ride an exercise bicycle to keep his legs in shape . . ."

Determined fellow, isn't he? And he does have a point: When does he use his rib cage anyway? Certainly not throwing, and barely swinging. Five dollars.

" 'It's better to take 15 days off now instead of six or eight weeks later,' Smith said."

Whoa. Ten dollars. Ozzie's hurting and doesn't know how old he's gotten.

He played in 155 games.

GARRY TEMPLETON	AB	HR	RBI	SB	BA	$
1987 SD	510	5	48	14	.222	5
1988 SD	362	3	36	8	.249	8
1989 SD	506	6	40	1	.255	8

If he keeps this up, he's going to outearn Ozzie yet. In 1997.

ANDRES THOMAS	AB	HR	RBI	SB	BA	$
1987 ATL	324	5	39	6	.231	5
1988 ATL	606	13	68	7	.252	17
1989 ATL	554	13	57	3	.213	8

Bad year on defense as well.

DICKIE THON	AB	HR	RBI	SB	BA	$
1987 HOU	66	1	3	3	.212	1
1988 SD	258	1	18	19	.264	10
1989 PHI	435	15	60	6	.271	19

He didn't steal the bases he did way back in 1983, but otherwise his offense—stretched out to the 619 at-bats he had that year—was every bit as effective.

JOSE URIBE	AB	HR	RBI	SB	BA	$
1987 SF	309	5	30	12	.291	11
1988 SF	493	3	35	14	.252	10
1989 SF	453	1	30	6	.221	2

Uribe only had six sacrifices all year and was intentionally walked 12 times—evidence of bad managing on both sides.

MATT WILLIAMS	AB	HR	RBI	SB	BA	S
1987 SF	245	8	21	4	.188	1
1988 SF	156	8	19	0	.205	4
1989 SF	292	18	50	1	.202	11

When the decision was made to resume the Series, he said, "The fans will come out cheering and hollering. But I don't know if they'll be stomping their feet much."

The other natural disaster last fall, Hurricane Hugo, just did miss the baseball season. But in the South Atlantic League so many ballparks were blown away, it's not certain when or where the opening days will be this year. The Myrtle Beach Blue Jays had minimal damage, like broken windows and bent foul poles. "We were pretty fortunate," the general manager, Dan Rajkowski, said. "But it's certainly going to affect our business for 1990. It'll be tough to sell advertising to people who don't have restaurants anymore."

Player Z
Joey Cora didn't hit quite as well at Las Vegas last year as his old rival, Bip Roberts, did the year before, but he earned a September call-up and batted .316. Sure, in only 19 at-bats, but it must have been fun to see his name above Bip's in the *USA Today* final averages. If Templeton's knees give out, the two might find themselves playing side by side, trying to plug the left side of the infield, which will look like a mismatch.

A player to watch in winter ball is—ready?—Rey Quinones.

NATIONAL LEAGUE THIRD BASEMEN

BOBBY BONILLA	AB	HR	RBI	SB	BA	S
1987 PIT	466	15	77	3	.300	19
1988 PIT	584	24	100	3	.274	29
1989 PIT	616	24	86	8	.281	30

Presenting the Rotisserie all-stars: Hojo at short, Bobo at third. In the appendix Bonilla is the giant of the position, $10 better than the next player. Twenty games into the season, he'll qualify at another position.

KEN CAMINITI	AB	HR	RBI	SB	BA	$
1987 HOU	203	3	23	0	.246	2
1988 HOU	83	1	7	0	.181	0
1989 HOU	585	10	72	4	.255	15

The 1989 line should be his 1988 line and Bonilla's 1988 line should be his 1989 line.

RON GANT	AB	HR	RBI	SB	BA	$
1988 ATL	563	19	60	19	.259	24
1989 ATL	260	9	25	9	.177	5

Pitchers found a hole; now he has to cover it. September was inconclusive.

JEFF HAMILTON	AB	HR	RBI	SB	BA	$
1987 LA	83	0	1	0	.217	−1
1988 LA	309	6	33	0	.236	3
1989 LA	548	12	56	0	.245	11

Seems to have cleared Tracy Woodson from the scene, which is fine by me.

CHARLIE HAYES	AB	HR	RBI	SB	BA	$
1989 PHI	304	8	43	3	.257	11

His predecessor—what was his name? Mike somebody?—won't go into the Rotisserie Hall of Fame. There are no refunds.

VANCE LAW	AB	HR	RBI	SB	BA	$
1987 MON	436	12	56	8	.273	13
1988 CHI N	556	11	78	1	.293	21
1989 CHI N	408	7	42	2	.235	7

Perhaps I should have scanned Luis Salazar and made Vance Law the scrub. The person I really like at third for the Cubs is McClendon; however, in the past, what I like and Don Zimmer likes have borne little resemblance.

TERRY PENDLETON	AB	HR	RBI	SB	BA	$
1987 STL	583	12	96	19	.286	24
1988 STL	391	6	53	3	.253	11
1989 STL	613	13	74	9	.264	20

Has to hit more homers with Guerrero on base if he wants more ribbies.

RANDY READY	AB	HR	RBI	SB	BA	$
1987 SD	350	12	54	7	.309	16
1988 SD	331	7	39	6	.266	11
1989 SD/PHI	254	8	26	4	.264	9

Worth paying, oh, $3 for instead of $2, since he can also be an outfielder.

BIP ROBERTS	AB	HR	RBI	SB	BA	$
1987 SD	241	1	12	14	.253	5
1988 SD	9	0	0	0	.333	0
1989 SD	329	3	25	21	.301	17

The Pro-Ball League bought Bip for $9. This tells me they hold their draft in July.

Really, what's going on here? Not one of the new leagues bought him, and 20 of the 25 established leagues passed. How could two teams bid Bip that high?

Mike Pagliarulo is his backup.

CHRIS SABO	AB	HR	RBI	SB	BA	$
1988 CIN	538	11	44	46	.271	29
1989 CIN	304	6	29	14	.260	12

The average salary for Sabo in the established leagues: $8. (In the new leagues: $21.) This is why owners forgave or at least forgot him, while they goddamned Darryl Stawberry to the bitter end.

Heath's tracking of Kevin Mitchell shows he was bought in drafts by 21 teams that finished first in the hypothetical final standings; no team that bought his monster season finished last. The second-best player by this reckoning was Roberto Alomar: 25 firsts, five lasts. He had the kind of season Sabo was meant to have, and like Sabo was underpriced ($11 in the established leagues) because in most cases he was a freeze.

Sabo ranks 99th (out of 180): 12 teams won, 14 finished last.

Now, there are very good reasons for finishing last, usually lots of them. It's the rare team that makes so many blatantly boneheaded decisions that it actually deserves to finish last.

But, expectations aside, Sabo was not one of the reasons. He still managed to earn $12; just as Heath's numbers suggest, he was a wash.

TIM WALLACH	AB	HR	RBI	SB	BA	$
1987 MON	593	26	123	9	.298	30
1988 MON	592	12	69	2	.257	16
1989 MON	573	13	77	3	.277	20

Last year is probably about right for him.

Player Z

Unlike first base, there are at least some who are worth mentioning: Ernie Riles, Greg Litton. Darrell Evans, if he hangs on long enough to play in 1990. Hojo and Matt Williams, if you're desperate.

Which you may be. The reason there are no Player Z's at first is that the position is so settled: with the addition of Esasky, 10 regulars to be spread among 10 Rotisserie teams. Owners will thus be looking for 20 regular third basemen, whereas at best there are seven or eight.

NATIONAL LEAGUE OUTFIELDERS

ERIC ANTHONY	AB	HR	RBI	SB	BA	$
1989 HOU	61	4	7	0	.180	2

Excellent candidate for the 1991 Sophomore of the Year award.

KEVIN BASS	AB	HR	RBI	SB	BA	$
1987 HOU	592	19	85	21	.284	25
1988 HOU	541	14	72	31	.255	27
1989 HOU	313	5	44	11	.300	16

By the end of the free-agent auction, he looked like a bigger bargain than Esasky, and if he keeps the Giants just one game ahead of the

Padres and everyone else, he's dirt cheap. In any event, he should function nicely batting between Butler and Clark.

BARRY BONDS	AB	HR	RBI	SB	BA	$
1987 PIT	551	25	59	32	.261	25
1988 PIT	538	24	58	17	.283	29
1989 PIT	580	19	58	32	.248	28

Continued to hit better against lefties. Continued to leave bundles of runners on base when dropped down in the lineup. Vastly improved his base-stealing, to stay in the leadoff position and make me look bad.

HUBIE BROOKS	AB	HR	RBI	SB	BA	$
1987 MON	430	14	72	4	.263	13
1988 MON	588	20	90	7	.279	28
1989 MON	542	14	70	6	.268	20

Hubie's only 33? He seemed older than that when he was a rookie. But gee, there's plenty of baseball left in him. Can't imagine the Dodgers won't buy him.

TOM BRUNANSKY	AB	HR	RBI	SB	BA	$
1987 MIN	532	32	85	11	.259	21
1988 (MIN)/STL	572	23	85	17	.240	26
1989 STL	556	20	85	5	.239	20

Bruno's lifetime batting average is .247. His high (his rookie year) is .272; his low (his sophomore year), .227. As the three-year scan shows, he's settled in the middle of that range just about exactly. For some reason, consistency at this level seems more remarkable than the steady performances of high-average hitters.

BRETT BUTLER	AB	HR	RBI	SB	BA	$
1987 CLE	522	9	41	33	.295	23
1988 SF	568	6	43	43	.287	28
1989 SF	594	4	36	31	.283	22

Getting whipped in the World Series has to be a whole lot preferable to getting whipped in Cleveland.

JOE CARTER	AB	HR	RBI	SB	BA	$
1987 CLE	588	32	106	31	.264	32
1988 CLE	621	27	98	27	.271	36
1989 CLE	651	35	105	13	.243	31

When Frank Robinson came over to the Orioles in 1966, at the same age as Carter now, there was talk that he was past his prime. A generation later, Carter doesn't have to listen to that kind of guff, but there's still plenty of pressure on him: Sandy Alomar Jr., Chris James, Carlos Baerga and $9.3 million, as opposed to Milt Pappas.

VINCE COLEMAN	AB	HR	RBI	SB	BA	$
1987 STL	623	3	43	109	.289	44
1988 STL	616	3	38	81	.260	34
1989 STL	563	2	28	65	.254	29

A truly bad second half. It was as if one thrown-out-stealing and, poof, end of season. He will not be playing for Whitey again.

KAL DANIELS	AB	HR	RBI	SB	BA	$
1987 CIN	368	26	64	26	.334	31
1988 CIN	495	18	64	27	.291	31
1989 CIN/LA	171	4	17	9	.246	7

Gibson, Shelby, Marshall, Daniels . . . Who *did* play the outfield for the Dodgers last year?

ERIC DAVIS	AB	HR	RBI	SB	BA	$
1987 CIN	474	37	100	50	.293	44
1988 CIN	472	26	93	35	.273	39
1989 CIN	462	34	101	21	.281	40

Benzinger, invited to comment on the fact that he was the only Reds regular not to go on the DL, said, "I should be the rule, not the exception. The whole team should be like me."

Todd, if the whole team were like you, the Reds might not finish .500, whereas if the whole team were ED, they'd win 130 games.

ANDRE DAWSON	AB	HR	RBI	SB	BA	$
1987 CHI N	621	49	137	11	.287	39
1988 CHI N	591	24	79	12	.303	34
1989 CHI N	416	21	77	8	.252	23

The heart sinks . . . Unless you were a Giants fan, it got to the point where you prayed he wouldn't come to bat.

In fact, I suddenly realize that when you have no particular rooting interest—or if you have strong rooting interests evenly divided—your emotions are zero sum. For me, Kirk Gibson's hobble around the bases will always be linked with the expression on Eckersley's face. Mookie and Billy Buck. Last year, oddly enough, it was two players on the same team: Dawson and Grace.

LENNY DYKSTRA	AB	HR	RBI	SB	BA	$
1987 NY N	431	10	43	27	.285	**19**
1988 NY N	429	8	33	30	.270	**20**
1989 NY N/PHI	511	7	32	30	.237	**16**

Ended up batting .222 against lefties. That's not all that bad; I mean, Van Slyke would take it. It was the .243 against righties that did Nails in.

KIRK GIBSON	AB	HR	RBI	SB	BA	$
1987 DET	487	24	79	26	.277	**26**
1988 LA	542	25	76	31	.290	**38**
1989 LA	253	9	28	12	.213	**9**

The opening game of the season last year may have been the most deceiving: Dodgers against the Reds in Cincinnati. Winning pitcher: Jackson (5 innings, 4 hits, 2 earned runs, 2 walks). Losing pitcher: Belcher (2.1, 6, 4, 2). Save: Franco (2, 0, 0, 0). Kirk Gibson: 2-for-4, home run, stolen base.

Four good reasons to hold your draft the Sunday before.

TOMMY GREGG	AB	HR	RBI	SB	BA	$
1989 ATL	276	6	23	3	.243	**6**

I've been comparing the market prices in new leagues and old leagues for well-established talent available to all, like Jack Clark and Eddie Murray. What about rookies?

For Tommy Gregg, the average salary in Chapter 1 is $3. The average salary in Heath's 25 veteran leagues is $9, a quite substantial difference.

Gregg made $3 for the rookies, lost $3 for the veterans, but with his injury that seems moot. In any case, what we're trying to decide is, which group of bettors showed more savvy in April?

A factor, of course, is once again the freeze lists. The older leagues have fewer openings and more money to spend per opening. The new leagues have so many attractive outfielders to bid on that Tommy Gregg is not going to be a priority.

But he's key to the fortunes of both groups. Why? Because $3 or $9, he has a big up side. Jack Clark—at either salary ($24 or $30)—really doesn't.

The older leagues learn this quickly and that's why they pore over the minors. I have no prejudice in their favor—as I've said, these five start-up leagues are much sharper than my league was in its infancy—but my vote in the matter of Mr. Gregg goes to the geezers.

On the other hand, he will be available in this year's draft in some of the older leagues (he'll only be available in the one start-up league that didn't buy him at all); some of the geezers went a little nuts.

Gone! For $14 to Dodge This (S&D league). For $16 to the Younguns (Victor). For $25—twentee-fiive-dolllarrs!—to Dad's Devils (All in the Family). They finished ninth, eighth, and eighth.

KEN GRIFFEY SR.	AB	HR	RBI	SB	BA	$
1987 ATL	399	14	64	4	.286	15
1988 ATL/CIN	243	4	23	1	.255	5
1989 CIN	236	8	30	4	.263	9

Borderline Player Z, but will Junior be playing when he's 40?

Stats Inc. has a book that lists all hitters in both leagues alphabetically. Buy the book just to compare the two boxes. Junior's is—let's see—$3/8''$ high; Senior's takes the bulk of the page. Breaking in with the Big Red Machine was a little tougher than the Mariners, so the first year that Senior played as many games as Junior did last year was his third season, 1975. He had much higher batting and on-base averages, a somewhat lower slugging average. Curiously, they both stole 16 out of 23 bases.

The Tigers should sign Senior; I promise Sparky he's better than Chester. I'd go to Seattle to see them playing in the same game.

MARQUIS GRISSOM	AB	HR	RBI	SB	BA	$
1989 MON	74	1	2	1	.257	1

Keep an eye on him in the Dominican League; like Anthony, he's been galloped along so fast that he didn't even appear in the *Sporting News Baseball Register* as a minor leaguer.

TONY GWYNN	AB	HR	RBI	SB	BA	$
1987 SD	589	7	54	56	.370	**42**
1988 SD	521	7	70	26	.313	**29**
1989 SD	604	4	62	40	.336	**37**

I've given up worrying about whether the Red Sox are going to deal Boggs or not. I almost hope they do—to the National League. He and Gwynn would be in each other's dreams.

BILLY HATCHER	AB	HR	RBI	SB	BA	$
1987 HOU	564	11	63	53	.296	**32**
1988 HOU	530	7	52	32	.268	**23**
1989 HOU/PIT	481	4	51	24	.231	**14**

His earnings are going . . . going . . . and he'll soon be gone.

MICKEY HATCHER	AB	HR	RBI	SB	BA	$
1987 LA	287	7	42	2	.282	**9**
1988 LA	191	1	25	0	.293	**6**
1989 LA	224	2	25	1	.295	**7**

He is Player Z material; but he's been Player Z for 11 years now, which is itself an accomplishment.

RON JONES	AB	HR	RBI	SB	BA	$
1988 PHI	124	8	26	0	.290	**9**
1989 PHI	31	2	4	1	.290	**2**

Knee still in a brace in November.

JOHN KRUK	AB	HR	RBI	SB	BA	$
1987 SD	447	20	91	18	.313	**28**
1988 SD	378	9	44	5	.241	**10**
1989 SD/PHI	357	8	44	3	.300	**15**

Other than 1987, in nine professional baseball seasons, Kruk has never hit more than 11 home runs. Except for 1981 in Walla Walla—and 1988, of course—he's never hit less than .300. A fine hitter who's back within himself.

FRED LYNN	AB	HR	RBI	SB	BA	$
1987 BAL	396	23	60	3	.253	12
1988 BAL/DET	391	25	56	2	.246	16
1989 DET	353	11	46	1	.241	9

Freddie's finally as old (38) as he acts. Why he's on this team, and Mark Davis isn't, beats the heck out of me.

LLOYD MCCLENDON	AB	HR	RBI	SB	BA	$
1987 CIN	72	2	13	1	.208	1
1988 CIN	137	3	14	4	.219	3
1989 CHI N	259	12	40	6	.286	15

A great scan! Improving in every category during his first three years. What are the odds? And more to the point, what are the odds he'll make it four years?

Except for batting average, damn good.

ODDIBE MCDOWELL	AB	HR	RBI	SB	BA	$
1987 TEX	407	14	52	24	.241	16
1988 TEX	437	6	37	33	.247	20
1989 CLE/ATL	519	10	46	27	.266	22

He batted so well in the National League, it was as if he was a rookie again. If so, pitchers have figured him out before.

WILLIE MCGEE	AB	HR	RBI	SB	BA	$
1987 STL	620	11	105	16	.285	23
1988 STL	562	3	50	41	.292	27
1989 STL	199	3	17	8	.236	6

Thompson filled in so well that the Cardinals really didn't miss him. Not that that's any comfort to people who didn't have Thompson.

KEVIN MCREYNOLDS	AB	HR	RBI	SB	BA	$
1987 NY N	590	29	95	14	.276	26
1988 NY N	552	27	99	21	.288	38
1989 NY N	545	22	85	15	.272	29

The pressure of playing in Kevin Mitchell's shadow finally got to him.

MIKE MARSHALL	AB	HR	RBI	SB	BA	$
1987 LA	402	16	72	0	.294	16
1988 LA	542	20	82	4	.277	25
1989 LA	377	11	42	2	.260	12

The Dodgers should offer him to the Orioles for Mike Devereaux.

DAVE MARTINEZ	AB	HR	RBI	SB	BA	$
1987 CHI N	459	8	36	16	.292	15
1988 CHI N/MON	447	6	46	23	.255	17
1989 MON	361	3	27	23	.274	15

Worth investing in if you plan to freeze Grissom.

KEVIN MITCHELL	AB	HR	RBI	SB	BA	$
1987 SD/SF	464	22	70	9	.280	20
1988 SF	505	19	80	5	.251	21
1989 SF	543	47	125	3	.291	45

Speaking of the devil.

He had a Willie Mays-type spring training in Phoenix. Was that the clue?

Hardly. Lots of players do in Arizona.

The market prices in the older leagues ($17 average, including freezes) give no more premonition of his season than the prices in the start-up leagues.

Now that he's here, though, we want to know, is he staying here? Not if you listen to Brett Butler; Mitchell, as we were told so often, is the good player having a great year.

You know, Brett? Even if you were right, I'd retract that.

But I don't think he's right. Mitchell is the good player having a few great years, like Roger Maris. I'd bet him back up to $40.

DALE MURPHY	AB	HR	RBI	SB	BA	$
1987 ATL	566	44	105	16	.295	36
1988 ATL	592	24	77	3	.226	19
1989 ATL	574	20	84	3	.228	17

It's taken Murph the last two years to earn what he earned in '87 and even so, the 1989 RBI total is misleading. His doubles and triples dropped from 39 to 16; strikeouts up, walks down. His intentional bases on balls in the last three seasons have gone from 29 to 16 to 10.

PAUL O'NEILL	AB	HR	RBI	SB	BA	$
1988 CIN	485	16	73	8	.252	20
1989 CIN	428	15	74	20	.276	27

The third year of this three-year scan should show a jump over '89 in the first three columns, a decrease in the fourth, and no change in the last two. How's that for specific?

TIM RAINES	AB	HR	RBI	SB	BA	$
1987 MON	530	18	68	50	.330	39
1988 MON	429	12	48	33	.270	25
1989 MON	517	9	60	41	.286	32

It's quite simple: Rock is a hard-nosed ballplayer who's been pounded to a pulp sliding into second. He's playing his own game, not Rickey's. Or ours.

R. J. REYNOLDS	AB	HR	RBI	SB	BA	$
1987 PIT	335	7	51	14	.260	12
1988 PIT	323	6	51	15	.248	14
1989 PIT	363	6	48	22	.270	19

All-time-great fifth outfielder, but don't promote him; he's getting on, and $8 of those $19 last year are wrapped up in stolen bases.

ROLANDO ROOMES	AB	HR	RBI	SB	BA	$
1989 CIN	315	7	34	12	.263	13

Might have had the worst strikeout frequency, combined with strike-outs-to-walks ratio, ever recorded by anyone who was meant to be a hitter.

JUAN SAMUEL	AB	HR	RBI	SB	BA	$
1987 PHI	655	28	100	35	.272	33
1988 PHI	629	12	67	33	.243	24
1989 PHI/NY N	532	11	45	42	.235	24

When the Mets were out of it and he was totally bummed, he kept hustling. Nothing to do with incentives or free agency; it's the way he is. That's why I'm very worried about him. Talent is harder to retrieve.

JOHN SHELBY	AB	HR	RBI	SB	BA	$
1987 (BAL)/LA	508	22	72	16	.272	21
1988 LA	494	10	64	16	.263	20
1989 LA	345	1	12	10	.183	−1

He's always seemed like, well, a pitcher.

DWIGHT SMITH	AB	HR	RBI	SB	BA	$
1989 CHI N	343	9	52	9	.324	21

The Cubs are supposedly willing to trade him. They're crazy.

LONNIE SMITH	AB	HR	RBI	SB	BA	$
1987 KC	167	3	8	9	.251	4
1988 ATL	114	3	9	4	.237	3
1989 ATL	482	21	79	25	.315	37

"Everybody knew about Lonnie Smith," a friend of mine said, rehashing the season. (Steve Levy, who introduced me years ago to *Baseball America*. "What? You've never heard of it?—Oh my god, what have I done? Telling Patton about *Baseball America* is like giving the A-bomb to the PLO!") Steve isn't even in a National League Rotisserie, and he noticed Lonnie in winter ball.

So let's go once more to the average salary in the geezer leagues . . . $10. Hmmm. I wouldn't say everybody knew, Steve, but that *is* twice what the new guys spent.

I'm pretty sure they've already sent in their subscriptions.

DARRYL STRAWBERRY	AB	HR	RBI	SB	BA	$
1987 NY N	532	39	104	36	.284	39
1988 NY N	543	39	101	29	.269	45
1989 NY N	476	29	77	11	.225	24

Say one thing for the Straw Man: He isn't stats-conscious. Two years ago he wouldn't steal second in the last week to get 30. Last year he didn't care about 30 homers. And that's all right. But the trouble is, he wouldn't play either. The Mets—Frank Cashen as well as Davey Johnson—are gutless wonders for allowing that.

It's worth noting that Hojo all by himself made up for the drop-offs by Strawberry and McReynolds. Their top three hitters had the same production as last year, and the team, even with the efforts of Hernandez and Carter, led the National League in home runs. They were third in RBIs, second in steals. Second in ERA. I don't see another Rotisserie team in the league to compete with them.

MILT THOMPSON	AB	HR	RBI	SB	BA	$
1987 PHI	527	7	43	46	.302	27
1988 PHI	378	2	33	17	.288	14
1989 STL	545	4	68	27	.290	26

Played a good center field, too.

ANDY VAN SLYKE	AB	HR	RBI	SB	BA	$
1987 PIT	564	21	82	34	.293	31
1988 PIT	587	25	100	30	.288	41
1989 PIT	476	9	53	16	.237	15

This is what a rib-cage injury can do to you if you're not Ozzie Smith.

JEROME WALTON	AB	HR	RBI	SB	BA	$
1989 CHI N	475	5	46	24	.293	22

Attention all passengers: Sophomore slump about to board.

GLENN WILSON	AB	HR	RBI	SB	BA	$
1987 PHI	569	14	54	3	.264	11
1988 SEA/(PIT)	410	5	32	0	.256	5
1989 PIT/HOU	432	11	64	1	.266	15

Seems to be back to his old self, which is more or less the average player.

GERALD YOUNG	AB	HR	RBI	SB	BA	$
1987 HOU	274	1	15	26	.321	14
1988 HOU	576	0	37	65	.257	27
1989 HOU	533	0	38	34	.233	14

Bad on-base average, horrendous stolen-base percentage, but he can catch the ball. Choices are to quit or go to the American League and bat ninth.

Player Z

There's Marvell Wynne. Don't laugh. In the past two years, he has hit well over .300 against lefties. With the kind of swing he has, it may not be a fluke. (But the only manager who might be inclined to find that out is Earl Weaver, busy with make-work in Florida.)

There's Mike Davis. I don't mind if you laugh.

There's Carmelo Martinez. He should have gone to Japan ages ago, but if he's still around, he also qualifies at first.

There's Herm Winningham. He may be self-destructing right now, and he may be in winter ball.

In fact, there's a lot of there here: Franklin Stubbs, Mike Aldrete, Geronimo Berroa, John Cangelosi, Terry Puhl, Pat Sheridan, Chris Ford, Dave Clark—just try not to have more than one of them on your team.

Don't try to save Jerald Clark until the end. Put him out early, I'm telling you. You saw what happened with Tommy Gregg.

NATIONAL LEAGUE PITCHERS

LARRY ANDERSEN	IP	W	SV	ERA	RATIO	$
1987 HOU	102	9	5	3.45	12.04	12
1988 HOU	83	2	5	2.94	11.11	7
1989 HOU	88	4	3	1.54	8.93	16

Could he throw this well in the ninth inning? If I were Houston, I'd find out.

No one else will get the chance to find out, thanks to the Elias rating system. Andersen's got to be ready to go on stri—to write his congressman about this issue alone.

If he were a Type C player after 1988, he'd have been a free agent this winter. Back when he signed with Houston, both sides thought he was Type C, but the Players Association—not exactly looking out for his interests—discovered some technicality that upgraded him to Type

B, and he became, at 37, eligible for arbitration instead. "I figured there would be some teams interested, so this could cost me," said Andersen. "I'm just confused how it happened."

STEVE BEDROSIAN	IP	W	SV	ERA	RATIO	$
1987 PHI	89	5	40	2.83	10.82	**43**
1988 PHI	74	6	28	3.75	12.35	**24**
1989 PHI/SF	85	3	23	2.87	10.10	**25**

A good old-fashioned fire sale. Unlike Rotisserie teams, the Phillies could just as well have fire-saled before the season, except that they have tickets to sell. They waited, fooling no one, and it could have backfired. If LaCoss had worked out for the Giants the way Jeff Russell did for Texas, no contender would have needed Bedrosian enough to pay the price. That's why the price wasn't higher than it was.

Perhaps because Bedrock used to be his teammate, it makes me think back to Dale Murphy. Why wasn't he fire-sold? Were real general managers as tuned in to a superstar's decline as Rotisserie owners? They seldom are. Or was it just their good fortune that Cox, as usual, had the fire-sale business all snarled in his head, asking the contending team to make *him* a contending team?

TIM BELCHER	IP	W	SV	ERA	RATIO	$
1987 LA N	34	4	0	2.38	9.79	**7**
1988 LA N	180	12	4	2.91	9.72	**19**
1989 LA N	230	15	1	2.82	10.25	**20**

If the season had gone a few weeks longer, he would have gotten that ratio under 10.

ANDY BENES	IP	W	SV	ERA	RATIO	$
1989 SD	67	6	0	3.51	11.07	**4**

His ratio and ERA went kablooey in his last game of the season. An auspicious start, to say the least.

MIKE BIELECKI	IP	W	SV	ERA	RATIO	$
1987 PIT	46	2	0	4.73	10.84	**1**
1988 CHI N	48	2	0	3.35	13.22	**−1**
1989 CHI N	212	18	0	3.14	11.36	**14**

Six of the 25 veteran leagues bought him in the draft.

JOE BOEVER	IP	W	SV	ERA	RATIO	$
1987 ATL	18	1	0	7.36	20.13	−5
1988 ATL	20	0	1	1.77	5.75	5
1989 ATL	82	4	21	3.94	12.24	17

Faded so badly that he barely returned any profits. As a matter of fact, the average salary in the older leagues was $17.

OIL CAN BOYD	IP	W	SV	ERA	RATIO	$
1987 BOS	37	1	0	5.89	13.75	−3
1988 BOS	130	9	0	5.34	13.05	−4
1989 BOS	59	3	0	4.42	11.59	1

A slick move by the Expos: the Can is bound to fill Pascual's shoes.

TOM BROWNING	IP	W	SV	ERA	RATIO	$
1987 CIN	183	10	0	5.02	12.89	−2
1988 CIN	251	18	0	3.41	9.66	18
1989 CIN	250	15	0	3.39	10.99	12

As long as those bases-empty homers don't bother him, they don't especially bother his owners.

TIM BURKE	IP	W	SV	ERA	RATIO	$
1987 MON	91	7	18	1.19	8.01	37
1988 MON	82	3	18	3.40	11.96	15
1989 MON	85	9	28	2.55	9.57	35

Terrific pitcher in two of the last three years. Without those salaries in front of us, we might think it was 3-for-3.

DON CARMAN	IP	W	SV	ERA	RATIO	$
1987 PHI	211	13	0	4.22	11.22	11
1988 PHI	201	10	0	4.29	12.56	−6
1989 PHI	149	5	0	5.24	14.34	−16

Occasionally, as a necessary caution, I leave a pitcher in the profiles who's probably become Player Ex.

NORM CHARLTON	IP	W	SV	ERA	RATIO	$
1988 CIN	61	4	0	3.96	11.74	0
1989 CIN	95	8	0	2.93	10.10	10

By every measurement except saves, he pitched much better than Franco, and slightly better than Myers.

MARTY CLARY	IP	W	SV	ERA	RATIO	$
1988 ATL	15	0	0	6.14	14.73	−3
1989 ATL	109	4	0	3.15	11.10	4

I'm probably getting him confused with Chuck Cary, but I keep checking to see if he's a lefty. Since he's not, I don't like him.

PAT COMBS	IP	W	SV	ERA	RATIO	$
1989 PHI	39	4	0	2.10	9.78	6

Everyone likes this fellow.

For as long as possible, I delay writing the comments (so much better to talk about a trade after it's happened); therefore I know what lurks later in the book, while readers presumably don't. If I want to give equal time, sometimes it has to come ahead of time.

Richard Gurnett of the FURL league in Wisconsin writes: "The most important change this year was going to the Ultra way of playing. It was great! The league unanimously voted to continue the system and then poured Yoo-Hoo over Rick Gaub's head. The waitresses at O'Shea's look forward to this each October, because we let them help us."

So they're not going to go along with what I say in Chapter 4.

Bruce Grabell of the Ron Hodges Memorial League in Connecticut says, "To be honest, the attitude of the owners who voted against Ultra [Notes, Hawks, Dogs] reflects their lack of effort and understanding; between them they have three money finishes ever and little prospect of the money this year."

So, evidently, only a few owners in this league are going to agree with me.

Mike Fenger of the dBBL league in California: "I liked the Ultra rules on the whole . . . I really don't think the reserve draft is any more of a crapshoot than the entire business . . . My own dark-horse pick, who I drafted late this year and still have my eye on to pick up cheap if I can, is Brian Jordan of the Cardinals' chain—it isn't a good sign, though, that he's currently on the Atlanta Falcons' injured reserve list.''

Another, albeit less rabid dissenter.

Which is okay. I'm glad they didn't feel hosed by a sexy-sounding, half-baked idea prominently featured on the cover of a book. But I've combed over the reserve lists of these and other Ultra leagues—God knows how many players, many more than 170, names like Newsome and Procter and Wilmet and Mussina—and I just can't seem to locate this 1988 first-round draft pick by the Phillies.

The lists are great. Every league plucks off Andy Benes, for instance, in a blink. But when you've got a crafty new lefty like Combs in there shutting your hitters down, he should play. He earned more than Viola, who should play also.

DAVID CONE	IP	W	SV	ERA	RATIO	$
1987 NY N	99	5	0	3.71	11.91	5
1988 NY N	231	20	0	2.22	10.04	26
1989 NY N	220	14	0	3.52	10.53	12

In the early part of the season he looked like a sportswriter trying to be a pitcher.

DENNIS COOK	IP	W	SV	ERA	RATIO	$
1988 SF	22	2	0	2.86	8.18	3
1989 SF/PHI	121	7	0	3.72	11.01	4

If it was the Giants' idea to showcase him to the Phillies when they called him up, he more than cooperated with a 1.90 ERA in two starts. How did the Giants know he wasn't Combs? What a shock it must have been for Cook.

JOHN COSTELLO	IP	W	SV	ERA	RATIO	$
1988 STL	50	5	1	1.81	12.50	6
1989 STL	62	5	3	3.32	9.82	8

I wonder if the law of competitive balance applies to ERA and ratio? Surely Costello lucked out of some runs in '88; last year it looks like some hard-luck runs were scored on him. That ratio and Worrell's injury make him mighty interesting.

RON DARLING	IP	W	SV	ERA	RATIO	$
1987 NY N	208	12	0	4.29	12.07	**7**
1988 NY N	241	17	0	3.25	10.40	**15**
1989 NY N	217	14	0	3.52	11.76	**6**

The appendix will show you that his wins were worth $10; in other words . . .

DANNY DARWIN	IP	W	SV	ERA	RATIO	$
1987 HOU	196	9	10	4.29	11.64	**19**
1988 HOU	192	8	13	3.84	11.11	**13**
1989 HOU	122	11	7	2.36	9.22	**23**

For the first time in his 12-year career, he never started a game, which clearly suited him just fine.

MARK DAVIS	IP	W	SV	ERA	RATIO	$
1987 SF/SD	133	9	2	3.99	12.32	**7**
1988 SD	98	5	28	2.01	10.25	**33**
1989 SD	93	4	44	1.85	9.42	**48**

Not surprisingly, there's a correlation between Heath's "winners and losers" and my top profit-makers in the previous chapter. Mark Davis (30 firsts, 4 lasts) ranks first among pitchers in the Heath leagues, Tim Burke (20 and 5), fourth; each averaged $23 in profits.

Pitchers two through four are starters who did well but didn't cost much: Jose DeLeon, Joe Magrane, and John Smiley (the cost of all three in the older leagues was $23, compared to $25 in the start-up leagues). After Burke, the ranking continues (with the average salaries in the older leagues): Tim Belcher ($7), Bryn Smith ($6), Randy Myers ($17), Mitch Williams ($22) . . . nothing terribly eye-catching. You have to go all the way to the 25th pitcher, Chris Carpenter ($6), before you find a Heath "winner" (9 and 5) who clearly lost money.

With the departure of Davis to the American League, all NL relievers—not just the obvious case of Craig Lefferts—should get higher salaries on the open market.

KEN DAYLEY	IP	W	SV	ERA	RATIO	$
1987 STL	61	9	4	2.66	12.54	**12**
1988 STL	55	2	5	2.77	10.90	**7**
1989 STL	75	4	12	2.87	11.11	**14**

His value has always been indexed with Worrell's, making it hard to figure this year.

JOSE DELEON	IP	W	SV	ERA	RATIO	$
1987 CHI A	206	11	0	4.02	11.97	8
1988 STL	225	13	0	3.67	11.34	5
1989 STL	245	16	0	3.05	9.31	23

Earned $10 with his ratio!

JIM DESHAIES	IP	W	SV	ERA	RATIO	$
1987 HOU	152	11	0	4.62	12.20	4
1988 HOU	207	11	0	3.00	10.26	13
1989 HOU	226	15	0	2.91	10.33	18

Very similar to Browning, except that he pitches in the Astrodome.

ROB DIBBLE	IP	W	SV	ERA	RATIO	$
1988 CIN	59	1	0	1.82	9.71	6
1989 CIN	99	10	2	2.09	9.18	18

A suggestion for Lou Piniella: Make him a starter, tell him to go like hell for five innings, then bring in Tommy John.

DOUG DRABEK	IP	W	SV	ERA	RATIO	$
1987 PIT	176	11	0	3.88	10.79	13
1988 PIT	219	15	0	3.08	10.01	17
1989 PIT	244	14	0	2.80	10.46	18

The explanation I'll be looking for in Syd Thrift's book is how he slipped Rhoden to the Yankees for Drabek, and then got hired by the Yankees after he was fired by the Pirates.

SID FERNANDEZ	IP	W	SV	ERA	RATIO	$
1987 NY N	156	12	0	3.81	11.37	12
1988 NY N	187	12	0	3.03	9.48	16
1989 NY N	219	14	0	2.83	9.52	21

Happened to catch El Sid's first major league home run on the tube;

replay showed his right leg went up à la Ott and was still in the air when he connected!

JOHN FRANCO	IP	W	SV	ERA	RATIO	$
1987 CIN	82	8	32	2.52	11.30	**38**
1988 CIN	86	6	39	1.57	9.10	**45**
1989 CIN	81	4	32	3.12	12.61	**27**

If he and Randy Myers have their games on VCR, as I imagine they do, they should get together to compare the boos they both heard in the second half. Franco, pitching much less effectively, no doubt was treated more politely. Now that Myers is gone, Mets fans feel a little guilty about their manners, since they secretly liked him a lot. Therefore, if Franco starts out pitching badly, he's going right off the boo meter.

McIlvaine must be satisfied that Franco's second half was one of those things (perhaps one of the many Pete Rose things), and that, of course, is the question before us: Was it? Do we discount his second half as a slump or do we give it extra weight precisely because it's the most recent evidence we have?

Mechanical projections of player stats have no sex appeal to me at all, but done carefully I guess they can't do any harm. John Benson, one of the more respectable touts to be found in the classifieds of *Baseball America* and *The Sporting News,* in the past has gone with the extra-weight theory. If he's still doing that this year, Franco's going to be hard to distinguish from Don Aase.

As the trade deadline approaches, to be sure, we also ponder the first half/second half splits. Just like a horse running in the Derby, if a player goes out "too fast," we're tempted to trade him.

At the all-star break last year, Franco had 22 saves and a 1.35 ERA. You look at his 1989 line above and say, Why didn't you take one of the offers, you knucklehead?

Here's why: At the halfway point the year before, Franco had 12 saves and 1.81 ERA; in the second half he managed 27 saves and a 1.31 ERA.

MARK GARDNER	IP	W	SV	ERA	RATIO	$
1989 MON	26	0	0	5.13	12.65	**−2**

Hope he's not Bob Sebra; he's listed here because I don't think he is, and because the Expos might have to get Bob Sebra back to play this season.

SCOTT GARRELTS	IP	W	SV	ERA	RATIO	$
1987 SF	106	11	12	3.22	10.61	24
1988 SF	98	5	13	3.58	11.57	12
1989 SF	193	14	0	2.28	9.08	25

So many of the Giant pitchers were obviously out of gas by the post-season that it's a shame the Padres didn't get their shot in the last three games; might have been interesting.

TOM GLAVINE	IP	W	SV	ERA	RATIO	$
1987 ATL	50	2	0	3.22	15.74	− 6
1988 ATL	195	7	0	4.56	12.16	− 8
1989 ATL	186	14	0	3.68	10.26	12

Huge swing from the red to the black that signifies, um—I'm not sure.

DWIGHT GOODEN	IP	W	SV	ERA	RATIO	$
1987 NY N	180	15	0	, 3.21	10.75	20
1988 NY N	248	18	0	3.19	10.84	14
1989 NY N	118	9	1	2.89	10.65	11

Keep your fingers crossed.

JIM GOTT	IP	W	SV	ERA	RATIO	$
1987 SF/PIT	87	1	13	3.12	12.52	13
1988 PIT	77	6	34	3.49	10.47	33
1989 PIT	1	0	0	0.00	27.00	0

His season ended on April 6, so you can pretty much tell which leagues held their drafts a week into the season by looking at his market prices. This year the big question will be how high the market wants to drive his price for the people who already have Jay Howell.

KEVIN GROSS	IP	W	SV	ERA	RATIO	$
1987 PHI	201	9	0	4.35	13.07	0
1988 PHI	232	12	0	3.69	11.58	3
1989 MON	201	11	0	4.38	12.34	− 3

He's pitched over 600 innings, winning 32 games, in the last three seasons, and it all adds up to zero.

GREG W. HARRIS	IP	W	SV	ERA	RATIO	$
1988 SD	18	2	0	1.50	8.00	**4**
1989 SD	135	8	6	2.60	10.53	**16**

No one who has him cheap is about to part with him. More effective setting up Davis than starting, he could end up being a more effective stopper than Lefferts.

OREL HERSHISER	IP	W	SV	ERA	RATIO	$
1987 LA	265	16	1	3.06	10.92	**26**
1988 LA	267	23	1	2.26	9.47	**34**
1989 LA	257	15	0	2.31	10.62	**22**

Here's the first very clear evidence (at least the first that I've noticed) of what the rabbit ball in '87 did to pitchers' earnings. Orel had a higher ERA and ratio than he did last year, but they were worth more.

The competitive-balance law—I'm not sure why we don't just call it the law of averages, or payback—hit him in the face in September. The Dodgers came close to equaling his streak of the year before, scoring six runs for him in his last 61 innings.

In Chapter 1 he looks like he's in Chapter 11, losing $13. The older leagues spent an average of $25, so he more or less breaks even (and, indeed, his record is 9 and 8 in the Heath leagues). But let's get to the point.

He's an absolutely sensational pitcher; has been in five of the last six years. The only player to win 20 games in each of the last three years, Dave Stewart, has earned an average of $22 over that period. Hershiser's averaged $27.

If the Dodgers had somehow gotten to the World Series again, with time out for the earthquake, they probably would have won it again.

KEN HILL	IP	W	SV	ERA	RATIO	$
1989 STL	197	7	0	3.80	13.04	**−5**

Much more impressive than his salary would suggest.

JAY HOWELL	IP	W	SV	ERA	RATIO	$
1987 OAK	44	3	16	5.89	14.01	**14**
1988 LA	65	5	21	2.08	9.00	**27**
1989 LA	80	5	28	1.58	9.26	**35**

People must have been afraid the Dodgers were hiding the fact that his arm was sore, and perhaps they were, yet his numbers in the end were even better than they appear here. Only three home runs and 16 unintentional walks.

KEN HOWELL	IP	W	SV	ERA	RATIO	$
1987 LA	55	3	1	4.91	13.58	−1
1988 LA	13	0	0	6.39	14.21	−2
1989 PHI	204	12	0	3.44	10.63	22

If there's a superficial resemblance to Dave Stewart's career, it doesn't stand up under inspection. Would Stewart say—after five wild pitches, one shy of the major league record—"I wish I could have broken it"?

BRUCE HURST	IP	W	SV	ERA	RATIO	$
1987 BOS	239	15	0	4.41	11.86	12
1988 BOS	217	18	0	3.66	11.92	13
1989 SD	245	15	0	2.69	10.30	20

The older leagues spent exactly the same as the new leagues ($21), and he gave a better return than either Murray or Clark.

Nevertheless, no profits. In the Heath rankings he's 5 and 8; that puts him quite far down (88 out of 125), but the middle ground is flukish (Dibble is 8 and 9). What's significant is that Hurst is either a winner or a loser in only 13 leagues.

But Bruce proved he didn't need Fenway Park, and the earnings show that he pitched better in the National League context than he had in the American League.

DANNY JACKSON	IP	W	SV	ERA	RATIO	$
1987 KC	224	9	0	4.02	13.18	4
1988 CIN	261	23	0	2.73	9.56	28
1989 CIN	116	6	0	5.60	13.93	−12

If a hitter's batting average rising from .273 to .560 is the wrong analogy, try picturing a .273 hitter dropping 287 points.

BOB KNEPPER	IP	W	SV	ERA	RATIO	$
1987 HOU	178	8	0	5.27	14.18	−9
1988 HOU	175	14	0	3.14	11.47	9
1989 HOU/SF	165	7	0	5.13	14.45	−16

The biggest loser in the Heath leagues. But, since I didn't have him, he gained in my esteem. After he blasted the Houston owner for being a carpetbagger, reporters asked Knepper what he thought now of the rumor he was going to be traded to Boston. He replied that he'd already listed with a realtor there.

Notice that it will be a long commute.

MIKE LACOSS	IP	W	SV	ERA	RATIO	$
1987 SF	171	13	0	3.68	13.00	8
1988 SF	114	7	0	3.62	11.49	3
1989 SF	150	10	6	3.17	12.45	9

He didn't cost much even in the older leagues (top bid $11), so his inability to do the job was uniformly predicted.

LES LANCASTER	IP	W	SV	ERA	RATIO	$
1987 CHI N	132	8	0	4.90	12.85	1
1988 CHI N	86	4	5	3.78	12.92	5
1989 CHI N	73	4	8	1.36	9.29	18

Another convincing display of the power of a middle reliever; his ERA and ratio were worth more than Reuschel's.

BILL LANDRUM	IP	W	SV	ERA	RATIO	$
1987 CIN	65	3	2	4.71	14.12	−1
1988 CHI N	12	1	0	5.84	16.05	−2
1989 PIT	81	2	26	1.67	9.78	31

The Pirates' management kept pointing to Gott's injury as one of the excuses for the team's poor season, yet Landrum pitched better last year than Gott did the year before. This year, more of the same from Landrum, for a fraction of what Gott's costing the Dodgers.

TIM LEARY	IP	W	SV	ERA	RATIO	$
1987 LA	108	3	1	4.76	13.08	−2
1988 LA	229	17	0	2.91	10.12	19
1989 LA/CIN	207	8	0	3.52	11.87	2

In December he was being shopped around rather furiously by the Reds.

That's because, by the time the Leary-Daniels trade was made last season, both teams were well out of it, and a time-honored tradition akin to fire sales was being observed: Slip each other your damaged goods.

CRAIG LEFFERTS	IP	W	SV	ERA	RATIO	$
1987 SD/SF	99	5	2	3.83	11.36	7
1988 SF	92	3	11	2.92	9.46	16
1989 SF	107	2	20	2.69	9.67	24

How come the Padres started counting pennies when it came time for a relief pitcher? You have to win to get your investment back when you've spent what they have, so you'd better spend more. A pitcher who is sure to blow five games, at least, that Mark Davis wouldn't have has somehow conned his way onto the team.

ROGER MCDOWELL	IP	W	SV	ERA	RATIO	$
1987 NY N	89	7	25	4.16	12.44	24
1988 NY N	89	5	16	2.63	11.22	19
1989 NY N/PHI	92	4	23	1.96	11.45	26

Nineteen saves, 1.11 ERA with the Phillies. (Bedrosian with the Giants: 17 saves, 2.65 ERA.)

GREG MADDUX	IP	W	SV	ERA	RATIO	$
1987 CHI N	156	6	0	5.61	14.71	−13
1988 CHI N	249	18	0	3.18	11.24	12
1989 CHI N	238	19	0	2.95	11.48	15

If Maddux had repeated his second-half form of 1988, 1989 would have been 1987 all over again.

JOE MAGRANE	IP	W	SV	ERA	RATIO	$
1987 STL	170	9	0	3.54	11.49	11
1988 STL	165	5	0	2.18	10.02	13
1989 STL	235	18	0	2.91	11.16	16

Got a good payback in the wins department, but he blew the Cy Young Award in September.

RICK MAHLER	IP	W	SV	ERA	RATIO	$
1987 ATL	197	8	0	4.98	13.57	−6
1988 ATL	249	9	0	3.69	11.60	1
1989 ATL	221	9	0	3.83	11.95	0

Won one game after June 8.

DENNIS MARTINEZ	IP	W	SV	ERA	RATIO	$
1987 MON	145	11	0	3.30	10.74	15
1988 MON	235	15	0	2.72	10.33	18
1989 MON	232	16	0	3.18	10.71	15

The average salary for him was $3 less than for Greg Maddux. There was more faith in Maddux, who'd only had one half of one good year, than in Martinez, who doesn't seem to have had a drink in years.

RAMON MARTINEZ	IP	W	SV	ERA	RATIO	$
1988 LA	36	1	0	3.79	12.36	−1
1989 LA	99	6	0	3.19	10.95	6

If his innings are stretched out to 232, he's Dennis's twin.

MIKE MORGAN	IP	W	SV	ERA	RATIO	$
1987 SEA	207	12	0	4.65	12.96	4
1988 BAL	71	1	1	5.43	11.73	−2
1989 LA	153	8	0	2.54	9.61	15

Six wins, 1.79 ERA at the all-star break.

RANDY MYERS	IP	W	SV	ERA	RATIO	$
1987 NY N	75	3	6	3.96	10.92	9
1988 NY N	68	7	26	1.72	8.21	35
1989 NY N	84	7	24	2.35	10.89	28

In the old days, when a general manager justified a move by saying, "We wanted somebody who could get right-handed batters out, too," we could only shrug. Nowadays we go to our Elias books. The batting averages against Franco by right-handers since 1987: .246, .210, and .269. Against Myers: .246, .193, and .219. While it's true Myers gave up four rather painful home runs last year, only two were to right-handers, one less than Franco.

All Piniella has to do is tell Myers and Dibble that they alternate in the set-up role, depending on whether a right-hander or left-hander started, and the Reds win every game they lead after six innings.

BOB OJEDA	IP	W	SV	ERA	RATIO	$
1987 NY N	46	3	0	3.88	10.76	4
1988 NY N	190	10	0	2.88	9.03	18
1989 NY N	192	13	0	3.47	12.05	5

Dennis Martinez came $4 cheaper than a pitcher who had chopped the tip of his finger off.

JEFF PARRETT	IP	W	SV	ERA	RATIO	$
1987 MON	62	7	6	4.44	12.05	9
1988 MON	92	12	6	2.65	10.90	16
1989 PHI	106	12	6	2.98	11.41	14

Won as many games as Youmans and Gross combined.

ALEJANDRO PENA	IP	W	SV	ERA	RATIO	$
1987 LA	87	2	11	3.50	12.31	12
1988 LA	94	6	12	1.91	9.73	22
1989 LA	76	4	5	2.13	9.47	13

Check out the breakdown of his earnings by categories in the appendix.

MARK PORTUGAL	IP	W	SV	ERA	RATIO	$
1987 MIN	44	1	0	7.77	16.77	−10
1988 MIN	58	3	3	4.50	11.95	3
1989 HOU	108	7	0	2.75	10.67	9

Would you believe, if your pitching staff consisted of all these Astros, that you finished ninth in ERA as the Astros did?

DENNIS RASMUSSEN	IP	W	SV	ERA	RATIO	$
1987 NY A/(CIN)	191	13	0	4.57	11.83	9
1988 CIN/SD	205	16	0	3.43	11.30	9
1989 SD	184	10	0	4.26	12.84	−5

He's at his best after he's traded.

RICK REUSCHEL	IP	W	SV	ERA	RATIO	$
1987 PIT/SF	227	13	0	3.09	9.87	**26**
1988 SF	245	19	0	3.12	10.43	**17**
1989 SF	208	17	0	2.94	10.76	**17**

Hitters should look at this three-year scan and hang their heads in shame.

JOSE RIJO	IP	W	SV	ERA	RATIO	$
1987 OAK	82	2	0	5.90	16.13	**−12**
1988 CIN	162	13	0	2.39	10.17	**17**
1989 CIN	111	7	0	2.84	12.08	**5**

The perfect excuse, all by himself, to go to Florida.

DON ROBINSON	IP	W	SV	ERA	RATIO	$
1987 PIT/SF	108	11	19	3.42	12.08	**25**
1988 SF	177	10	6	2.45	10.24	**20**
1989 SF	197	12	0	3.43	10.10	**13**

Time for him to move over to the American League and DH.

CALVIN SCHIRALDI	IP	W	SV	ERA	RATIO	$
1987 BOS	84	8	6	4.41	12.37	**11**
1988 CHI N	166	9	1	4.38	12.39	**−4**
1989 CHI N/SD	100	6	4	3.51	12.15	**5**

Four solid starts with the Padres.

MIKE SCOTT	IP	W	SV	ERA	RATIO	$
1987 HOU	245	16	0	3.23	10.21	**26**
1988 HOU	219	14	0	2.92	8.85	**22**
1989 HOU	229	20	0	3.10	9.51	**24**

If he goes elsewhere, how much will he miss the Astrodome? Not as much as he used to, judging by his road ERAs for the last three years: 4.26, 3.61, and 3.21.

ERIC SHOW	IP	W	SV	ERA	RATIO	$
1987 SD	206	8	0	3.84	11.93	8
1988 SD	235	16	0	3.26	9.74	18
1989 SD	106	8	0	4.23	12.87	−1

With his splendid '88 season right in front of us, it's easy to see why even the crusty older leagues spent as much as $22 on him.

JOHN SMILEY	IP	W	SV	ERA	RATIO	$
1987 PIT	75	5	4	5.76	14.28	−2
1988 PIT	205	13	0	3.25	10.14	13
1989 PIT	205	12	0	2.81	9.77	18

Hats off to Doug MacNeil and Steve Fulkman of the B-B-Q League in San Diego: In their rookie year their Roasted Chickens unseated one of those obnoxious dynasties, the Blue Sox, owned by Frank Kastelic (my informant; see the thanks you get, Frank?). One Roasted Chicken was named Smiley and another was named Smoltz.

BRYN SMITH	IP	W	SV	ERA	RATIO	$
1987 MON	150	10	0	4.37	11.70	6
1988 MON	198	12	0	3.00	9.59	16
1989 MON	216	10	0	2.84	9.64	18

Karl Junkersfeld of Brooklyn included this note with the record of the Sporting Club's auction: "Unfortunately, I became very ill with the flu and had to draft by phone from my bed. I had to draft quickly so I wouldn't faint from fatigue. Consequently my team was not exactly what I would have preferred."

I haven't heard how his team did yet, but he came away with a three-man rotation of Bryn Smith, Magrane, and Deshaies, for a total of $38. Karl can't be sorry that all three of them are now in great pitchers' parks.

DAVE SMITH	IP	W	SV	ERA	RATIO	$
1987 HOU	60	2	24	1.65	9.00	30
1988 HOU	57	4	27	2.67	12.40	25
1989 HOU	58	3	25	2.64	10.55	25

For five years he's averaged 27 saves—rarely pitching more than an inning and always acting like his arm is about to fall off.

ZANE SMITH	IP	W	SV	ERA	RATIO	$
1987 ATL	242	15	0	4.09	12.50	8
1988 ATL	140	5	0	4.30	13.02	−7
1989 ATL/MON	147	1	2	3.49	11.82	0

By the end of last year he was lost in Pitcher Zeedom, but he actually did quite well in relief (two saves, 1.50 ERA). Since the end of the season, though, he's moved steadily up in the rotation.

JOHN SMOLTZ	IP	W	SV	ERA	RATIO	$
1988 ATL	64	2	0	5.48	15.05	−9
1989 ATL	208	12	0	2.94	10.04	16

The prices for Smoltz in the start-up leagues give him the short shrift he earned in his rookie season. However, in the other leagues, we see the veterans coming out of their lairs and having at it: $6 average salary. Some small wars even: the Procrastinators in Babi-NL, $10; the Cockroaches in the PTL Clubs, $13; the Phillies in the Columbia National, $14.

Despite his outstanding season, these aren't smart skirmishes, in my view. The fights that took Smoltz to $6–8 were smart; after that you've got people who are hooked on their own scouting powers. They've been in Florida themselves, watching the movement on Smoltz's pitches. They'd rather have him than poopy old Sutcliffe.

Well, we know they got away with it, so how'd they do?

Procrastinators 10th, Cockroaches 2nd, Phillies 1st.

Meanwhile, many more than three teams will swear they bid $9, $12, or $13.

MIKE STANTON	IP	W	SV	ERA	RATIO	$
1989 ATL	24	0	7	1.50	9.38	9

While I was combing the Ultra reserve drafts for Combs, I kept my eye out for Stanton. Didn't see him.

RICK SUTCLIFFE	IP	W	SV	ERA	RATIO	$
1987 CHI N	237	18	0	3.68	12.49	13
1988 CHI N	226	13	0	3.86	12.03	1
1989 CHI N	229	16	0	3.66	10.65	12

Rick, it's like this: Last year I would have rather had you; this year I prefer Smoltz.

FERNANDO VALENZUELA	IP	W	SV	ERA	RATIO	S
1987 LA	251	14	0	3.98	13.55	3
1988 LA	142	5	1	4.24	13.78	−8
1989 LA	197	10	0	3.43	12.95	0

It hurts, but I can't quarrel with the Elias rating for Fernando: Type C free agent.

FRANK VIOLA	IP	W	SV	ERA	RATIO	S
1987 MIN	252	17	0	2.90	10.57	32
1988 MIN	255	24	0	2.64	10.22	34
1989 MIN/NY N	261	13	0	3.66	11.03	13

If Bedrosian was an old-fashioned fire sale, Mark Langston—with a contract that was about to expire—represented the new kind, the one in which life imitates Rotisserie baseball. Once the Expos had Langston, McIlvaine had to go shopping. Inasmuch as he still has Viola, he can take some satisfaction, but McIlvaine will hold his breath for several years—watching Aguilera, West, and Tapani—before he thumbs his nose at Dombrowski.

Fire sales are a plague; we could have told him that. It's amazing how quickly you can deplete your assets. All the Mets have left is money. If I had been McIlvaine, I would have proposed to Nelson Doubleday that buying Langston would have been the best revenge.

BOB WALK	IP	W	SV	ERA	RATIO	S
1987 PIT	117	8	0	3.31	12.15	8
1988 PIT	213	12	0	2.71	10.50	15
1989 PIT	196	13	0	4.41	12.54	−3

Do we ever get a handle on ratio? I'll bet few people can tell, without looking in the appendix, whether Walk's ratio or ERA was worse last year.

JOHN WETTELAND	IP	W	SV	ERA	RATIO	S
1989 LA	103	5	1	3.77	10.08	6

Another wild-pitch fiend like Ken Howell. Means he's got good stuff.

EDDIE WHITSON	IP	W	SV	ERA	RATIO	$
1987 SD	206	10	0	4.73	11.40	5
1988 SD	205	13	0	3.77	10.83	7
1989 SD	227	16	0	2.66	9.75	23

McKeon says he's become one hell of a pitcher. So do Patton $.

MITCH WILLIAMS	IP	W	SV	ERA	RATIO	$
1987 TEX	109	8	6	3.23	12.96	14
1988 TEX	68	2	18	4.63	12.57	13
1989 CHI N	82	4	36	2.76	13.56	30

First base should have been open when he faced Will Clark. The reason it wasn't was certainly not Bielecki's fault. Before Thompson batted, everyone realized Bielecki had nothing left. Possibly Zimmer didn't, although I doubt it, but Bielecki definitely did. A walk's never as good, or bad, as a hit, and it's not even close with runners on second and third. Bielecki made the sensible decision to throw meatballs out of the strike zone as long as Zimmer left him in.

TODD WORRELL	IP	W	SV	ERA	RATIO	$
1987 STL	95	8	33	2.66	11.37	39
1988 STL	90	5	32	3.00	10.30	32
1989 STL	52	3	20	2.96	11.85	19

My guess is, he'll be back earlier than expected, then get hammered; you might not want to activate him until next year.

Pitcher Z
He abounds.

From A to Y: Agosto, Armstrong, Carpenter, DiPino, Downs, Eave, Grant, Gullickson, Hammaker, Heaton, Hesketh, Horton, Kipper, Kramer, Lilliquist, Mulholland, Musselman, Jose Nunez, Perry, Pico, Power, Ron Robinson, Ruffin, Terrell, Terry, Steve Wilson, Trevor Wilson, Youmans.

And those are the good Pitcher Z's. Well, maybe not Youmans, who told the Phillies that batters wouldn't be turning on his fastball later in the season but didn't tell them why. Still, I haven't mentioned any of the codgers who are going to be at camps, like Tudor and Rhoden and I'm not including the minor leaguers in Chapter 5 or other young fellers like Mike Harkey and Rickey Bones.

From Andersen to Worrell is some 80 pitchers. Sixty-eight pitchers were profiled last year, 42 of whom ended up among the top 90 pitchers in this year's appendix. At the same success rate this year, there are roughly 40 openings for Pitcher Z.

AMERICAN LEAGUE CATCHERS

SANDY ALOMAR JR.	AB	HR	RBI	SB	BA	$
1989 SD	19	1	6	0	.211	1

For our purposes, he probably won't do too much. I had to bump several hitters who earned more Patton $ to include him in the minor league chapter, and his rookie year could resemble Andy Allanson at his peak. Yet he should work his way up to the Terry Steinbach level, and if he catches like Joel Skinner, as they say he does, the Indians have got a player.

BOB BOONE	AB	HR	RBI	SB	BA	$
1987 CAL	389	3	33	0	.242	1
1988 CAL	352	5	39	2	.295	11
1989 KC	405	1	43	3	.274	8

By heaping praise on Parrish, the Angels pitchers were of course trashing Boonie. A few of the Royals pitchers seemed to like his style. And his lifetime batting average continues to rise.

CARLTON FISK	AB	HR	RBI	SB	BA	$
1987 CHI A	454	23	71	1	.256	13
1988 CHI A	253	19	50	0	.277	15
1989 CHI A	375	13	68	1	.293	17

So, as a matter of fact, does Pudge's batting average, and he's a month older.

The Elias ratings do produce one interesting revelation: Fisk is fifth in the league in plate appearances by catchers over the last two seasons. So, you see, all you teams that owned him really shouldn't have moaned so much. Boone, for instance, ranks three behind him. What? Oh, it must be walks. How often does Fisk walk anyway?

If you add up both players' walks, hit-by-pitches, sacrifice bunts and sacrifice flies over the past two years, and add these totals to their at-bats, you get 716 for Fisk, 861 for Boone. You still get the strong impression Boone played more.

In fact, Elias agrees about Boone: 861 plate appearances. But Fisk somehow managed to appear 901.64 times.

What's .64 of a plate appearance? A 2-1 count?

What's that, Elias? That's how many times he would have appeared if he hadn't been hurt? Oh. Plate appearances are a category, but not if it's not the player's fault that he didn't get enough of them. Somewhere in here, I suspect, is a message for Larry Andersen.

BOB GEREN	AB	HR	RBI	SB	BA	$
1989 NY A	205	9	27	0	.288	9

Tailed off, but he showed enough—defensively, as well—to send Slaught out of town.

BRIAN HARPER	AB	HR	RBI	SB	BA	$
1987 OAK	17	0	3	0	.235	0
1988 MIN	166	3	20	0	.295	5
1989 MIN	385	8	57	2	.325	17

The PCL in 1988 was not the first time he bashed minor league pitching. Other good-to-great seasons in the minors: 1978, 1979, 1981, 1982, and 1987. From 1983 through 1985 he was in the majors, getting a total of 295 at-bats.

MIKE HEATH	AB	HR	RBI	SB	BA	$
1987 DET	270	8	33	1	.281	7
1988 DET	219	5	18	1	.247	4
1989 DET	396	10	43	7	.263	13

A healthy Nokes should reduce his playing time.

TIM LAUDNER	AB	HR	RBI	SB	BA	$
1987 MIN	288	16	43	1	.191	4
1988 MIN	375	13	54	0	.251	10
1989 MIN	239	6	27	1	.222	4

The Rotisserie owner's nightmare: at his worst when something is expected of him.

MATT NOKES	AB	HR	RBI	SB	BA	$
1987 DET	461	32	87	2	.289	21
1988 DET	382	16	53	0	.251	12
1989 DET	268	9	39	1	.250	8

Had such a good spring training, I'm surprised his average salary wasn't higher than $23.

LANCE PARRISH	AB	HR	RBI	SB	BA	$
1987 PHI	466	17	67	0	.245	10
1988 PHI	424	15	60	0	.215	11
1989 CAL	433	17	50	1	.238	11

Given virtually the identical salary ($13) in the established leagues as in the start-ups.

As for the improvement in the Angels pitchers, if they even thought he should get some credit, then I guess he should.

TONY PENA	AB	HR	RBI	SB	BA	$
1987 STL	384	5	44	6	.214	3
1988 STL	505	10	51	6	.263	15
1989 STL	424	4	37	5	.259	9

No pull hitter, he's in trouble if the screen beckons, but if the Red Sox catch even half of his spirit, it's a great acquisition.

GENO PETRALLI	AB	HR	RBI	SB	BA	$
1987 TEX	202	7	31	0	.302	7
1988 TEX	351	7	36	0	.282	9
1989 TEX	184	4	23	0	.304	7

Good hitter. Big jump in RBIs due.

TERRY STEINBACH	AB	HR	RBI	SB	BA	$
1987 OAK	391	16	56	1	.284	12
1988 OAK	351	9	51	3	.265	11
1989 OAK	454	7	42	1	.273	10

We're waiting, Terry; we certainly don't expect your earnings to continue making like a Cape Canaveral countdown.

B. J. SURHOFF	AB	HR	RBI	SB	BA	$
1987 MIL	395	7	68	11	.299	16
1988 MIL	493	5	38	21	.245	14
1989 MIL	436	5	55	14	.248	13

Countdown II. Can B. J. be over the hill at 25?

MICKEY TETTLETON	AB	HR	RBI	SB	BA	$
1987 OAK	211	8	26	7	.194	4
1988 BAL	283	11	37	0	.261	9
1989 BAL	411	26	65	3	.258	20

Comparatively speaking, was not a good DH. Compared to other designated hitters he was fine, that is, but he hit much better as a catcher. Doesn't much matter to those who own Tettleton, but it will probably mean something to Bob Melvin's owners.

DAVE VALLE	AB	HR	RBI	SB	BA	$
1987 SEA	324	12	53	2	.256	9
1988 SEA	290	10	50	0	.231	8
1989 SEA	316	7	34	0	.237	5

In the start-up leagues, Scott Bradley was the better buy, but we all keep thinking that Valle's got a bit of Mickey Tettleton in him.

ERNIE WHITT	AB	HR	RBI	SB	BA	$
1987 TOR	446	19	75	0	.269	13
1988 TOR	398	16	70	4	.251	15
1989 TOR	385	11	53	5	.262	13

Boone and Fisk just seem to keep egging old Ernie on. He's got another year, at least.

Many of the established leagues spent more on Pat Borders—what was that all about? The Hamilton Burghers of the Washington Ghost AL, for example, paid $8 for Whitt; probably prepaid. They then spent $13 for Borders. I would call that uninsuring your investment. Since the Burghers finished first, I feel certain they could care less what I call it.

Player Z

Even counting backups like Borders, the number of catchers mentioned so far falls well short of 24. Problem is, I don't know who else to mention. Ron Hassey? Bill Schroeder? Lenny Webster? I'll mention them, but please don't spend more than a dollar on them. Once-heralded prospects, like Derek Parks and Todd Pratt, failed to cut it in Double A last year. I can't even foolishly recommend Francisco Cabrera anymore, not here, since he's gone to the National League.

Where most of the good catching prospects already reside.

Recently the flow of talent, both from the minors and between major leagues, has favored the NL more than people realize. Even the people who are paid to watch closely have missed this point. Peter Pascarelli, who writes "NL Beat" for *The Sporting News,* headlined one of his November columns, "Series Is Further Evidence of NL Inferiority." Like so many things, it all comes down to Whitey Herzog: ". . . Perhaps the success of the Cardinals made too many teams concentrate too much on slap-hitting . . . clubs became too intent on building a team to fit their ballpark rather than acquiring the best players available."

Pascarelli will get no argument from AL Rotisserie leagues, which from the inception have prided themselves on having the action, the exciting hitters to follow.

In the masochist chapter I show how ever-so-slightly less exciting the slap hitters in the National League were last year, even with so many injuries, but let's not depend on that chapter for rebuttal. Let's try slugging average.

The best in baseball belonged to Mitchell—obviously—almost a hundred points better than Sierra's. But three other National League hitters also had better slugging averages than Sierra: Howard Johnson, Will Clark, and Eric Davis. Two of these added some action with their feet.

Much of Bill James's "leader board" is too abstruse for me to tell exactly what's being measured, but surely he's measuring "action." The special hitting categories that he's cooked up are Offensive Winning Percentage, Power/Speed Number, Runs Created, Secondary Average, and Isolated Power; in all five cases the NL leader is better than the AL leader *and* the tenth best NL player is better than the tenth best AL player.

The defections of Joe Carter and Nick Esasky to the National League would seem to guarantee the same situation this year. American League aficionados, like it or not, will have to fill the void of these stalwarts with subtler action: Tony Pena going ape over the Clemens fastball, Sandy Alomar trying to decide whether to call another Candiotti knuckleball. Both are things I look forward to.

AMERICAN LEAGUE FIRST BASEMEN

STEVE BALBONI	AB	HR	RBI	SB	BA	$
1987 KC	386	24	60	0	.207	7
1988 KC/SEA	413	23	66	0	.235	14
1989 NY	300	17	59	0	.237	13

Pretty good numbers for half a season. Qualified at first in the last week.

GEORGE BRETT	AB	HR	RBI	SB	BA	$
1987 KC	427	22	78	0	.290	17
1988 KC	589	24	103	14	.306	34
1989 KC	457	12	80	14	.282	23

His home runs at home over these three years: 14, 13, 3.

GREG BROCK	AB	HR	RBI	SB	BA	$
1987 MIL	532	13	85	5	.299	18
1988 MIL	364	6	50	6	.212	6
1989 MIL	373	12	52	6	.265	14

Since 1987, in 350 at bats, his batting average against lefties has been .282. Without injuries or Joey Meyer, he might have a decent year.

ALVIN DAVIS	AB	HR	RBI	SB	BA	$
1987 SEA	580	29	100	0	.295	22
1988 SEA	478	18	69	1	.295	20
1989 SEA	498	21	95	0	.305	26

So what *is* Offensive Winning Percentage? The top six in the American League last year provide an interesting mix: Alvin, Yount, McGriff, Boggs, Sierra, Rickey.

KEITH HERNANDEZ	AB	HR	RBI	SB	BA	$
1987 NY N	587	18	89	0	.290	19
1988 NY N	348	11	55	2	.276	15
1989 NY N	215	4	19	0	.233	3

Almost everything Keith said he looked forward to—new cities, new parks, new teams, new teammates—he may wind up regretting, yet from the Indians' standpoint this was a good deal. They have two years to find a first baseman, and in the meantime they've basically got O'Brien.

KENT HRBEK	AB	HR	RBI	SB	BA	$
1987 MIN	477	34	90	5	.285	23
1988 MIN	510	25	76	0	.312	25
1989 MIN	375	25	84	3	.272	23

Tiger Stadium may have been tempting to Hrbie—compared to, oh, Royals Stadium. Compared to the Metrodome, where he hit 17 of his homers last year? Get serious.

WALLY JOYNER	AB	HR	RBI	SB	BA	$
1987 CAL	564	34	117	8	.285	27
1988 CAL	597	13	85	8	.295	24
1989 CAL	593	16	79	3	.282	21

Two home runs at the all-star break. The year before, he had four. The year before that, he had 20. That was the year they changed baseballs at the break to protect Roger Maris. Wally was a sophomore; as a rookie he had hit 22 home runs. Why wouldn't he think he was going to hit 30 or 40 a year for the next decade?

In the National League comments I pointed out how a similar fluke of fate seems to have affected John Kruk. But Wally never missed a beat. What an ego.

RON KITTLE	AB	HR	RBI	SB	BA	$
1987 NY A	159	12	28	0	.277	7
1988 CLE	225	18	43	0	.258	12
1989 CHI A	169	11	37	0	.302	11

Was on his way to being Walt Hriniak's greatest triumph before he was injured.

GENE LARKIN	AB	HR	RBI	SB	BA	$
1987 MIN	233	4	28	1	.266	4
1988 MIN	505	8	70	3	.267	13
1989 MIN	446	6	46	5	.267	11

Has anyone ever been more consistent in batting average in his first three years (or any three years)? If he doesn't snap out of it, he'll find his at-bats consistently declining.

DON MATTINGLY	AB	HR	RBI	SB	BA	$
1987 NY A	569	30	115	1	.327	29
1988 NY A	599	18	88	1	.311	25
1989 NY A	631	23	113	3	.303	31

The Stats Inc. book, which I highly recommend (its official handle is the *1990 Major League Handbook*), examines 25 star players in exhaustive depth. With its help, you can ponder such questions as, Should Mattingly walk more?

The 3-2 pitch, I think, is the key to baseball. The umpire's strike zone unquestionably expands and contracts at different stages in the count. Borderline pitches on 3-and-1 get called strikes; borderline pitches on 2-and-2 get called balls. By the time the count is full, there's no more slack. The umpire has a weighty decision to make when this pitch is taken, and if it's close he doesn't appreciate it. He blames the hitter. So the umpire's strike zone is a little larger when the count is full, making the strike zone of many hitters much larger.

Not counting intentional walks, Mattingly took ball four 33 times all year—13 times on 3-0 counts, 12 on 3-1 counts, and eight on full counts. He had 23 swings (or more, counting foul balls) with full counts; at how many bad pitches, I wonder?

The Stats scorers don't presume to tell us that. But they record that

Mattingly had 10 hits in those 23 at bats; with the count full, he batted .417.

FRED MCGRIFF	AB	HR	RBI	SB	BA	$
1987 TOR	295	20	43	3	.247	10
1988 TOR	536	34	82	6	.282	29
1989 TOR	551	36	92	7	.269	31

McGriff was at the other extreme from Mattingly: 17 walks on 3-0 pitches, 29 on 3-1, 61 on 3-2. With the count full, he struck out 31 times (Mattingly four) and batted .213. All together he worked the count to 3-and-2 136 times, compared to Mattingly's 31, whereupon they both drove in seven runs.

MARK MCGWIRE	AB	HR	RBI	SB	BA	$
1987 OAK	557	49	118	1	.289	30
1988 OAK	550	32	99	0	.260	24
1989 OAK	490	33	95	1	.231	22

A truly alarming batting average, and somewhat mystifying; he had his career high in walks and career low in strikeouts.

RANDY MILLIGAN	AB	HR	RBI	SB	BA	$
1988 PIT	82	3	8	1	.220	2
1989 BAL	365	12	45	9	.268	15

While it was still April, I was trying to convince Bruce Buschel of the BB Guns to take this guy for Medina. Not straight-up, of course; I was offering Honeycutt as a sweetener. He resisted. I asked why? He said, "Because the Mets traded Milligan." I said, so? Bruce said, "They don't *make* bad trades."

It was from that day forward that Mitchell began to tear up the league, that the Mets began thinking they needed to upgrade in center field and find another starter, and that even Milligan began to play respectably. For the BB Guns.

PETE O'BRIEN	AB	HR	RBI	SB	BA	$
1987 TEX	569	23	88	0	.286	18
1988 TEX	547	16	71	1	.272	17
1989 CLE	555	12	55	3	.259	13

The $4 drop by O'Brien last year is probably accounted for by Cleveland Stadium, so how much will The Kingdome add? My guess is he'll hit as well as but no better than he hit in Texas.

RAFAEL PALMEIRO	AB	HR	RBI	SB	BA	$
1987 CHI N	221	14	30	2	.276	9
1988 CHI N	580	8	53	12	.307	22
1989 TEX	559	8	64	4	.275	15

Did pitchers find a hole in that sweet swing? The July 10 issue of Baseball America had him on the cover with Will Clark.

GREG WALKER	AB	HR	RBI	SB	BA	$
1987 CHI A	566	27	94	2	.256	16
1988 CHI A	377	8	42	0	.247	7
1989 CHI A	233	5	26	0	.210	2

It says here he's going to come back.

Player Z

I've listed more than 12 first baseman, but none, I see, for the Tigers. Oh dear. Maybe next year.

Dave Bergman has a grade A first baseman's mitt, and a perfectly acceptable bat for a second baseman or shortstop. For many years now—can it be since Norm Cash?—the Tigers have conceded runs to the opposition by adopting such a cavalier attitude toward their production from this position. Torey Lovullo, safely back at Toledo, played third last year. The Toledo first baseman was someone named Rich Wieligman: 5 home runs, batted .286. Jim Lindeman, anyone?

Nor do the Red Sox have a first baseman, now, but at least they had one last year. For this season they may try Carlos Quintana at first, they may platoon him with Sam Horn, and they may rush Maurice Vaughan to the scene. After all that has failed, they'll bring Dwight Evans back in.

Paul Sorrento of the Twins showed good power in Orlando; he's a threat to Larkin. McGriff has nothing to worry about from John Olerud, but the latter very well might send Rance Mulliniks and/or Lee Mazzilli to other pastures. Tino Martinez, who so far has looked more like Al Chambers than Alvin Davis, may have found it in the instructional league, hitting well over .300; since they now have O'Brien for the next four years, maybe the Mariners will consider loaning Tino to the Tigers or the Red Sox.

AMERICAN LEAGUE SECOND BASEMEN

WALLY BACKMAN	AB	HR	RBI	SB	BA	$
1987 NY N	300	1	23	11	.250	5
1988 NY N	294	0	17	9	.303	9
1989 MIN	299	1	26	1	.231	1

I knew he was slowing down, but only two steal *attempts?* The Twins were so disenchanted that they're giving Chip Hale a shot.

Al Newman played the same number of games as Backman at second—and will play more than Chip, I imagine—but has been listed at shortstop, the weaker position.

MARTY BARRETT	AB	HR	RBI	SB	BA	$
1987 BOS	559	3	43	15	.293	15
1988 BOS	612	1	65	7	.283	14
1989 BOS	336	1	27	4	.256	5

The Fourteen Marty Barretts would have been an awful team last year. He'll be a hell of a lot better bargain this year for Rotisserie owners than for Mrs. Yawkey.

JERRY BROWNE	AB	HR	RBI	SB	BA	$
1987 TEX	454	1	38	27	.271	18
1988 TEX	214	1	17	7	.229	2
1989 CLE	598	5	45	14	.299	19

In the 30 Heath leagues that I have prices for, he returned good-to-excellent profits 29 times. The exception? The Baseball League of America, where the Smithsonian Institute paid $22. Remember, someone has to help you do this. Sparks were flying all over the place: $56 for Henke, $42 for Boggs, $54 for Lee Smith, $31 for Saberhagen, $68 for Rickey, $46 for Brett, $63 for Canseco, $52 for Reardon, $31 for Welch, $42 for Bell.

Let's see . . . Looks like everyone else was frozen.

SCOTT FLETCHER	AB	HR	RBI	SB	BA	$
1987 TEX	588	5	63	13	.287	16
1988 TEX	515	0	47	8	.276	11
1989 TEX/CHI A	546	1	43	2	.253	5

Did he or did he not qualify at short in real baseball?

JULIO FRANCO	AB	HR	RBI	SB	BA	$
1987 CLE	495	8	52	32	.319	26
1988 CLE	613	10	54	25	.303	28
1989 TEX	548	13	92	21	.316	33

He and Sierra had a combined record of 38-4 (first-place vs. last-place teams) in the Heath leagues.

MIKE GALLEGO	AB	HR	RBI	SB	BA	$
1987 OAK	124	2	14	0	.250	1
1988 OAK	277	2	20	2	.209	0
1989 OAK	357	3	30	7	.252	7

Should beat Blankenship out for this position and play it as well as Phillips.

JIM GANTNER	AB	HR	RBI	SB	BA	$
1987 MIL	265	4	30	6	.272	7
1988 MIL	539	0	47	20	.276	16
1989 MIL	409	0	34	20	.274	14

Spare-us-the-details department. *The Sporting News,* giving us the good news that Gantner seemed to be recovering nicely: "The medial collateral ligament was repaired and the interior cruciate ligament was replaced with an artificial one."

TIM HULETT	AB	HR	RBI	SB	BA	$
1987 CHI A	240	7	28	0	.217	2
1988			did not play in majors			
1989 BAL	97	3	18	0	.278	4

If he's got the leather, he's got the bat—compared to the competition, anyway.

NELSON LIRIANO	AB	HR	RBI	SB	BA	$
1987 TOR	158	2	10	13	.241	6
1988 TOR	276	3	23	12	.264	10
1989 TOR	418	5	53	16	.263	16

Seems to have beaten out Manny Lee once and for all. Now he's got to worry about Luis Sojo.

TONY PHILLIPS	AB	HR	RBI	SB	BA	$
1987 OAK	379	10	46	7	.240	8
1988 OAK	212	2	17	0	.203	−1
1989 OAK	451	4	47	3	.262	8

What did *he* eat? Raised his average 20 points in the last month, almost won the batting title for Lansford with an unbelievable play against Puckett, hit the long ball in the World Series. I definitely would have bid $3 for him at Oakland and will bid $5 for him now.

JOHNNY RAY	AB	HR	RBI	SB	BA	$
1987 PIT/(CAL)	599	5	69	4	.289	13
1988 CAL	602	6	83	4	.306	20
1989 CAL	530	5	62	6	.289	16

After getting 30 or more doubles for seven straight years, he suddenly dropped to 16. Whether it was his bat or his legs, it doesn't bode well.

HAROLD REYNOLDS	AB	HR	RBI	SB	BA	$
1987 SEA	530	1	35	60	.275	28
1988 SEA	598	4	41	35	.283	25
1989 SEA	613	0	43	25	.300	22

No matter who his manager is, he's still allowed to get nailed at second at a suicidal rate. Chop $10 off his salary if you think this is the year the Mariners will tell him not to bother.

STEVE SAX	AB	HR	RBI	SB	BA	$
1987 LA	610	6	46	37	.280	21
1988 LA	632	5	57	42	.277	27
1989 NY A	651	5	63	43	.315	37

Average salary in the established leagues: $26. Profits across the board of over 40 percent; might be a good idea to trade him for somebody else's profits this year.

LOU WHITAKER	AB	HR	RBI	SB	BA	$
1987 DET	604	16	59	13	.265	15
1988 DET	403	12	55	2	.275	14
1989 DET	509	28	85	6	.251	24

The same thing for Lou, although it won't be as easy.

FRANK WHITE	AB	HR	RBI	SB	BA	$
1987 KC	563	17	78	1	.245	10
1988 KC	537	8	58	7	.235	9
1989 KC	418	2	36	3	.256	6

This old guy, on the other hand, has probably faded about as far as he's going to for a while, and nobody else in Kansas City can play any better. I'd have him rated right in there with Tony Phillips.

Player Z

This was a productive position last year; including Newman, Fred Manrique, and Jody Reed, all listed at shortstop, the second basemen provided more offense than the third basemen. That's unlikely to continue to be the case this year. Mark McLemore, Lance Blankenship, and Mike Brumley are all light hitters who might do a bit of running if the position falls their way.

Steve Lyons got enough playing time and indeed played well enough to deserve his own profile—if the profiles were retrospective; I don't see him playing much this season. But he does qualify at both corners and in the outfield as well, so he's worth having for that reason alone.

AMERICAN LEAGUE SHORTSTOPS

ALVARO ESPINOZA	AB	HR	RBI	SB	BA	$
1988 NY A	3	0	0	0	.000	0
1989 NY A	503	0	41	3	.282	8

Ignored in 12 of the 25 established leagues. As usual, I'm more curious about the leagues that didn't ignore Alvaro Espinoza. The Johnsons in the Dewey Bush League paid $5 for him. They finished 11th. The Goners in South Main Street paid $4. They finished first. Doesn't really satisfy my curiosity.

TONY FERNANDEZ	AB	HR	RBI	SB	BA	$
1987 TOR	578	5	67	32	.322	28
1988 TOR	648	5	70	15	.287	21
1989 TOR	573	11	64	22	.257	21

Prices for him, as with Jim Gott in the National League, give a fair indication of when teams drafted; it's pretty obvious that two of the start-up leagues held their auctions after Tony's face was smushed.

GREG GAGNE	AB	HR	RBI	SB	BA	$
1987 MIN	437	10	40	6	.265	9
1988 MIN	461	14	48	15	.236	15
1989 MIN	460	9	48	11	.272	16

If you know your league's hypothetical final standings, figure out how many points the Fourteen Greg Gagnes would have been worth. I bet it's between 30 and 34.

OZZIE GUILLEN	AB	HR	RBI	SB	BA	$
1987 CHI A	560	2	51	25	.279	17
1988 CHI A	566	0	39	25	.261	16
1989 CHI A	597	1	54	36	.253	22

Had an okay year, but he forgot the little he seemed to have learned about drawing walks. He must have given Hriniak fits.

JEFF KUNKEL	AB	HR	RBI	SB	BA	$
1987 TEX	32	1	2	0	.219	0
1988 TEX	154	2	15	0	.227	1
1989 TEX	293	8	29	3	.270	9

The American Dreams, as I reported last year, tried a partial cure to fire sales: All players traded during the season whose salaries are under $15 automatically jump to $15 the following season. (We modified the rule to $10 and $10 for starting pitchers.) How'd it work?

On the whole, very well. Perhaps a few honest trades were discouraged, but not many. Only one team, the Wssox, had players who would be tempting at $15, and since they were the only team that wanted to fire-sale, that was fine. Meanwhile, an unexpected blessing was that there were seemingly dozens of crapshoot players who were moved as small pieces in big trades and subsequently blossomed.

Jeff Kunkel, $2? Excellent keeper. How can you miss? But Jeff Kunkel, $15? You can miss. Good-bye, fellow. You were a great scrub.

FRED MANRIQUE	AB	HR	RBI	SB	BA	$
1987 CHI A	298	4	29	5	.258	5
1988 CHI A	345	5	37	6	.235	7
1989 CHI A/TEX	378	4	52	4	.294	13

The assumption is that you like a wide-open draft. Having to put your money down on who's going to be the Rangers' shortstop—that's the sort of thing that keeps many more Rotisserie owners than Rangers fans awake nights.

It's an intriguing question. Neither is worth a lick on defense, so probably by season's end they both will have been replaced by Player Z. But until then, who's going to hit better, Jeff Kunkel or Fred Manrique?

Kunkel's got the wrists, the snappy swing, but he uppercuts, striking out a lot. Manrique's got—he's got whatever Hriniak taught him, I guess, but he didn't seem to forget it in Texas. He drove in more runs than Baines.

Manrique's 28, so the Ranger brass will prefer Kunkel, who's—28. Scratch that.

Kunkel's truly got talent; last year he was going to be a pitcher . . . Manrique at least knows who he is . . .

AL NEWMAN	AB	HR	RBI	SB	BA	$
1987 MIN	307	0	29	15	.221	5
1988 MIN	260	0	19	12	.223	5
1989 MIN	446	0	38	25	.253	15

I saw him huffing and puffing in a rubber jacket at the end of spring training, while the Red Sox were having BP. He'd trot 10 yards, stop, look up, and watch one of Mike Greenwell's arching drives soar into the adjacent football stadium.

So I steered clear of Al Newman in the draft. And as soon as I bought Greenwell, I penciled in 30 homers.

JODY REED	AB	HR	RBI	SB	BA	$
1987 BOS	30	0	8	1	.300	1
1988 BOS	338	1	28	1	.293	7
1989 BOS	524	3	40	4	.288	11

The Wall is perfect for him: turns warning-track line drives into doubles.

CAL RIPKEN JR.	AB	HR	RBI	SB	BA	$
1987 BAL	624	27	98	3	.252	16
1988 BAL	575	23	81	2	.264	20
1989 BAL	646	21	93	3	.257	21

With Worthington occupying half his former territory, he's again an excellent shortstop. Yet there seems no question he'd be a better hitter if he took the odd day off. His father probably cared about his streak, but why does Frank Robinson?

His market price in the established leagues is $28, almost the same as in the start-ups. It may be a shade too high. However, with a nod to position scarcity and a bow to his amazing durability, he's definitely worth $25.

DICK SCHOFIELD	AB	HR	RBI	SB	BA	$
1987 CAL	479	9	46	19	.251	13
1988 CAL	527	6	34	20	.239	12
1989 CAL	302	4	26	9	.228	6

Has been successful in 80 percent of his stolen-base attempts lifetime . . . Struggling hard to find something exciting about him.

GARY SHEFFIELD	AB	HR	RBI	SB	BA	$
1988 MIL	80	4	12	3	.238	4
1989 MIL	368	5	32	10	.247	9

He's inevitably discussed, however briefly, in the minor league section. The thing is, he'd be better off if it wasn't major league parks but major league pitchers that caused him grief; that he could do something about, and I still think he will.

BILL SPIERS	AB	HR	RBI	SB	BA	$
1989 MIL	345	4	33	10	.255	9

But if Sheffield bitches about not playing shortstop, he's gone from Milwaukee.

KURT STILLWELL	AB	HR	RBI	SB	BA	$
1987 CIN	395	4	33	4	.258	5
1988 KC	459	10	53	6	.251	12
1989 KC	463	7	54	9	.261	13

Has earned $9 more in two years than Danny Jackson.

ALAN TRAMMELL	AB	HR	RBI	SB	BA	$
1987 DET	597	28	105	21	.343	38
1988 DET	466	15	69	7	.311	23
1989 DET	449	4	43	10	.243	9

According to Heath's "winners and losers," the damage was mild (6–8). But that's only 14 leagues; if Jerry tracked all the finishes, I assume it would be much worse.

My cumbersome manual search on leagues at random: Kenny Punk Ports of Bos-Wash, $29 for Trammell; finished third. Camp's Champs of Red Rose, $35; finished 10th. Battermore Oreos of Babi-AL, $19; finished first. Gashouse Gang of Cowtown, $24; finished 10th. Mike Hammers of Tucson Slug, $47; finished eighth. Hall Stars of Sour Grapefruit, $27; finished 12th. Amazon of Washington Ghost-AL, $31; finished fourth. River Rats of Columbia American, $28; finished fifth.

All in all, not as bad as I expected.

WALT WEISS	AB	HR	RBI	SB	BA	$
1987 OAK	26	0	1	1	.462	2
1988 OAK	452	3	39	4	.250	6
1989 OAK	236	3	21	6	.233	5

Might get 15–20 stolen bases.

Player Z

Felix Fermin and Omar Vizquel are the only clear, everyday players in either league that I just couldn't see my way to elevating above

Player Z. They should not complain; in the past, when I said this about Alfredo Griffin and Steve Jeltz, I turned their careers around.

Word is that Luis Rivera is not an everyday player, but the Red Sox will let him keep putting pressure on Reed, which will put pressure on Barrett.

I still say Dale Sveum will be a factor on the Brewers. He just heals slowly.

AMERICAN LEAGUE THIRD BASEMEN

WADE BOGGS	AB	HR	RBI	SB	BA	S
1987 BOS	551	24	89	1	.363	29
1988 BOS	584	5	58	2	.366	25
1989 BOS	621	3	54	2	.330	19

George Brett cost Boggs his batting title.

It comes as no surprise that the Stats Inc. pitch count shows Boggs combining the best of Mattingly and McGriff. He reached the 3-2 count 124 times last year (McGriff reached it even more often, which is surprising). He got 35 walks (compared to McGriff's 61 and Mattingly's eight); in 89 at-bats, he hit .348 and had 12 RBIs. His on-base average was .528, his slugging average .494—the former lower, the latter higher than McGriff's. Mattingly was laughably better in both (.581 and .739); he's definitely a better 3-2 hitter—the rare day in the week he takes the count that far.

Mattingly probably puts the ball in play more often per swing than any hitter in baseball; but Boggs shows even better bat control by fouling unpleasant pitches off. The pitches he takes, he stares right into the glove, and then glares at the umpire, daring him to increase the strike zone on *him*.

Which, of course, is where Brett enters. "There will be a woman president before he gets called out on strikes," quoth George. I'd love to know how many backward K's Boggs had last year. His strikeouts rose from 34 to 51. His unintentional walks dropped from 107 to 88.

Nevertheless, he remained the second-best leadoff hitter in baseball, and the second best of all time. Indeed, he tied with Henderson in runs scored. But . . . should he be a leadoff hitter?

I don't think so, for two reasons. The first is, as usual, I have him on my team. The second is that all his singles and doubles would be even nicer with men on base. He had more total bases last year than either Greenwell or Evans.

Joe Morgan did give him a fairly long tryout in the third spot, abandoning it because Boggs only drove in 15 runs in 123 at-bats, about a 75-RBI pace. In those 123 at-bats, Boggs hit .407, with a .561 slugging average. If Boggs had Boggs leading off, he'd drive in 120 runs. If he had Rickey, he'd drive in 150.

Anyway, that's my problem. And whoever replaces Morgan's. Let's get to the important stuff. I really don't think Margo had any effect on the umpires—it was all Brett—but to some extent she helped his on-base average: He was hit by pitches seven times, up 133 percent.

STEVE BUECHELE	AB	HR	RBI	SB	BA	S
1987 TEX	363	13	50	2	.237	7
1988 TEX	503	16	58	2	.250	13
1989 TEX	486	16	59	1	.235	11

Missed qualifying at second by two games. The Rangers were still threatening over the winter to move Franco to first, Buechele to second, and bring in Coolbaugh. The idea is to make Palmeiro hit a little better than Pete O'Brien.

DARNELL COLES	AB	HR	RBI	SB	BA	S
1987 DET/(PIT)	268	10	39	1	.201	3
1988 PIT/(SEA)	406	15	70	4	.261	16
1989 SEA	535	10	59	5	.252	12

Don't know where the Mariners will play him, but this is where we will.

GARY GAETTI	AB	HR	RBI	SB	BA	S
1987 MIN	584	31	109	10	.257	22
1988 MIN	468	28	88	7	.301	29
1989 MIN	498	19	75	6	.251	19

He only dropped to his lifetime batting average, approximately, but fell 40 points past his career slugging average.

KELLY GRUBER	AB	HR	RBI	SB	BA	$
1987 TOR	341	12	36	12	.235	9
1988 TOR	569	16	81	23	.278	29
1989 TOR	545	18	73	10	.290	25

Did Gaetti at least keep up the good work in the field, earning his Gold Glove? If he did, it's not discernible in the fielding statistics. Going by stats alone, Jack Howell, of all people, should have gotten the Gold Glove. Combining stats with observation, I'd vote for Gruber.

JACK HOWELL	AB	HR	RBI	SB	BA	$
1987 CAL	449	23	64	4	.245	12
1988 CAL	500	16	63	2	.254	14
1989 CAL	474	20	52	0	.228	11

His continued helplessness against lefties makes the future of Bobby Rose just a little bit sweeter.

BROOK JACOBY	AB	HR	RBI	SB	BA	$
1987 CLE	540	32	69	2	.300	21
1988 CLE	552	9	49	2	.241	7
1989 CLE	519	13	64	2	.272	15

Before you look at the appendix, which do you think was worth more—Jacoby's speed or his batting average?

CARNEY LANSFORD	AB	HR	RBI	SB	BA	$
1987 OAK	554	19	76	27	.289	27
1988 OAK	556	7	57	29	.279	25
1989 OAK	551	2	52	37	.336	34

While you're there, it's sort of interesting to see how Carney pulls ahead of Molly.

CARLOS MARTINEZ	AB	HR	RBI	SB	BA	$
1988 CHI A	55	0	0	1	.164	−1
1989 CHI A	350	5	32	4	.300	11

I'm tempted to say he won't last long above Player Z, but I have such faith in Hriniak that I'm not sure. One of the nicest things about Hriniak is that he obviously gives equal time to the scrubs.

PAUL MOLITOR	AB	HR	RBI	SB	BA	$
1987 MIL	465	16	75	45	.353	40
1988 MIL	609	13	60	41	.312	38
1989 MIL	615	11	56	27	.315	32

Over 1200 at-bats in the past two years—who would have thought? Molly's such a straight arrow he put on a fantastic salary drive even though his contract wasn't up. Maybe he was just running along next to his buddy Yount, pacing him to the finish: "Get rich, Robin, but please don't leave."

JIM PRESLEY	AB	HR	RBI	SB	BA	$
1987 SEA	575	24	88	2	.247	14
1988 SEA	544	14	62	3	.230	10
1989 SEA	390	12	41	0	.236	7

Hit .328 and slugged .491 against lefties. With so many right-handed pitchers, the Mariners still have a big hole at third. Presley's at-bats show they kept trying to fill it with Edgar Martinez, which didn't work either.

KEVIN SEITZER	AB	HR	RBI	SB	BA	$
1987 KC	641	15	83	12	.323	26
1988 KC	559	5	60	10	.304	19
1989 KC	597	4	48	17	.281	18

Had as dramatic a drop in doubles as Johnny Ray. Since it can't be his legs, it's very disturbing.

RANDY VELARDE	AB	HR	RBI	SB	BA	$
1988 NY A	115	5	12	1	.174	1
1989 NY A	100	2	11	0	.340	4

The challenge facing the Yankees is simple: Stop pretending you have a chance when you don't. Play for next year, starting with Velarde.

ROBIN VENTURA	AB	HR	RBI	SB	BA	$
1989 CHI A	45	0	7	0	.176	0

I got to see him play a few times and he seemed to be hitting into some tough outs. But he's got to silence the whispers that he's got his sights set on being Dave Magadan.

CRAIG WORTHINGTON	AB	HR	RBI	SB	BA	$
1988 BAL	81	2	4	1	.185	0
1989 BAL	497	15	70	1	.247	13

Hard to say who was more outrageous—Worthington playing 10 yards wide of third or Devereaux playing only a little farther in back of second. They both made the Orioles just a whole lot of fun to watch.

Player Z

At the bewitching hour—well into the end of the winter meetings—the Tigers suddenly realized the Strange Schu didn't fit. They had tried other pumpkins last year at third as well (Chris Brown, Torey Lovullo, Al Pedrique), and seemed perfectly prepared to get no production from either corner position again, when someone must have whispered in Monaghan's ear: Tom, we're getting into the late rounds and you still have $260 left.

So that's how Tony Phillips became a Tiger. He's not Kent Hrbek but he's versatile (he qualifies at third, although on most Rotisserie teams he'll be a second baseman), and he can help out at first, too, if he has to.

If Sandy Alomar's stats for Las Vegas are just ordinary in the hitting-minded PCL, what's to be made of his teammate, Carlos Baerga, who came to the Indians with him? Not much, in my book.

Other teams have brighter prospects. In addition to Coolbaugh, Dean Palmer will be trying out for the Rangers. In addition to Rose, Jeff Manto for the Angels. I do hope the Yankees give Velarde his chance. He's 27. Hensley Meulens is still only 23.

AMERICAN LEAGUE OUTFIELDERS

HAROLD BAINES	AB	HR	RBI	SB	BA	$
1987 CHI A	505	20	93	0	.293	18
1988 CHI A	599	13	81	0	.277	17
1989 CHI A/TEX	505	16	72	0	.309	21

For some reason he didn't hit very well for the Rangers, but he should fit their offense nicely. Qualifying only at DH last year, he didn't cost much and won't be available in many drafts.

JESSE BARFIELD	AB	HR	RBI	SB	BA	$
1987 TOR	590	28	84	3	.263	17
1988 TOR	468	18	56	7	.244	15
1989 TOR/NY A	521	23	67	5	.234	17

At about the time the Yankees were signing him up at a raise, Rotisserie owners who bought for him anything over $15 were trying hard to trade him. Every now and then his bat seemed to find the ball, but for the most part he looked all snarled up.

GEORGE BELL	AB	HR	RBI	SB	BA	$
1987 TOR	610	47	134	5	.308	35
1988 TOR	614	24	97	4	.269	24
1989 TOR	613	18	104	4	.297	27

People bet on his coming back even better than he did ($33 average salary in the older leagues), so he will be widely available. However, he's the type of player you might want to hold on to at $33 if there are a lot of underpriced players being carried over, including some of your own. The market would quickly push Bell back up to the high 30s.

JOEY BELLE	AB	HR	RBI	SB	BA	$
1987 CLE	218	7	37	2	.225	6

Might start the season in the minors and might start in the place of any number of questionable veterans.

PHIL BRADLEY	AB	HR	RBI	SB	BA	$
1987 SEA	603	14	67	40	.297	31
1988 PHI	569	11	56	11	.264	18
1989 BAL	545	11	55	20	.277	22

As he traveled from the Mariners to the Phillies to the Orioles, Bradley's spirit must have sunk. And then soared.

GREG BRILEY	AB	HR	RBI	SB	BA	$
1988 SEA	36	1	4	0	.250	1
1989 SEA	394	13	52	11	.266	17

Hit fine against lefties the few chances he got. Why not let him hack away full-time and see what happens? If he were four inches taller, they'd let him.

GLENN BRAGGS	AB	HR	RBI	SB	BA	$
1987 MIL	505	13	77	12	.269	16
1988 MIL	272	10	42	6	.261	12
1989 MIL	514	15	66	17	.247	20

A $12 season without his stolen bases.

JAY BUHNER	AB	HR	RBI	SB	BA	$
1987 NY A	22	0	1	0	.227	0
1988 NY A/SEA	261	13	38	1	.215	7
1989 SEA	204	9	33	1	.275	9

One of the more guts-ball trades in my league last year was Tartabull for Buhner and Sosa. Not a fire-sale trade; a gamble by the BB Guns that Buhner and Sosa would outperform Tartabull, and while all three were healthy they did.

ELLIS BURKS	AB	HR	RBI	SB	BA	$
1987 BOS	558	20	59	27	.272	23
1988 BOS	540	18	92	25	.294	34
1989 BOS	399	12	61	21	.303	26

Was on a pace to do slightly better than 1988.

RANDY BUSH	AB	HR	RBI	SB	BA	$
1987 MIN	293	11	46	10	.253	11
1988 MIN	394	14	51	8	.261	15
1989 MIN	391	14	54	5	.263	15

Must be something in the milk in Minnesota that makes players extremely stable. I've never seen two seasons that were as like each other as these last two by Randy Bush. He's starting to get some recognition in Rotisserie circles as the all-star fifth outfielder.

IVAN CALDERON	AB	HR	RBI	SB	BA	$
1987 CHI A	542	28	83	10	.293	24
1988 CHI A	264	14	35	4	.212	8
1989 CHI A	622	14	87	7	.286	23

Ike's not president of the Walt Hriniak fan club; he wants to know where his homers went.

JOSE CANSECO	AB	HR	RBI	SB	BA	$
1987 OAK	630	31	113	15	.257	25
1988 OAK	610	42	124	40	.307	56
1989 OAK	227	17	57	6	.269	17

Random thumb-through of rosters to see how the people who bought Jose fared:

Safe Sex of the Santa Ana Oxymorons, $27; finished seventh. Minimum Contacts of Cowtown (AIDS on our minds, would you say?), $42; finished fourth. Stones of Red Rose, $29; finished eighth. Albany Machine of Bos-Wash, $46; finished 12th. Wssox of the American Dreams, $43; finished fifth. N.Y. Giants of Columbia American, $32; finished 12th. Krafty O's of Babi-AL, $40; finished fourth. Peking Ducks of Washington Ghost-AL, $35; finished ninth. Poetic Justus of Sour Grapefruit, $33; finished seventh.

So they'll get theirs this year.

An interesting thing is that the vast majority of these teams (all save the Krafty O's and Poetic Justus) did better or as well in the hypothetical final standings; they had better teams, that is, coming out of the draft than at the end of the year. It would seem that once they bought Canseco, they put themselves into a fire-sale mentality, come what may.

And, of course, most of these teams will not be rewarded this year. Canseco hit the ball a ton once he got going; however, his last year's earnings prorated to 600 at-bats is $45. He was Kevin Mitchell only. The prices are attractive, but few are bargains for the non-running version of Canseco.

And, now that Henderson has signed with the A's, why would he run? Jose may not follow baseball too closely, but he can tell when he's outclassed. During the playoffs, more knocked out by Rickey than anybody, he said, "If he was as big as me, he'd hit a ball to Mars."

HENRY COTTO	AB	HR	RBI	SB	BA	$
1987 NY A	149	5	20	4	.235	4
1988 SEA	386	8	33	27	.259	19
1989 SEA	295	9	33	10	.264	13

Fine fifth outfielder.

CHILI DAVIS	AB	HR	RBI	SB	BA	$
1987 SF	500	24	76	16	.250	20
1988 CAL	600	21	93	9	.268	24
1989 CAL	560	22	90	3	.271	23

Was it yesterday or the day before that Chili was a sleek, all-the-tools stud patrolling in the footsteps of Willie Mays? Now his legs seem so heavy that he looks like he's wading across a creek going after a routine fly. He held the ball, though, this year, and hit as well as anyone expects him to now.

ROB DEER	AB	HR	RBI	SB	BA	$
1987 MIL	474	28	80	12	.238	17
1988 MIL	492	23	85	9	.252	22
1989 MIL	466	26	65	4	.210	14

His minus seven dollars in batting average is the biggest I can find in the appendix, at least for the American League. The second worst is Cory Snyder. The third is a tie between Lloyd Moseby and Chad Kreuter.

JIM EISENREICH	AB	HR	RBI	SB	BA	$
1987 KC	105	4	21	9	.238	6
1988 KC	202	1	19	9	.218	4
1989 KC	475	9	59	27	.293	27

It's a shame he'll be available in so few drafts. What would you bid on him?

CECIL ESPY	AB	HR	RBI	SB	BA	$
1988 TEX	347	2	39	33	.248	19
1989 TEX	475	3	31	45	.257	25

Despite his promising '88, the market prices in Chapter 1 showed little faith in him. Despite the profits, Gary Pettis means he's still not a keeper.

DWIGHT EVANS	AB	HR	RBI	SB	BA	$
1987 BOS	541	34	123	4	.305	29
1988 BOS	559	21	111	5	.293	28
1989 BOS	520	20	100	3	.285	25

This is the year, alas, that I would withdraw my faith in Dewey.

JUNIOR FELIX	AB	HR	RBI	SB	BA	$
1989 TOR	415	9	46	18	.258	17

He had cooled off when I finally got to see him, and he didn't look so hot. But he's clearly got a very live bat. Probably will start out platooning with Glenallen Hill, and then one or the other will take over.

DAN GLADDEN	AB	HR	RBI	SB	BA	$
1987 MIN	438	8	38	25	.249	14
1988 MIN	576	11	62	28	.269	25
1989 MIN	461	8	46	23	.295	23

Has risen from fifth-outfielder status to third, easily.

MIKE GREENWELL	AB	HR	RBI	SB	BA	$
1987 BOS	412	19	89	5	.328	23
1988 BOS	590	22	119	16	.325	39
1989 BOS	578	14	95	13	.308	30

Carl Yastzremski, I guarantee, didn't have a .320 batting average after his first three years, and they didn't talk about trading him.

KEN GRIFFEY JR.	AB	HR	RBI	SB	BA	$
1989 SEA	455	16	61	16	.264	22

In the comment on his old man, I point out that his first full year was in some ways better than his phenom son's. Now I look again and see he had virtually the same batting average and a slightly better on-base average and slugging average *last year* than his son. But, no, I don't expect the similarity to persist.

MEL HALL	AB	HR	RBI	SB	BA	$
1987 CLE	485	18	76	5	.280	16
1988 CLE	515	6	71	7	.280	16
1989 NY A	361	17	58	0	.260	14

Turned himself into a Yankee Stadium hitter. As long as he doesn't get himself kicked off the team while he's waiting for the chance, he'll get some at-bats.

DAVE HENDERSON	AB	HR	RBI	SB	BA	$
1987 BOS/(SF)	205	8	26	3	.234	**4**
1988 OAK	507	24	94	2	.304	**27**
1989 OAK	579	15	80	8	.250	**18**

Still shaking my head over Hendu. I mean, he's dependable. Average the last two seasons and you've probably got his upcoming stats, but in most leagues he'll still be working on a long-term contract.

RICKEY HENDERSON	AB	HR	RBI	SB	BA	$
1987 NY A	358	17	37	41	.291	**27**
1988 NY A	554	6	50	93	.305	**56**
1989 NY A/OAK	541	12	57	77	.274	**48**

The top five prices in both the start-up and existing leagues: $70 (MLB), $68 (BLA), $65 (WGA), $64 (ADL), $61 (AFL).

John Candelaria has to take some of the credit. Remember? He said he couldn't wait to watch Rickey play for free agency, and then he didn't wait and there wasn't much to see anyway, I have to admit. Rickey dogged it in New York. He had earned $14 at the point that he was traded. He was headed for a $32 season. He did better than that for Oakland alone; his performance there, over the whole year, would have been worth $60—best Rotisserie season ever.

But he wasn't dogging it because he wanted to make middle-aged males jump from bridges; he was depressed himself. The horrible team he was playing for thoroughly bummed him. That was the main thing. But also, the fans never appreciated him. For some reason, Rickey Henderson was a flop in New York. A great show that would have closed after one week on Broadway. It happens.

He scored 513 runs for the Yankees. In four and a half years. And how he scored them! Wade Boggs—you barely notice him scoring; but not Rickey. Boggs needs help, he needs to be tiddlywinked around; Rickey just flares his nostrils, heads for second, heads for third. Boggs brushes the plate absently on his way to the dugout; Rickey slows down to savor the moment. He's so pleased with what he's done, he can barely decide which foot to use.

In this age of infinite stats, someone must have a record of how many runs Rickey Henderson scored for the Yankees before Mattingly or Winfield ever got the chance to knock him in. These aren't just single digits on the scoreboard, either; they are runs that hurt. The entire country saw how much they hurt Ernie Whitt, Kelly Gruber, the whole Toronto team. But he never caught on in New York.

It's a sad scene, as everyone knows, in Yankee Stadium these days. By the seventh inning and 15th beer, too many Yankee fans can hardly see Don Mattingly. They never did see Rickey. I don't know why. You would think the combination of 15 beers and Rickey Henderson would have been explosive!

I live in New York and obviously get a fair amount of enjoyment out of watching him play, yet I hope he stays in Oakland. I'm confident he will, because if money was all that mattered, he would have never left.

PETE INCAVIGLIA	AB	HR	RBI	SB	BA	$
1987 TEX	509	27	80	9	.271	**20**
1988 TEX	418	22	54	6	.249	**17**
1989 TEX	453	21	81	5	.236	**18**

In a dismal season, he did manage to whiff less often. Like Cory Snyder the year before, he seemed determined to work on it. Like Cory, there's probably no solution in the end.

BO JACKSON	AB	HR	RBI	SB	BA	$
1987 KC	396	22	53	10	.235	**12**
1988 KC	439	25	68	27	.246	**29**
1989 KC	515	32	105	26	.256	**38**

Bo marched into the All-Star Game with $27 already earned; he looked like he was headed for the all-time Rotisserie season.

Yet another thing Jerry Heath produces is a graph of how all the teams in a league did week by week. Naturally, you get out your Magic Marker and plot your own team as it zigzags through the season. If we could see something that charts the teams that had Bo vs. the ones with Rickey, what would it look like?

They both had such powerful years, but concentrated in different halves, that you would assume it would be noticeable. The Bo people riding high in July, well above the Rickey line. Then Bo's graph faltering, Rickey's starting to rise . . .

At the end, it's a very close finish. Bo's teams went 13 and 4; Rickey's 12 and 5.

CHRIS JAMES	AB	HR	RBI	SB	BA	$
1987 PHI	358	17	54	3	.293	**15**
1988 PHI	566	19	66	7	.242	**18**
1989 PHI/SD	482	13	65	5	.243	**15**

Won't make the fans forget Joe Carter but he should be able to hold his own with Dion, Candy, and the rest.

DION JAMES	AB	HR	RBI	SB	BA	$
1987 ATL	494	10	61	10	.312	19
1988 ATL	386	3	30	9	.256	8
1989 ATL/CLE	415	5	40	2	.287	10

Batted two points higher for Cleveland (.306) than Oddibe did for Atlanta.

LANCE JOHNSON	AB	HR	RBI	SB	BA	$
1987 STL	59	0	7	6	.220	2
1988 CHI A	124	0	6	6	.185	1
1989 CHI A	180	0	16	16	.300	11

When we bring a player off the reserve list in my league, he gets a salary next year of $15 (starting pitchers $10). Often it seems to put players right on the cusp. What would you do with Lance Johnson if you could keep him at $15 (as I can)?

What will he earn? What will people bet on him? I really think he's going to earn more than $15. Maybe $20. I think the bidding might stop around $11 or $12. I really doubt it will go as high as $18. So what do I do?

ROBERTO KELLY	AB	HR	RBI	SB	BA	$
1987 NY A	52	1	7	9	.269	5
1988 NY A	77	1	7	5	.247	3
1989 NY A	441	9	48	35	.302	30

At an average salary of $10 in the established leagues (and $7 in the start-ups), there won't be any head-scratching over Roberto.

CHET LEMON	AB	HR	RBI	SB	BA	$
1987 DET	470	20	75	0	.277	14
1988 DET	512	17	64	1	.264	15
1989 DET	414	7	47	1	.237	6

Chet, make sure you warn the first baseman before you try that headfirst slide of yours in the Senior League.

JEFF LEONARD	AB	HR	RBI	SB	BA	$
1987 SF	503	19	63	16	.280	20
1988 (SF)/MIL	534	10	64	17	.242	16
1989 SEA	566	24	93	6	.254	23

Did anyone actually bid $23 for Jeff Leonard? Let me see . . . None of the new leagues . . . None of the old ones.
The question is, Will they keep him at the salaries they paid ($10 and $11)?

LLOYD MOSEBY	AB	HR	RBI	SB	BA	$
1987 TOR	592	26	96	39	.282	35
1988 TOR	472	10	42	31	.239	20
1989 TOR	502	11	43	24	.221	16

Tiger Stadium, with its deep center field, is not the right place for Moseby, offensively or defensively. Furthermore, as with Dawson in Wrigley Field, it's too late for its forgiving surface to save Moseby's knees.

The Skydome, by the way, is ominous. Just when it looks like there's going to be a swing in the direction of grass fields and cozy stadiums, Giamatti dies, an earthquake kills the new stadium in San Francisco, and this thing comes along.

JOE ORSULAK	AB	HR	RBI	SB	BA	$
1987 PIT	did not play in majors					
1988 BAL	379	8	27	9	.288	13
1989 BAL	390	7	55	5	.285	14

When you see "did not play," as you will for Winfield, it's a downer. It's the opposite when you see "did not play in majors." Hulett had the same line, telling what kind of season the Orioles had. If it keeps up, and even if it doesn't, when their cozy grass ballpark is built, I'm piling on the train and heading on down.

DAN PASQUA	AB	HR	RBI	SB	BA	$
1987 NY A	318	17	42	0	.233	6
1988 CHI A	422	20	50	1	.227	11
1989 CHI A	246	11	47	1	.248	10

What Hriniak did for Kittle he was supposed to do for Pasqua. Maybe he just needed more time.

GARY PETTIS	AB	HR	RBI	SB	BA	$
1987 CAL	394	1	17	24	.208	5
1988 DET	458	3	36	44	.210	19
1989 DET	444	1	18	43	.257	21

If you have to kiss off a category, this is the one you want. Stolen bases are not only unredundant, they're often counterproductive. Players like Pettis and Otis Nixon have all their coordination from their waist down. Hitters as extreme as they are can in fact hurt you in three categories. If the average player gets 11 home runs, and you have Pettis on your team, and you want an above-average offense . . .

But if you are interested in stolen bases, he may be your man. His on-base average rose from .285 to .375. And once he's on base—what separates Gary and Otis from people like Jose and Darryl—he knows what he'd better do.

LUIS POLONIA	AB	HR	RBI	SB	BA	$
1987 OAK	435	4	49	29	.287	20
1988 OAK	288	2	27	24	.292	17
1989 OAK/NY A	433	3	46	22	.300	21

Red Sox could use some speed. Think Mrs. Yawkey would take him for Boggs?

KIRBY PUCKETT	AB	HR	RBI	SB	BA	$
1987 MIN	624	28	99	12	.332	33
1988 MIN	657	24	121	6	.356	42
1989 MIN	635	9	85	11	.339	31

Many times, I notice, when hitters' home runs go down, their doubles go up. You wonder if it's not just a matter of hitting the ball too square on the nose. So Kirby should have had 60 doubles last year. But he got his batting title, which is like Juan Marichal getting a Cy Young Award, and rattled the ball around to the tune of almost 300 total bases. He's averaged 338 total bases over the last four years, the greatest statistical accomplishment of anybody in that span. Nice center fielder, too.

CARLOS QUINTANA	AB	HR	RBI	SB	BA	$
1987 BOS	6	0	2	0	.333	0
1988 BOS	77	0	6	0	.208	0

They love him in Boston, but in 83 at-bats he still hasn't hit a home run. Or earned a dollar.

RUBEN SIERRA	AB	HR	RBI	SB	BA	$
1987 TEX	643	30	109	16	.263	25
1988 TEX	615	23	91	18	.254	27
1989 TEX	634	29	119	8	.306	37

The Peter Gammons campaign to make Yount the MVP will pay off for the Rangers. Injured pride, especially Latin pride, is a great incentive clause.

As for the merits of the campaign, probably Yount did have the better year. Played center field. Had a few more Runs Created, the yardstick used by Bill James to measure hitters outside of the team context. And, in fact, Yount did have fewer at-bats with runners on (285 vs. 319), doing slightly better in those opportunities.

But that's getting tricky, and if we're going to be that way, why not vote for Saberhagen? No, he's not an "everyday player," but the opposition had 961 at-bats against him, so he must have played a little bit.

If I had the vote, I'd have kept it simple. Sierra led the league in RBIs, slugging average, and total bases. In a year that had no clearly more valuable player, go with the steak and eggs.

CORY SNYDER	AB	HR	RBI	SB	BA	$
1987 CLE	577	33	82	5	.236	15
1988 CLE	511	26	75	5	.272	23
1989 CLE	489	18	59	6	.215	12

Even closer to going back to college than Inky.

SAMMY SOSA	AB	HR	RBI	SB	BA	$
1989 TEX/CHI A	183	4	13	7	.257	6

Looked bad in Texas and quite promising in Illinois.

PAT TABLER	AB	HR	RBI	SB	BA	$
1987 CLE	553	11	86	5	.307	19
1988 CLE/KC	444	2	66	3	.282	12
1989 KC	390	2	42	0	.259	5

When you're as quiet as this two years in a row, you turn into Player Z.

DANNY TARTABULL	AB	HR	RBI	SB	BA	$
1987 KC	582	34	101	9	.309	30
1988 KC	507	26	102	8	.274	28
1989 KC	441	18	62	4	.268	18

In the trade that sent Buhner and Sosa to the Guns, the Bags received Tartabull. He became their fourth outfielder, after Bo Jackson, Kirby Puckett and Mike Greenwell. This was June. The second-place, pitching-rich, hitting-poor Bags had already traded Montgomery, Bosio, and Chili Davis to get Puckett (and Carmelo Martinez); Guillen and Inky to get Greenwell (and Jody Reed); Bo they'd had since he stepped down from Krypton.

The results? They dropped from eighth in home runs to tied-for-tenth, from eighth in RBIs to ninth. The only one of the four big boppers who approached or exceeded form was Bo, and by June he'd mostly done it. Who said hitters were reliable?

But they held on to second because their pitchers still gained 42 pitching points.

GREG VAUGHAN	AB	HR	RBI	SB	BA	$
1989 MIL	113	5	23	4	.265	7

A serious threat to either Braggs or Deer. At last sighting, he was doing well in Puerto Rico.

CLAUDELL WASHINGTON	AB	HR	RBI	SB	BA	$
1987 NY A	312	9	44	10	.279	12
1988 NY A	455	11	64	15	.308	24
1989 CAL	418	13	42	13	.273	18

Was an excellent fourth outfielder for the Angels, although their organizational charts probably had him listed a little higher.

DEVON WHITE	AB	HR	RBI	SB	BA	$
1987 CAL	639	24	87	32	.263	28
1988 CAL	455	11	51	17	.259	18
1989 CAL	636	12	56	44	.245	29

Instead of the 25 superstars, Stats Inc. should chart the riddles like Devon White. Does he take too many pitches, does he never bunt, does he not hustle to first when he nubs the ball? Does he simply not have the mental toughness to play the full season?

MOOKIE WILSON	AB	HR	RBI	SB	BA	$
1987 NY N	385	9	34	21	.299	**17**
1988 NY N	378	8	41	15	.296	**18**
1989 NY N/TOR	487	5	35	19	.251	**14**

It would have been splendid if the Mookster had rampaged through the playoffs—the Mets management, along with Steinbrenner, strangling themselves in their box seats.

WILLIE WILSON	AB	HR	RBI	SB	BA	$
1987 KC	610	4	30	59	.279	**29**
1988 KC	591	1	37	35	.262	**21**
1989 KC	383	3	43	24	.253	**16**

He and Mookie are the same age. Who's had a better career? Oh, Willie's far ahead statistically, but stats are only everything in our game. Which career would you take for yourself?

DAVE WINFIELD	AB	HR	RBI	SB	BA	$
1987 NY A	575	27	97	5	.275	**21**
1988 NY A	559	25	107	9	.322	**35**
1989 NY A			did not play			

Ranks 208 out of 213 in the Heath tracking. Seems kind of severe, since, unlike Mike Schmidt, he made his mind up before most leagues had held their drafts. The average salary in Heath's established leagues was $12 and no team paid more than $19. Plenty of players above Winfield lost more than he did (Trammell ranks 139), which leads me to believe that buying him, like buying Canseco, either reflected or induced a fire-sale mentality. Next year we'll have to compare how each player paid off.

Schmidt's rank in the National League, by the way, is 162 out of 180, one better than Strawberry.

ROBIN YOUNT	AB	HR	RBI	SB	BA	$
1987 MIL	635	21	103	19	.312	**31**
1988 MIL	621	13	91	22	.306	**33**
1989 MIL	614	21	103	19	.318	**38**

Has earned more than Joe Carter in the last three years; might be time to pay him more.

Player Z

In 1988, Rick Leach and Dave Clark were outfielders number 58 and 59 in the appendix, both earning $3. Last year, not only was the 60th outfielder (Lemon) worth $6, so were the next five players listed in the appendix. Far greater depth of position, in other words. (The strength of position actually declined; it was $18.72 in 1988.)

The situation looks similar this year—all sorts of Outfielder Zees to choose from: Armas, Boston, Carmen Castillo, Felder, Finley, Gallagher, Heep, Javier, Jefferson, Tracy Jones, Komminsk, Maldonado, Moses, Romine, Thurman, Ken Williams. A veteran I hope gets nominated late—when $13 might blow away the field—is Mitch Webster.

Juan Gonzales—not Denny, not Rene, not Jose—bears watching on the Rangers. Rob Richie certainly should make the Tigers. Other prospects are mentioned above or are in the minor league chapter, and others—like Rob Ducey? Derek Bell?—are going to be surprises.

Just like Tom Lawless in the playoffs. Awful transition, but I have to mention him. He alone kept the A's from winning eight straight games. Had the Blue Jays won three more, he'd be famous forever. Only got into 12 games all year at third, so if you want him on your team, and you're in a callous league like mine, he's got to be an outfielder.

DESIGNATED HITTERS

BRIAN DOWNING	AB	HR	RBI	SB	BA	$
1987 CAL	567	29	77	5	.272	**19**
1988 CAL	484	25	64	3	.242	**16**
1989 CAL	544	14	59	0	.283	**16**

For compensation purposes, Elias lumps outfielders, first basemen, and designated hitters in one group. By being the second-best DH (behind Baines, who we know is really an outfielder), Downing finds himself in pretty good company as a Type-A player. The three players above him are Alvin Davis, Baines, and Ellis Burks; the three below are Ruben Sierra, George Brett, and Don Mattingly.

DAVE PARKER	AB	HR	RBI	SB	BA	$
1987 CIN	589	26	97	7	.253	20
1988 OAK	377	12	55	0	.257	11
1989 OAK	553	22	97	0	.264	21

Parker is sandwiched between Kent Hrbek and Joe Carter. Even more amazing: He hit as well as they did last year. Question, though . . . did the Brewers sign him to babysit Sheffield or—and it can't be both—appease Yount?

KEN PHELPS	AB	HR	RBI	SB	BA	$
1987 SEA	332	27	68	1	.259	14
1988 SEA/NY A	297	24	54	1	.263	17
1989 NY A/OAK	194	7	29	0	.242	5

Just when it looked like he would be a star in either Japan or the Senior League, Parker offered him something much more enticing: the chance to really contribute to a World Series ring.

JIM RICE	AB	HR	RBI	SB	BA	$
1987 BOS	404	13	62	1	.277	11
1988 BOS	485	15	72	1	.264	15
1989 BOS	209	3	28	1	.234	3

It's time for his golf clubs, which he always seemed to get more of a kick out of anyway.

LARRY SHEETS	AB	HR	RBI	SB	BA	$
1987 BAL	469	31	94	1	.316	25
1988 BAL	452	10	47	1	.230	6
1989 BAL	304	7	33	1	.243	6

Listed to pad this section.

Player Z

Baseball agreed with the dismay I expressed last year over the deterioration at this—position. Teams tried to pump new blood into their DH spot with the likes of Luis Medina, Dave Clark, Joey Meyer, and Terry Francona. I've made much ado about the rise of the National League average hitter; the American League continues to watch its natural DHs—Esasky being the latest example—ship out.

The practical effect for us, oddly, is to boost the prices of Parker and Downing. The one-dollar DH gambit is passé; no reason to keep the DH slot open to fill it with Jerry Hairston.

AMERICAN LEAGUE PITCHERS

JIM ABBOTT	IP	W	S	ERA	RATIO	$
1989 CAL	181	12	0	3.92	13.10	3

Bad ratio was due to hits, not walks. From what I saw of his fastball, it won't keep happening. The bidding will go briskly to $10, and then the nail-biting begins.

RICK AGUILERA	IP	W	S	ERA	RATIO	$
1987 NY N	115	11	0	3.60	12.29	9
1988 NY N	25	0	0	6.93	14.23	−5
1989 NY N/MIN	145	9	7	2.79	10.86	17

Six of these dollars earned for the Twins, in only 11 starts.

DOYLE ALEXANDER	IP	W	S	ERA	RATIO	$
1987 (ATL)/DET	206	14	0	3.01	12.36	28
1988 DET	229	14	0	4.32	11.87	5
1989 DET	223	6	0	4.44	12.96	−6

Doyle's such a sourpuss he probably enjoyed playing on the Tigers last year.

ALLAN ANDERSON	IP	W	S	ERA	RATIO	$
1987 MIN	12	1	0	5.42	21.90	−3
1988 MIN	202	16	0	2.45	10.50	26
1989 MIN	197	17	0	3.80	12.22	10

The confidence gained in 1988 seemed to take him through the rough patches last year. Needs confidence, since he's one of those lefties with good movement but not much velocity.

JEFF BALLARD	IP	W	S	ERA	RATIO	$
1987 BAL	70	2	0	6.59	17.44	−13
1988 BAL	153	8	0	4.40	12.27	1
1989 BAL	215	18	0	3.43	12.41	12

Not much velocity, and really not that much movement. When your ERA drops but your ratio rises, it tells you—not that he was lucky, necessarily, but the Orioles did have that kind of year. Ballard will continue to use his outfielders, and he may win 15, but not for me. I'm a big fan of his type of pitching at the ballpark, not in the box scores.

SCOTT BANKHEAD	IP	W	S	ERA	RATIO	$
1987 SEA	149	9	0	5.42	12.36	0
1988 SEA	135	7	0	3.07	10.20	13
1989 SEA	210	14	0	3.34	10.70	17

He operated at full tilt and almost matched Tartabull playing on one cylinder.

JUAN BERENGUER	IP	W	S	ERA	RATIO	$
1987 MIN	112	8	4	3.94	11.81	12
1988 MIN	100	8	2	3.96	12.15	6
1989 MIN	106	9	3	3.48	12.14	9

The Nine Juan Berenguers, in my league's hypothetical final standings, would have finished third in wins, 10th in saves, third in ERA, and eighth in ratio. He's said to be worth a little more than the average pitcher ($8.67), and his 28 pitching points are a little better than average (26).

BUD BLACK	IP	W	S	ERA	RATIO	$
1987 KC	122	8	1	3.60	11.84	11
1988 KC/CLE	81	4	1	5.00	12.89	−2
1989 CLE	222	12	0	3.36	10.73	16

The Indians had quite good pitching last year (they were the only team with an ERA under 4.00 and a losing record), and Black was their best starter by the end. Since he's in the second year of peanut contracts in virtually every league, bettors will be spared wondering if he can do it again.

BERT BLYLEVEN	IP	W	S	ERA	RATIO	$
1987 MIN	267	15	0	4.01	11.80	16
1988 MIN	207	10	0	5.43	12.63	−7
1989 CAL	241	17	0	2.73	10.05	28

In comparing prices between the start-up leagues and the existing leagues, we've seen the hitters who were available in both auctions almost invariably bringing more money in the older leagues. In part, the explanation is freeze lists; in part, it's explained by the different salaries for a pitcher like Blyleven: $8 paid by the newcomers who saw Bert's wins over the years and didn't give much thought to the other junk, $4 paid by the shell-shocked veterans.

MIKE BODDICKER	IP	W	S	ERA	RATIO	$
1987 BAL	226	10	0	4.18	11.55	11
1988 BAL/BOS	236	13	0	3.39	11.86	12
1989 BOS	212	15	0	4.00	12.25	7

Fenway Park seems to be an okay place for him, oddly enough.

CHRIS BOSIO	IP	W	S	ERA	RATIO	$
1987 MIL	170	11	2	5.24	12.55	4
1988 MIL	182	7	6	3.36	11.27	15
1989 MIL	235	15	0	2.95	10.47	23

Bosio, by the anti-fire-sale legislation that was first adopted in my league, would have cost $15 this year, since he was traded during the season. In modifying the rule to $10 for starting pitchers, we've made him considerably more attractive. The grand tradition of selling out has not been abolished, by any means.

KEVIN BROWN	IP	W	S	ERA	RATIO	$
1988 TEX	23	1	0	4.24	15.81	−2
1989 TEX	191	12	0	3.35	11.17	14

Eight veteran leagues, along with all five new leagues, didn't even buy him in the draft. Activated from a reserve list or claimed from the free-agent pool, he's $10 this year by our rules. A keeper? Perhaps. But the free ride is over.

TODD BURNS	IP	W	S	ERA	RATIO	$
1988 OAK	103	8	1	3.16	11.13	11
1989 OAK	96	6	8	2.24	8.78	22

The A's have no problem replacing Storm Davis, but who will replace Burns?

TOM CANDIOTTI	IP	W	S	ERA	RATIO	$
1987 CLE	211	7	0	4.78	12.20	2
1988 CLE	217	14	0	3.28	11.55	15
1989 CLE	206	13	0	3.10	10.62	19

In four of the last five years, he's been among the best starting pitchers in baseball.

CHUCK CARY	IP	W	S	ERA	RATIO	$
1987 ATL	17	1	1	3.60	11.50	1
1988 ATL	8	0	0	4.00	12.22	−1
1989 NY A	99	4	0	3.10	10.62	9

Chuck Cary is 30? Looks younger, throws younger. Hope he's still around in the crapshoot.

JOHN CERUTTI	IP	W	S	ERA	RATIO	$
1987 TOR	151	11	0	4.40	12.07	8
1988 TOR	124	6	1	3.13	11.79	8
1989 TOR	205	11	0	3.07	11.70	13

He's 30. Probably repeated a few years at Amherst.

ROGER CLEMENS	IP	W	S	ERA	RATIO	$
1987 BOS	281	20	0	2.97	10.60	35
1988 BOS	264	18	0	2.93	9.51	32
1989 BOS	253	17	0	3.13	10.94	21

This is the logical place to confess that I had Clemens last year. All season long. Bought him in the draft. $32.

How it happened exactly—well, the memory blurs. I think I was enforcing prices. I don't have precise bidding points for pitchers, so there was no definite cutoff that would have stopped me. It was early in the draft. I was in high spirits; I seem to recall making a previous bid in the high 20s for Clemens. When I heard $31, I merrily said $32.

And silence.

Think there was a conspiracy? Could have been. The funny thing, though, is that far from throwing me off my feed for the rest of the day, I was pleased. Roger Clemens? On my team? Golly!

And thus $11 bit the dust. No big deal. I bought McGwire for about the same amount and about the same amount bit the dust. Clemens in real baseball is twice as valuable as McGwire and, in fact, has earned more Patton $ than McGwire in the past three years. He had a damn fine season—not the Saberhagen season that I secretly expected, but Moose Factory has no complaints.

Having said that, I admit I'm dropping Clemens. I'm keeping McGwire.

CHUCK CRIM	IP	W	S	ERA	RATIO	$
1987 MIL	130	6	12	3.67	11.91	20
1988 MIL	105	7	9	2.91	10.54	19
1989 MIL	118	9	7	2.83	11.47	17

He's almost as valuable to Treblehorn as he is to us.

STORM DAVIS	IP	W	S	ERA	RATIO	$
1987 SD/OAK	93	3	0	5.23	14.03	−5
1988 OAK	202	16	0	3.70	13.48	5
1989 OAK	169	19	0	4.36	13.55	4

If he had pitched a respectable number of innings, the way a 19-game winner is supposed to, he would have been worthless.

ElRoy Face, by the way, pitched 93 innings the year he won 18 games in relief. Bob Stanley won 15 games in 142 innings (three starts) in 1978. Whitey Ford not only pitched better than Davis, but, despite his reputation, consistently pitched over 200 innings. Don Gullett is the only starter I can find who approaches Davis, winning 15 games in 160 innings in 1975. He had a 2.42 ERA.

Davis pitched fewer than nine innings—including losses and no-decisions—for each victory. The average Rotisserie team gets around 1300 innings. At the rate Storm Davis was collecting them, you'd have 146 wins.

He'll collect 10–12 wins for KC.

JOHN DOPSON	IP	W	S	ERA	RATIO	$
1988 MON	169	3	0	3.04	11.10	**4**
1989 BOS	169	12	0	3.99	12.49	**5**

He gave up more hits and walks in the same number of innings, but one less home run; not bad, considering the change of venue.

RICH DOTSON	IP	W	S	ERA	RATIO	$
1987 CHI A	211	11	0	4.17	12.24	**9**
1988 NY A	178	12	0	4.80	13.45	**−3**
1989 CHI A	151	5	0	4.46	14.21	**−8**

It was quite clear from the pitchers they were signing why the Royals had Tartabull on the winter trading block: They're moving the fences back to where only Bo can reach them.

DENNIS ECKERSLEY	IP	W	S	ERA	RATIO	$
1987 OAK	116	6	16	3.03	9.03	**34**
1988 OAK	73	4	45	2.35	7.80	**50**
1989 OAK	58	4	33	1.56	5.46	**43**

Trails only Henderson in three-year earnings. If another pitcher in either league's scans shows improvement each year in both ERA and ratio, no one begins where the Eck does. His ratio last year in 58 innings was worth more than Mike Moore's in 242. Mattingly goes to the full count more often than Eckersley: 12 times all year—one hit, three walks. Never a walk on fewer than six pitches. Must be the first person in the history of the game to give up fewer bases on balls than home runs. And yet—is it just me, or is he somehow a bit sleepy-making? Why do I go for a beer while he's coming in, knowing full well the game will be over before I'm back?

STEVE FARR	IP	W	S	ERA	RATIO	S
1987 KC	91	4	1	4.15	13.95	1
1988 KC	83	5	20	2.50	11.32	25
1989 KC	63	2	18	4.12	13.78	12

His bad ratio was due to hits, not walks—the last thing you want from a relief pitcher.

JOHN FARRELL	IP	W	S	ERA	RATIO	S
1987 CLE	69	5	0	3.39	11.74	7
1988 CLE	210	14	0	4.24	12.11	6
1989 CLE	208	9	0	3.63	11.55	8

For those who subscribe to good second-half performances, this is your man.

CHUCK FINLEY	IP	W	S	ERA	RATIO	S
1987 CAL	91	2	0	4.67	14.39	−4
1988 CAL	194	9	0	4.17	12.64	1
1989 CAL	200	16	0	2.57	11.40	21

The Don Zimmer League in Boston nearly ceased to function in May. Classic case of cutthroat veteran taking advantage of callow newcomer, ruining a tight pennant race. The culprit? John Benson of the Strokers (the very name should have been a warning). The victim? Joe Hyman of the Monte Verdi's.

The trade?

Chuck Finley and Jody Reed for Mark Langston and Gary Sheffield.

MIKE FLANAGAN	IP	W	S	ERA	RATIO	S
1987 BAL	144	6	0	4.06	12.44	5
1988 BAL/TOR	211	13	0	4.18	12.80	3
1989 TOR	172	8	0	3.93	12.22	3

Will cool off Amos Otis in the Senior League.

WILLIE FRASER	IP	W	S	ERA	RATIO	S
1987 CAL	177	10	0	3.92	11.36	13
1988 CAL	195	12	0	5.41	13.08	−7
1989 CAL	92	4	2	3.24	10.11	10

Managers increasingly are discovering what we've found out: Good middle relievers are dynamite.

WES GARDNER	IP	W	S	ERA	RATIO	$
1987 BOS	90	3	10	5.42	14.05	5
1988 BOS	149	8	2	3.50	11.05	11
1989 BOS	86	3	0	5.97	15.07	−11

His 81 strikeouts mean he should and will get more chances.

TOM GORDON	IP	W	S	ERA	RATIO	$
1988 KC	16	0	0	5.17	13.22	−1
1989 KC	163	17	1	3.64	11.48	14

If I were Flash Gordon and the unmentionable happens this spring, I know what I'd do: go work out in Japan. He'd show them a curveball or two and his fastball would look like Walter Johnson's.

Really, if there is a delay to the season, what's to stop everyone from underpaid keepers to Jose Canseco from earning a few yen on the side?

MARK GUBICZA	IP	W	S	ERA	RATIO	$
1987 KC	242	13	0	3.98	13.05	8
1988 KC	270	20	0	2.70	10.68	29
1989 KC	255	15	0	3.04	11.12	20

A three-category pitcher who last year exactly divided his earnings between the cumulative and qualitative categories.

LEE GUETTERMAN	IP	W	S	ERA	RATIO	$
1987 SEA	113	11	0	3.81	12.07	10
1988 NY A	41	1	0	4.65	13.94	−2
1989 NY A	103	5	13	2.45	10.83	21

A four-category pitcher who, last year anyway, was worth more than Gubicza.

MARK GUTHRIE	IP	W	S	ERA	RATIO	$
1989 MIN	57	2	0	4.55	13.66	−3

If Ben McDonald doesn't watch out, this guy's going to be getting all the attention when they go back to the city of New Orleans.

ERIK HANSON	IP	W	S	ERA	RATIO	S
1988 SEA	42	2	0	3.24	10.15	4
1989 SEA	113	9	0	3.18	10.72	11

In Las Vegas, I'd take whatever the odds are that he'll win the Cy Young Award. In the auction, I'll maybe bid as high as $11 for him.

PETE HARNISCH	IP	W	S	ERA	RATIO	S
1988 BAL	13	0	0	5.54	15.23	−2
1989 BAL	103	5	0	4.62	14.02	−5

Excellent pickup in the endgame, but he walks more people when he's in the majors, which is not a good sign.

BRYAN HARVEY	IP	W	S	ERA	RATIO	S
1988 CAL	76	7	17	2.13	9.36	28
1989 CAL	55	3	25	3.44	12.60	22

For some reason lefties can't hit Harvey even a little bit (.160 batting average). Righties (.206) don't exactly feast on him. And last year was a slump.

ANDY HAWKINS	IP	W	S	ERA	RATIO	S
1987 SD	118	3	0	5.05	13.77	−6
1988 SD	218	14	0	3.35	11.25	9
1989 NY A	208	15	0	4.80	13.57	−4

Some of the most memorable box scores of the season. In one game he gave up about 15 unearned runs. But he literally spared lives in the last week of the season. A handful of teams that owned him were actually still in the running. I know this because in the Heath trackings, Hawkins was 129 out of 141—only—and because I had him. In any event, Andy had two starts that week, and it's just lucky the sequence wasn't reversed. Had Hawkins picked up his Storm Davis special in the first one, owners would have gone into the last day of the season with hopes high, and *then* he would have given up eight earned runs in one-third of an inning.

TOM HENKE	IP	W	S	ERA	RATIO	$
1987 TOR	94	0	34	2.49	8.33	**49**
1988 TOR	68	4	25	2.91	11.12	**27**
1989 TOR	89	8	20	1.92	9.20	**33**

Of the teams that took big dives between the hypothetical final standings and their actual finishes, how many unloaded Henke? Early in the year he had two big obstacles to get over: Jimy Williams and no fastball. Without the former correction, the other may never have occurred.

MIKE HENNEMAN	IP	W	S	ERA	RATIO	$
1987 DET	97	11	7	2.98	10.76	**23**
1988 DET	91	9	22	1.87	9.46	**36**
1989 DET	90	11	8	3.70	13.50	**11**

When you find you have a $35 dog on your hands as the trade deadline approaches, what are your choices?

1) Keep wishing. You will be laughed at behind your back.

2) Try to trade him for somebody else's $35 player. You will be laughed at to your face.

3) Trade him for somebody else's $35 dog. One of you will laugh last.

4) Trade him for somebody else's $20 player. If it was Henneman you traded, you laugh; if it was Henke, he does.

You can't go lower than $20. If your dog has no more appeal than that, you have to eat him.

GUILLERMO HERNANDEZ	IP	W	S	ERA	RATIO	$
1987 DET	49	3	8	3.67	13.41	**10**
1988 DET	68	6	10	3.06	10.77	**16**
1989 DET	31	2	15	5.75	14.94	**9**

How many people who picked him up for $5 succeeded in trading Guillermo for a $20 player? I know everyone who owned him tried.

GREG HIBBARD	IP	W	S	ERA	RATIO	$
1989 CHI A	137	6	0	3.21	11.99	**6**

Might be Allan Anderson. Might be Ballard. Might be LaPoint.

TEDDY HIGUERA	IP	W	S	ERA	RATIO	$
1987 MIL	262	18	0	3.85	11.11	**22**
1988 MIL	227	16	0	2.45	8.99	**34**
1989 MIL	135	9	0	3.46	11.51	**9**

He'll never pitch this badly again. I'm almost sure.

BRIAN HOLMAN	IP	W	S	ERA	RATIO	$
1988 MON	100	4	0	3.23	12.11	**1**
1989 MON/SEA	191	9	0	3.67	12.75	**2**

A most deceiving salary, since he lost $3 for the Expos.

RICK HONEYCUTT	IP	W	S	ERA	RATIO	$
1987 (LA)/OAK	139	3	0	4.72	13.69	**−4**
1988 OAK	80	3	7	3.50	11.19	**10**
1989 OAK	77	2	12	2.35	9.63	**19**

If he and Nelson hadn't taken pity on the Giants, the final score would have been 32–6.

It reminds me that it's time to tell it like it is (now) about Tim McCarver. He's always talked too much. Now he says things you'd as soon not hear. When the Giants, down 3–0 in games and 8–2 in this one, were scampering around the bases against Honeycutt and Nelson, McCarver cried, "The A's have gone from domination to abomination!" It's the kind of thing you hope was ad-libbed—just burbled up because Tim's that kind of guy—but you suspect was pre-canned, like all of Vin Scully's much tamer distractions.

It was worse than distracting, of course, in that it wasn't true. If it were true, it would have been funny. McCarver lapsed more seriously from his primary duty earlier in the same game when Donnell Nixon was called out on an inning-ending force at second. "See that?" says Tim, during the replay. "He hook-slides into second!" Sure enough, he does. "If he doesn't hook-slide, he's safe!" cries Tim. The replay shows Donnell sliding again. He's still hook-sliding. "Donnell Nixon by hook-sliding instead of going straight in cost the Giants the inning!" says Tim. The replay shows it again. And again he's sliding, and again—whatever way he slides—he's out.

McCarver gets points for noticing the hook-slide. Without the replay, he could have speculated endlessly about Donnell's wrong choice of slide. He could even have observed that most ballplayers these days don't have two slides to choose from. But with each replay, he should have admitted it didn't matter.

CHARLIE HOUGH	IP	W	S	ERA	RATIO	$
1987 TEX	285	18	0	3.79	11.43	22
1988 TEX	252	15	0	3.32	11.71	15
1989 TEX	182	10	0	4.35	13.01	−1

Tom House, watching Hough and his new pitcher (the one from Houston) pitching in the spring, said Hough had better mechanics. Tells me maybe I should have McCarver's job, but not House's.

MIKE JACKSON	IP	W	S	ERA	RATIO	$
1987 PHI	109	3	1	4.20	11.89	3
1988 SEA	99	6	4	2.63	10.60	15
1989 SEA	99	4	7	3.17	12.23	10

The beauty of these middle relievers is not so much what they earn as what you pay for them: only $2 for Mike Jackson in the start-up leagues. That the older leagues have caught on is indicated by the fact that they paid $6 for him.

RANDY JOHNSON	IP	W	S	ERA	RATIO	$
1988 MON	26	3	0	2.42	10.38	4
1989 MON/SEA	161	7	0	4.82	13.61	−8

Unless something happens to Schooler, $6 is about the limit for Mike Jackson. He'll never hurt you the way Randy Johnson did, overall, last year. However, $6 won't fetch Johnson this year, and it shouldn't. My bid ($8 or $9) probably won't either.

DOUG JONES	IP	W	S	ERA	RATIO	$
1987 CLE	91	6	8	3.15	12.36	16
1988 CLE	83	3	37	2.27	9.18	42
1989 CLE	81	7	32	2.34	9.93	39

The Indians have quite a pitching staff, when you think about it.

JIMMY KEY	IP	W	S	ERA	RATIO	S
1987 TOR	261	17	0	2.76	9.52	**39**
1988 TOR	131	12	0	3.29	10.76	**14**
1989 TOR	216	13	0	3.88	10.54	**14**

Slipped into the hospital for more surgery after the season. Little touching up of the rotator cuff.

ERIC KING	IP	W	S	ERA	RATIO	S
1987 DET	116	6	9	4.89	13.27	**9**
1988 DET	69	4	3	3.41	12.32	**6**
1989 CHI A	159	9	0	3.39	11.75	**9**

The White Sox had the best minor league record of any franchise last year; they bought Hriniak; they keep getting far the better in trades. Someday it's got to show.

MARK KNUDSON	IP	W	S	ERA	RATIO	S
1987 MIL	62	4	0	5.37	14.81	**−3**
1988 MIL	16	0	0	1.13	10.69	**2**
1989 MIL	124	8	0	3.35	10.12	**12**

Threw as well as anybody in the last month.

MARK LANGSTON	IP	W	S	ERA	RATIO	S
1987 SEA	272	19	0	3.84	11.78	**20**
1988 SEA	261	15	0	3.34	11.43	**17**
1989 SEA/MON	250	16	14	2.74	11.16	**19**

He'll be a great keeper in all the leagues that feared bidding for Langston last year because he might go to the National League.

CHARLIE LEIBRANDT	IP	W	S	ERA	RATIO	S
1987 KC	240	16	0	3.41	11.59	**21**
1988 KC	243	13	0	3.19	11.33	**17**
1989 KC	161	5	0	5.14	13.98	**−11**

If he was a right-hander, I'd say he was finished.

AL LEITER	IP	W	S	ERA	RATIO	S
1988 NY A	57	4	0	3.92	12.87	**1**
1989 NY A/TOR	33	1	0	5.67	14.85	**−4**

All he has to do is look good in Florida and we'll all start thinking a lot more about him than we do Jesse Barfield; we won't pay much for Leiter, but whoever gets him knows anything's possible.

KIRK MCCASKILL	IP	W	S	ERA	RATIO	$
1987 CAL	75	4	0	5.67	14.22	−4
1988 CAL	146	8	0	4.31	13.29	−1
1989 CAL	212	15	0	2.93	11.08	19

Around the trading deadline for most leagues, McCaskill went into the kind of slump that made him untouchable.

LANCE MCCULLERS	IP	W	S	ERA	RATIO	$
1987 SD	123	8	16	3.72	12.73	18
1988 SD	98	3	10	2.48	11.48	12
1989 NY A	85	4	3	4.57	12.76	1

Steve Sax he wasn't.

BEN MCDONALD	IP	W	S	ERA	RATIO	$
1987 BAL	7	1	0	8.59	14.73	−1

In the Florida Instructional League he was putting alligators in people's showers. I wouldn't try that on Frank Robinson.

BOB MILACKI	IP	W	S	ERA	RATIO	$
1988 BAL	25	2	0	0.72	6.48	8
1989 BAL	243	14	0	3.74	11.89	10

A rookie who seemed like he was in his 10th season; was as important to the Orioles as Olson.

GREG MINTON	IP	W	S	ERA	RATIO	$
1987 CAL	99	6	11	3.17	12.69	19
1988 CAL	79	4	7	2.85	11.51	12
1989 CAL	90	4	8	2.20	11.30	15

Average salary in the established leagues: $4.

JEFF MONTGOMERY	IP	W	S	ERA	RATIO	$
1987 CIN	19	2	0	4.00	12.22	−2
1988 KC	63	7	1	3.45	12.06	6
1989 KC	92	7	18	1.37	8.90	33

Furious bids from his owners for Mark Davis.

MIKE MOORE	IP	W	S	ERA	RATIO	$
1987 SEA	231	9	0	4.71	13.71	−3
1988 SEA	229	9	1	3.78	10.19	15
1989 OAK	242	19	0	2.61	10.28	29

This is the kind of payoff you can't get from the likes of Minton. The second-best pitcher (16 firsts, 3 lasts) in the Heath rankings, behind Russell (20-1), ahead of Saberhagen (15-3).

In descending order of how they ranked, the other pitchers who earned $29 or more and their "won-lost" records: Eckersley (13-4), Schooler (11-3), Doug Jones (10-3), Thigpen (8-2), Olson (9-4), Pleasac (7-2), Henke (7-2), Montgomery (2-3), and Reardon (7-10).

All quite rational—even Reardon, for whom the average salary was more than hefty ($30 in the older leagues)—except Montgomery. Only two firsts? German Gonzalez (4-0) ranks 49 places ahead of him.

JACK MORRIS	IP	W	S	ERA	RATIO	$
1987 DET	266	18	0	3.38	10.83	28
1988 DET	235	15	0	3.94	11.80	10
1989 DET	170	6	0	4.86	13.10	−7

The list above is just those pitchers who earned at least $29; plenty of other starters besides Moore and Saberhagen figure in the top 25: Hanson (14-3), Key (13-3), Bosio (12-3), Black (8-2), Swindell (9-4), Blyleven (7-3), Gardner (6-2), Storm Davis (10-6), and Bankhead (10-6). Most of them make sense.

The other end of the heap makes sense, too. In ascending order from the worst pitcher in the Heath leagues last year: Niedenfuer (1-10), Candelaria (4-13), Rawley (3-11), Reuss (5-13), LaPoint (4-11), and Jack Morris (3-10).

Is it over, not-so-old Tiger Jack? 2794 IP take their toll? After 13 seasons, finally one with a losing record? You took a lot of tough losses, I see in Bill James's leader board: as many as Alexander, Clemens, and Viola (6); only Hough had more. Turn four of those around and you go 10–10. Yet the Tigers are going to continue to give you tough losses.

Who knows? I'll say this for Jack Morris: He'll get a higher bid from me than Charlie Leibrandt, right-handed or not.

ROB MURPHY	IP	W	S	ERA	RATIO	$
1987 CIN	101	8	3	3.04	10.96	**14**
1988 CIN	85	0	3	3.08	11.37	**3**
1989 BOS	105	5	9	2.74	11.83	**15**

Breeds Rotisserie racehorses.

JAMIE NAVARRO	IP	W	S	ERA	RATIO	$
1989 MIL	110	7	0	3.12	12.39	**6**

Cool customer with a hot arm.

GENE NELSON	IP	W	S	ERA	RATIO	$
1987 OAK	124	6	3	3.93	11.28	**12**
1988 OAK	112	9	3	3.06	10.56	**15**
1989 OAK	80	3	3	3.26	10.13	**9**

In 50 games for this team, he couldn't scrounge more wins or saves? He maybe owed a few.

TOM NIEDENFUER	IP	W	S	ERA	RATIO	$
1987 (LA)/BAL	68	4	14	4.50	13.10	**15**
1988 BAL	59	3	18	3.51	11.90	**18**
1989 SEA	36	0	0	6.69	15.11	**−7**

Everyone was puzzled when the Mariners signed him for the money they did. He also cost two picks in the amateur draft, neutralizing what little compensation they got for Mike Moore.

GREGG OLSON	IP	W	S	ERA	RATIO	$
1988 BAL	11	1	0	3.27	16.36	**0**
1989 BAL	85	5	27	1.69	10.91	**34**

Terry Bucher of the Bo Belinsky League in Virginia sent word that they, too (like the BBQ League in the NL), suffered the indignity of losing the pennant to callow newcomers. The Nuclear Nubbs prevailed against the Old Chapel Gang, who had a freeze list that included McGriff, Chili D, and Devon White for a total of $15; against the Royal Blossoms, who had Plesac for $4; against the Wapner Judges, who had Eckersley, Henneman, and Harvey for $17. How could that happen?

Partly luck: $30 for Saberhagen—far too much for an erratic starting pitcher.

Partly more luck: $1 for Montgomery.

Partly the other teams should be ashamed: $10 for Schooler.

And more ashamed: $1 for Olson. His average salary in the older Heath leagues was $10 (high of $24), and even in the start-ups it was $4.

Throw in Blyleven for $5, McCaskill for $7, Flanagan for $2, Kevin Brown for $1, and Bautista for $7 (thank God—they are mortal), and what do you have?

$64 for a clean sweep: 48 pitching points.

JESSE OROSCO	IP	W	S	ERA	RATIO	$
1987 NY N	77	3	16	4.44	12.74	**13**
1988 LA	53	3	9	2.72	12.06	**10**
1989 CLE	78	3	3	2.08	9.23	**14**

Seems to be an important and effective part of the Indians' pitching scheme.

MELIDO PEREZ	IP	W	S	ERA	RATIO	$
1988 CHI A	197	12	0	3.79	11.79	**9**
1989 CHI A	183	11	0	5.01	13.60	**−7**

During the last week of the season, I made a point of visiting a friend who owns a satellite dish. We settled in to watch the White Sox take on Minnesota at Comiskey. Melido pitching. I had picked him up on waivers a few weeks before, and he'd so far held his own. Tonight the wind was howling toward home plate with the temperature in the 40s. I explained to my friend, who doesn't ordinarily watch baseball, what a break I was catching.

Melido lasted four innings. Larkin and, hell, even Puckett hit home runs off him. Six earned runs, seven hits, five walks. All Melido could think of was getting his ass into a hot shower.

PASCUAL PEREZ	IP	W	S	ERA	RATIO	$
1987 MON	70	7	0	2.30	8.74	15
1988 MON	188	12	0	2.44	8.47	24
1989 MON	198	9	0	3.31	10.12	11

Pascual's a better pitcher than the Yankees are a baseball team; compared to what the franchise earns, he's underpaid.

DAN PLESAC	IP	W	S	ERA	RATIO	$
1987 MIL	79	5	23	2.61	9.80	36
1988 MIL	52	1	30	2.41	9.98	30
1989 MIL	61	3	33	2.35	9.39	36

But for one slight glitch, he'd make me revise one of my statements in the Eckersley comment.

ERIC PLUNK	IP	W	S	ERA	RATIO	$
1987 OAK	95	4	2	4.74	14.49	−1
1988 OAK	78	7	5	3.00	11.65	12
1989 OAK/NY A	104	8	1	3.28	12.59	6

With the right breaks, could go from a starter to the stopper on the Yankees.

JEFF REARDON	IP	W	S	ERA	RATIO	$
1987 MIN	80	8	31	4.39	10.98	32
1988 MIN	73	2	42	2.47	10.23	42
1989 MIN	73	5	31	4.07	9.86	31

Just looking at this thing superficially in December—he's older than Lee Smith, doesn't throw nearly as hard, and costs more. It must be that the Braves will take Lee Smith for Esasky.

DAVE RIGHETTI	IP	W	S	ERA	RATIO	$
1987 NY A	95	8	31	3.51	13.17	38
1988 NY A	87	5	25	3.52	12.72	23
1989 NY A	69	2	25	3.00	12.91	22

He'll be a moderately effective starter. If not, it's still a reasonable gamble to take with someone who's still relatively young and strong but no longer a very effective reliever.

JEFF ROBINSON	IP	W	S	ERA	RATIO	$
1987 DET	127	9	0	5.37	13.15	−1
1988 DET	172	13	0	2.98	10.10	20
1989 DET	78	4	0	4.73	14.08	−4

The sign of a successful season: Steve Levy, reviewing the performances of the players he bought, said, "Jeff Robinson was a bust." If his Hackers had finished anywhere else but first, he would have said Jeff Robinson was a bum.

JEFF RUSSELL	IP	W	S	ERA	RATIO	$
1987 TEX	97	5	3	4.44	14.89	0
1988 TEX	189	10	0	3.82	11.88	7
1989 TEX	73	6	38	1.98	8.55	45

Sabermetricians' pitcher of the year. Tom House, Craig Wright, et al., looked in their computers, and decided this was a guy who should be a reliever.

But I still don't see what they were looking at. In 1988, the first nine batters hit .270 against him (compared to .257 overall). The batting average against him with runners on was .314. In 16 at-bats with the bases loaded, he gave up three home runs. Lefties feasted on him (.292) and every team has one or two lefties on the bench.

Lefties batted .205 against him last year. No home runs. In 112 at-bats they whiffed 33 times (in 600, that's 177). Right-handers took him deep four times, but batted .165. In 1988 Russell struck out 88 batters in 189 innings. At the rate he was going last year, if he pitched that many innings, he would have had 200 strikeouts.

Even though it's not a category, I know I'm not the only one who studies a pitcher's K's. Steve Levy was trying to peddle Russell last March at $15 and got no takers, chiefly because, no matter what House or Russell himself said, he looked like a meatball pitcher. We all told Levy we planned to buy him in the draft, after he dropped him, for about $12. He said he wasn't going to drop him, which was a bluff; we called it and he had to keep him.

NOLAN RYAN	IP	W	S	ERA	RATIO	$
1987 HOU	212	8	0	2.76	10.23	22
1988 HOU	220	12	0	3.52	11.17	6
1989 TEX	239	16	0	3.20	9.78	25

Nolan Ryan has pitched the 4786 best innings of any pitcher ever.

I'm not a sabermetrician, but I'm competitive, and each spring I do battle with seventh- and eighth-graders at a school where I used to teach. The science teacher, Eric Lindow, has written a program that simulates baseball games; it's Strat-O-Matic taken to the nth degree, counting virtually every "how" stat a player can compile (for pitchers—hits, unintentional walks, strikeouts, home runs, wild pitches, balks, hit batsmen, even double-play grounders) and none of the "what" (wins, losses, and ERA). You learn fast in this game; before we start playing our season—which is based on last year's stats—you can rest assured the team that owns Nolan Ryan isn't about to trade him for Dave Stewart. No kid is going to fall for that.

But suppose the offer is Mike Scott or Joe Magrane? (Yes, mixed league; the game is for children, after all.) The bewildering assortment of pros and cons of all their stats is a little harder to size up. Put it this way: If Ryan's owner comes to me asking for Magrane, I want to be prepared.

I devised a formula for evaluating how pitchers will perform. It's an involved sort of reverse ratio (IP divided by different weights for hits, home runs, walks, wild pitches, and so forth) that gives an accurate rating: a total average for pitchers, in essence, that is much more valid than Boswell's for hitters. The ratings for the pitchers mentioned are Ryan .961, Scott .937, Magrane .872, and Stewart .761. Playing on the same team in the computer league, Ryan will win more games than Magrane. The only pitcher who will win more games than Ryan is Saberhagen (1.041).

Ryan has a better three-year rating than every pitcher except Hershiser and Clemens. He's not close to third in wins over the last three years.

Lifetime? Well, I'm still waiting for my copy of *Total Baseball* (when will they start offering a hauling fee to remove it from stores?) and the *Baseball Encyclopedia* doesn't give enough information. However, Ryan's career rating (.898) is far better than Steve Carlton's (.837), for a comparison. Nine of Ryan's 23 seasons have been spent in the American League, facing the DH. Carlton, playing for much worse teams, won 329 games. Ryan, in 29 fewer starts, has won 40 fewer games.

There's got to be some reason why Ryan hasn't done better. In over two decades he can't have run into one long string of bad luck. Somehow he creates it. A mesmerizing effect on his teammates? I doubt it ever will be located by sabermetrics, but it's there.

Still, he's 43 and just finished striking out more batters per inning than ever before. At a glance, I'd say his .961 pitcher rating was also the best of his career. One shouldn't be too critical.

BRET SABERHAGEN	IP	W	S	ERA	RATIO	$
1987 KC	257	18	0	3.36	10.47	**29**
1988 KC	261	14	0	3.80	11.39	**12**
1989 KC	262	23	0	2.16	8.65	**45**

He's on top of the world right now, yet if a hitter had this three-year scan, you'd be leery. Strawberry, with a better performance both overall and in terms of peaks and valleys, currently resides in the Rotisserie Hall of Shame.

One suggestion: If you spend mega-bucks to get Saberhagen, let everything ride on him and keep your innings down. Last year, if you were able to come in right at 1000 innings, his ERA would have been worth $16, his ratio $20; in all he would have been worth $52.

MIKE SCHOOLER	IP	W	S	ERA	RATIO	$
1988 SEA	48	5	15	3.54	12.85	**15**
1989 SEA	77	1	33	2.81	11.69	**31**

Gave up more than a hit an inning, but it hardly seems to have mattered.

LEE SMITH	IP	W	S	ERA	RATIO	$
1987 CHI N	83	4	36	3.12	12.58	**34**
1988 BOS	84	4	29	2.80	11.73	**30**
1989 BOS	70	6	25	3.58	11.01	**26**

For the fifth straight year, more than a strikeout an inning; 96 K's for the third straight year (check his innings). Whatever shape his knees are in, that's a lot of heat.

ROY SMITH	IP	W	S	ERA	RATIO	$
1987 MIN	16	1	0	4.96	14.33	**−1**
1988 MIN	37	3	0	2.68	9.97	**5**
1989 MIN	172	10	1	3.92	12.06	**6**

In real baseball, a breakthrough season. In Rotisserie baseball, he barely improved.

DAVE STEWART	IP	W	S	ERA	RATIO	$
1987 OAK	261	20	0	3.68	11.34	**24**
1988 OAK	276	21	0	3.23	11.43	**22**
1989 OAK	258	21	0	3.32	11.49	**20**

Royalty on the mound.

DAVE STIEB	IP	W	S	ERA	RATIO	S
1987 TOR	185	13	0	4.09	12.21	11
1988 TOR	207	16	0	3.04	10.24	23
1989 TOR	207	17	0	3.35	10.45	20

The power of confounded ratio: four fewer wins than Stewart, worse ERA, worth the same.

TODD STOTTLEMYRE	IP	W	S	ERA	RATIO	S
1988 TOR	98	4	0	5.69	14.23	−9
1989 TOR	128	7	0	3.88	12.76	2

Erik Hanson moves to the majors and keeps whiffing them at pretty much the same pace; Todd doesn't. That's not good, but he did show all kinds of fortitude against the Orioles after Bradley smoked him.

GREG SWINDELL	IP	W	S	ERA	RATIO	S
1987 CLE	102	3	0	5.10	13.15	−3
1988 CLE	242	18	0	3.20	10.38	24
1989 CLE	184	13	0	3.37	10.79	15

This year's Saberhagen or 1987's Swindell.

FRANK TANANA	IP	W	S	ERA	RATIO	S
1987 DET	219	15	0	3.91	11.18	18
1988 DET	203	14	0	4.21	12.28	5
1989 DET	224	10	0	3.58	12.11	7

One of the great fourth starters in baseball; we even will allow him on our teams.

BOBBY THIGPEN	IP	W	S	ERA	RATIO	S
1987 CHI A	89	7	16	2.73	11.12	29
1988 CHI A	90	5	34	3.30	12.90	31
1989 CHI A	79	2	34	3.76	11.62	30

He's 26. The only reason for the White Sox to trade him is that they think their future is a mirage.

DUANE WARD	IP	W	S	ERA	RATIO	$
1988 TOR	112	9	15	3.30	12.98	**18**
1989 TOR	115	4	15	3.77	11.93	**15**

When things go well for him they go great, and when they go bad they go awful.

BOB WELCH	IP	W	S	ERA	RATIO	$
1987 LA	252	15	0	3.22	10.36	**25**
1988 OAK	245	17	0	3.64	11.70	**14**
1989 OAK	210	17	0	3.00	11.55	**18**

Bid no more than he earned in 1988.

DAVID WELLS	IP	W	S	ERA	RATIO	$
1987 TOR	29	4	1	3.99	15.03	**2**
1988 TOR	64	3	4	4.62	13.43	**1**
1989 TOR	86	7	2	2.40	9.80	**15**

If he wants it badly enough—which is by no means clear—he could share some of the action with Henke.

DAVID WEST	IP	W	S	ERA	RATIO	$
1988 NY N	6	1	0	4.00	12.22	**1**
1989 NY N/MIN	39	3	0	6.41	15.33	**0**

Normally the team a player is traded from commences the bad-mouthing; in this instance, the Twins brass gave poor grades to West's mechanics after they acquired him. A funny way to cover your butt; if I were the owner, I'd can them all.

MARK WILLIAMSON	IP	W	S	ERA	RATIO	$
1987 BAL	125	8	3	4.03	11.74	**11**
1988 BAL	118	5	2	4.90	12.62	**−1**
1989 BAL	107	10	9	2.93	11.32	**19**

Another Oriole to be wary of, I'm afraid.

BOBBY WITT	IP	W	S	ERA	RATIO	S
1987 TEX	143	8	0	4.91	15.99	−9
1988 TEX	174	8	0	3.92	12.13	4
1989 TEX	194	12	0	5.14	13.71	−8

His last chance to lose this much.

MIKE WITT	IP	W	S	ERA	RATIO	S
1987 CAL	247	16	0	4.01	12.24	14
1988 CAL	250	13	0	4.15	12.62	3
1989 CAL	220	9	0	4.54	12.27	−1

Would seem to be the odd-man-out on the Angels.

In the last six years he has averaged 247 IP. Six years ago he was 23 and 6' 7". A possible explanation of his decline? Something for Randy Johnson's owners to think about in 1995.

CURT YOUNG	IP	W	S	ERA	RATIO	S
1987 OAK	203	13	0	4.08	10.55	18
1988 OAK	156	11	0	4.15	12.20	5
1989 OAK	111	5	0	3.73	13.30	0

He's walking more batters and giving up fewer home runs each season; in other words, he's learning he's not a very good pitcher.

CLINT ZAVARAS	IP	W	S	ERA	RATIO	S
1989 SEA	52	1	0	5.19	13.67	−4

When a pitcher gets as much praise as he does, while his numbers are this dreadful—in the majors and the minors—he's worth watching.

Pitcher Z

Who's this year's Jeff Russell? Who that I don't mention in Pitcher Z or the minors, much less the profiles, is going to be the most valuable player in the Heath leagues?

Roger Salkeld? No, because I just mentioned him.

Willie Banks? I'm getting desperate.

Those already on the scene who easily could be in the top 108 of next year's appendix, who in fact are in the top 108 of this year's: Aquino, Bailes, Dubois, Filer, Guante, Hall, Jeffcoat, Dave Johnson,

Lamp, Long, Olin, Pall, Reed, Rogers, Swift, Tapani, Thurmond, Tibbs, Wills.

But it's the nature of the Pitcher Z beast to exchange places above and below the Mendoza line, so here are some of last year's duds to consider: Akerfelds, Aldrich, Appier, Arnsberg, August, Barfield, Bautista, Cadaret, John Davis, Dyer, Gibson, Gonzales, Gene Harris, Hetzel, Hillegas, Holton, Kilgus, Leach, Mielke, Ritz, Jeff (Pinstripe) Robinson, Sanderson, Searcy, Wegman, Wojna.

In case you think I named everybody, I don't believe in Mauro Gozzo and have given up on Mike Dunne.

The preceding pages, for better or worse, do take a big bite out of the book, so this chapter is going to be packed pretty tight. The subjects are freeze lists, reserve lists, waiver claims, and trades—all the things that determine a team's fate before and after the hours of the draft.

Freeze Lists

The question I'm most often asked by people in existing leagues is: How do underpriced players carried over from the year before affect my prices? The answer is that they don't affect my prices at all, but they do affect market prices.

Leagues vary on the number of players that may be kept from the year before and the method of determining their salaries; however, the purpose is always the same: to go into the draft with an existing nucleus of players that you're sure would cost you more if you had to buy them on the open market.

These aren't necessarily cheap players, just underpriced. Normally, you assume that they are underpaid also; that they are going to earn more than they cost, that you are fleecing them. Occasionally, you will keep a player, like Rickey Henderson, at a hefty salary that he probably won't earn, because you figure he'll fetch an even heftier salary in the open market (so, in a sense, you're still fleecing him). The team that has the best freeze list is the one that ends up fleecing its players the most, turning the greatest profits. The team that appears to have the best freeze list before the draft is the one that you predict will turn the greatest profits.

Who would you rather have this season, if each had a salary of $30: Don Mattingly, Julio Franco, or Mike Schooler?

Yes, it's a tough call. They each earned about the same last year; what you're worried about is what they're going to do this year.

If you have each player at a salary of $10, it's exactly the same dilemma, except it's a more pleasant one. You're not going to miss with any of the three. They won't earn a penny more, but each is guaranteed to have a $20 greater profit.

Conversely, when you see other teams freezing players of this magnitude for $10, you start getting nervous. When one team has all three of them, you start hoping its owner will be transferred to Singapore. Even though he starts out in the auction with $230 to your $260, you know he's got more money to spend.

The key, though, is: How much more?

Here you're kind of hazy, and so is he. He has as much more to spend than you do, initially, as he has profits built into his freeze lists. But this is April, and neither of you can know what those profits will be until October. In practice, he has as much more money to spend as he *thinks* he has; it may turn out that he was woefully deluded.

To illustrate, let's go back to April of last year, and look at the 1989 freeze lists of the Legal Baseball League (for which I owe thanks to Joe David Jackson in Atlanta).

The Bag Boys froze seven players for $78: Craig Biggio $10, Robert Alomar $10, Paul O'Neill $10, Tom Brunansky $10, Jim Gott $17, Dennis Rasmussen $11, and Kevin Gross $10.

On a scale of one to 10, how strong is this list? I'd give it an eight. Cheap power, cheap speed, cheap relief. Some might have quarrelled with the starting pitchers then, but Gross had just gone to Montreal and Rasmussen had won 16 games with a 3.43 ERA the year before. Either or both could go to the $15 range in the draft. The more dubious freeze, for me, is Biggio. The Bag Boys obviously picked him up late in 1988—perhaps they had him on reserve—and, having watched him closely, like him a lot. Still, would he go for $10 in the draft? The market prices in Chapter 1 indicate he wouldn't. But if there is one other person in the Legal Baseball League who you know covets him, and if you have $10 faith in Biggio, then go ahead and keep him.

So what kind of profits are represented here? You can pencil in your rough estimates of what they will earn—Biggio $15, Alomar $25, etc.—and figure it out. That's the best way.

Another way that works just fine for large numbers of players is to pencil in what they earned the year before. You don't have to sit there and ponder each case; you're trying to size up the league as a whole, not individual teams.

By this strictly mechanical method, the seven frozen Bag Boys earned $109 in 1988 (including zero for Biggio); subtract their $78 in salaries, and the projected 1989 profit is $31. The league as a whole froze 58 players for $551; their 1988 earnings totaled $929, for a projected profit of $378.

At the league level, big numbers; the mind blurs. It's much easier to go back to the Bag Boys to try to answer the question, so what?

The so-what is that the Bag Boys have $31 of anticipated profits. If they can just break even on the 16 players they buy in the auction, they leave with $291 worth of players. The team is in contention and will have to blow it to not finish in the money.

Isn't that right?

No. My eagle-eyed interlocutor would have jumped all over the $378 total profits for the league. Divide it by 10 and you have $38 per team; the Bag Boys don't even have one of the better freeze lists in the league. They're headed for the second division, it now seems.

The profits of some other teams, projected in this same mechanical way (1989 salaries subtracted from 1988 earnings): Generals $72, III Stooges $67, Torts R Us $46, Terminators $45, Frogs $40.

Supposedly all these teams, by just breaking even with the players they have to buy, are $300 teams. Five teams guaranteed to win or at least finish second. Sounds like the invitations I get in the mail to buy land in the Poconos. What's the catch?

There are two catches.

First, they can't all break even in the draft. Overall, the league is going to lose exactly $378. The game is zero sum; the profits contained among the frozen players are obtained from the drafted players, not pulled out of thin air.

The second is that the frozen players aren't going to do nearly as well as they are expected to.

Here are the figures for all 10 teams, ranked in order of their projected profits:

	#	1989 SALARY	1988 EARNED	1989 EARNED	PROJ. PROFIT	ACT. PROFIT
GENERALS	10	89	161	179	72	90
III STOOGES	5	24	91	65	67	41
TORTS R US	9	149	195	150	46	1
TERMINATORS	6	39	84	45	45	6
FROGS	8	68	108	106	40	38
ROCKY'S REVIVAL	3	32	63	52	31	20
BAG BOYS	7	78	109	94	31	16
SENATORS	2	24	47	−10	23	−34
NUKERS	2	2	24	19	22	17
DISARMERS	6	46	47	55	1	9
TOTAL	58	551	929	755	378	204

The seven Bag Boys weren't worth $109, they were worth $94. The projected profit is cut in half. Who are the culprits? Not Brunansky, O'Neill, Alomar, and certainly not Biggio. The pitchers bombed out totally.

Gott was injured, but hitters get hurt, too. The Disarmers froze their Biggio, Ron Jones, at $10, for an $8 loss. The Disarmers also froze three starting pitchers at $10 each—Jose DeLeon, Greg Maddux, and Ramon Martinez—which to me would have seemed like a much less wise decision than the Bag Boys' pitching freezes, yet they got nice profits from all three of them, so the lesson is not that starting pitchers aren't worth investing in.

Here are the raw totals for two American League leagues, the Lone Stars and the Dirty Dozen:

LEAGUE	#	1989 SALARY	1988 EARNED	1989 EARNED	PROJ. PROFIT	ACT. PROFIT
LSL	123	1378	1949	1656	571	278
DDL	116	1365	2033	1610	668	245

The lesson is that even a mechanical method of evaluating freezes, which I'm quite sure is more conservative than the guesswork method, is too optimistic. We freeze players who did well last year; as a group, they're not going to do as well this year.

Back to how this affects market prices.

Let's say you're the Torts R Us in the Legal Baseball League. You've frozen nine players and you've pre-committed $149. That's $16.5 per player, but you don't think you're in bad shape, because these players are dynamite. Projected profits of $49—*conservatively*—and plenty of money left to buy what you need. Hell, you've already got your pitching staff (Hershiser, Rijo, Show, Dave Smith, Jay Howell); you're loaded with speed (Butler, Hudler, Otis Nixon); all that's missing is a couple of bangers, and you've 111 big ones left for them.

But the bangers are expensive. Van Slyke $37, McReynolds $36. You chase them, but in the end you feel you can't afford their stolen bases. You do get Galarraga for $34, and you're pretty pleased about that.

Which leaves you with $77 left to spend on 10 players.

Everyone seems to *just* slip out of reach. Will Clark $35? Hell, Galarraga's better than he is. Glenn Davis $33? In the Astrodome? Probably you should have chased him a little farther anyway. But you didn't.

Andre Dawson, bad knees and all, goes for $32.

Should you have gone to $33? But that would leave you with those bad knees, and $44 for 9 players.

You're sitting there, biding your time in the sixth round, when you can't believe your ears—the bidding's pooping out on Bob Ojeda at $14. Bobby O? He's going to be awesome this year; his patched-up finger is going to make his dead fish go kerplop! You'll put him in there with Orel, if these suckers will let you.

They do, for $15.

Which leaves $62 for nine players.

Jody Davis? All right, a bum, but you do need a catcher and maybe you can nickel-and-dime your power. Six dollars for Jody—are they nuts? You try seven. He goes for 10.

Carmelo Martinez, $13.

Terry Pendleton, $12.

Maybe you should have grabbed Pendleton; at least he was a good value.

In the seventh round, Juan Samuel looks like he's going to barely make it to $20. Big up side on that guy . . . hits some dingers . . . You say $22, because it's just too good a value, and you get him.

Forty dollars for eight players.

I'm assuming the Torts R Us are depressed at this point. Maybe they're not. They've bought three pretty good players, after all, and have $5 per player to spend as the auction nears the endgame.

The reason *I'm* depressed is that I've got hindsight. I know that Galarraga, Ojeda, and Samuel will together lose $15 (have cost $71, will earn $56), and I know the team didn't have that kind of margin to begin with: The actual profits of the Torts R Us freeze list will amount to $1.

This is a second-division team. (In fact, so were the Bag Boys. They finished seventh, Torts R Us sixth.) But it's not because of any blatantly silly misplay. Oh, I could point out that Kevin Mitchell slipped through for $23—before, not after, Ojeda—but $23 for Mitchell in April of last year was like $37 for Van Slyke.

This is a tough, no-nonsense draft; in view of the freeze lists, the prices are restrained; and still, adding up all the players mentioned so far not bought by the Torts R Us, including Mitchell, the league has lost $27.

The teams that actually turned out to have good freeze lists, hence really did have "extra" money for the draft, were the Generals, the III Stooges, and the Frogs. They finished fourth, first, and fifth. I'd like to be able to report wild overspending by the Generals and Frogs, but I don't see any. Indeed, the Generals only spent $38 to get Eric Davis, and the Frogs bought Mitchell. The overall picture is of a league betting on players to match or just slightly exceed their form. A league willing to accept slight losses.

To sum it up, underpriced players on freeze lists definitely influence the prices of players in the auction. The more underpriced the frozen players are, the more overpriced will be the ones in the auction. A team with a clearly superior freeze list—and you better compare yours to the others before you say this—can afford to pay the full price and maybe then some on the Cadillac ballplayers. Teams with good profits going into the draft sure don't want to risk their money pursuing more profits; they're happy just to hang onto it, and so they salt it away in Eric Davis, and McReynolds, and Van Slyke.

Which is still, I realize, not answering the question.

What people really want is some sort of math to tailor Patton $ to the specific realities of their league's draft. Isn't there any? There is, here it comes, and I'm not sure I recommend it.

The freeze lists of the three leagues that we've looked at have roughly the same drops from 1988 to 1989 earnings, about 20 percent. So when you get the freeze lists in your league this year, you can total up the 1989 earnings of the frozen players and chop that figure by 20 percent.

In the Legal Baseball League, multiply .8 times $929; that's $743, quite close to the actual 1989 earnings of $755—excellent.

Subtract the $743 that the frozen players will earn from the amount of money available ($2600) to find out what the players in the draft will earn: $1857.

You know what the players in the draft are going to cost ($2600 − $551): $2049.

The cost to earnings ratio is 2049/1857 or 1.1. Patton's prices are fair; costs and earnings are the same; their ratio is one. So multiply Patton $ by 1.1.

In plainer English, there's going to be about a 10 percent loss overall. The way you lose is by overspending, so overspend by 10 percent. If you think Will Clark's going to earn $40, pay $44.

Trouble is, if everyone does that, everyone ends up with a team worth $260. Every team comes in fifth-and-a-half.

Reserves and Waivers

The big event before the draft is the handing in of the freezes. Increasingly, the big event after the draft is the real draft, picking reserve players.

Here again, leagues vary as to how they do this. Some only select a few and others—practitioners of something called Ultra Rotisserie—select a whopping 17 players, the idea being to end up with 40-man rosters. A ludicrous conceit, if you ask me, that has even less relation to real baseball than the importance we attach to steals.

Where the RLBA boys went astray was in their understanding of the purpose of reserves in the first place. It was their perception, when they copied the idea of a reserve list from the American Dreams League, that the point was to have a farm system in the event of injuries or substandard performance. That wasn't it at all.

You have a reserve list because what you buy in the regular draft is only a portion of the pie. You've spent to your salary cap, and now you've got this population of players whose statistics are going to decide the standings—but wait a minute.

All sorts of players are going to emerge on the real baseball scene who weren't bought and in many cases weren't even available in the draft. As game-players, we have two options: keep these players out of our original populations—don't let them pollute the statistics—or let them filter in on some vaguely rational, at least not hopelessly unfair, basis.

The point of the reserve lists is to help them filter in.

In the early stages (way back in the early '80s), we were uninformed about baseball. We had little idea how much turnover took place. Now we know that every season there's going to be just a huge plateful of goodies sitting out of reach of our draft rosters—exciting our hunger, provoking our greed, and, if we don't watch out, sending us to war.

This was the loot that was not bought in the American Dreams draft last year:

HITTERS	AB	HR	RBI	SB	BA
ADL draft	62789	1501	7606	1349	.263
Final AL	77004	1718	9179	1512	.261
Difference	14215	217	1573	163	.250

PITCHERS	IP	W	S	ERA	RTO
ADL draft	12798	772	527	3.778	11.94
Final AL	20181	1133	582	3.883	12.20
Difference	7383	361	55	4.066	12.66

There are three sources of all the unbought loot.

Even though the best thing about Rotisserie baseball (give the RLBA boys credit here) is how deep it goes into major league rosters, it still doesn't sponge up all the players who are available on opening day. Somebody sitting on the very end of the pines, like Greg Briley, plans to grab a position, and he will. Pitchers? You need a mop for all of them.

Then there are the players in the minors who will be arriving throughout the season.

And, of course, that most unfair thing of all, even when you've been warned by seven different newspapers that the Mariners have figured out they boo-booed by letting Mike Moore go for nothing—interleague trades.

Keeping all three of these populations in quarantine is fine; that's fair. It's like throwing all players back into the pool each season: much the most sensible, but not much fun.

So what do you do?

I'm not one for laying down the rules; I think each league should tinker with the game until they have it the way they like it. Yet there's one rule that many leagues still adhere to that I find colossally idiotic: You're allowed to reach for the goodies when, and only when, one of your drafted players is injured. Or demoted. Or retires. You know you've got it wrong when you create a bidding war for Chris Brown.

What do you do?

You can have some sort of in-season procedure, periodic grab bags. A waiver system. That works pretty well. Most leagues let the season get fairly far along, then pick in reverse order of the standings. I've heard it argued that it rewards incompetence. True. But people in the hunt for the money would rather see the incompetent rewarded than the team right behind them.

What else can you do?

The only other thing that anyone's so far been able to think of is a reserve list. If you're so smart, and you know Langston's going to be traded, and you're in a National League Rotisserie, put him on your reserve list. If you know Joey Belle has been born again, or at least has grown up—if you've even heard of Joey Belle—put him on your reserve list.

Reserves are just more options, another set of variables, in this complex game. They give you the semblance of being in control. They give you reason to try to anticipate the season ahead, to pay attention to that dreary other league, to scour the minors. They do not give you the sense of being a general manager. Let us not kid ourselves.

When Langston gets traded, the Mariners can't skip every fourth game. They have to pitch someone in his place. They have to call up a rookie or give a start to Jerry Reed. You don't. You may be sorry to see him go, but you'd be absolutely beside yourself if you had to claim the rookie. In fact, nobody in the American Dreams would touch any of those Montreal pitchers at first, they all started out so badly.

Very few Rotisserie teams get or want enough innings to complete the season; all we want is a thousand.

If the object is to feel like real general managers, we'd make everyone who paid $30 or more for Danny Jackson keep him.

Nevertheless, if leagues insist on the charade, they might consider letting a week pass after the auction. That way they'd have time to familiarize themselves with their 23-man rosters; it's not humanly possible to have pre-studied the best farm system for them.

Bruce Grabell of the Ron Hodges Memorial Baseball Association tells me that, in their first year of Ultra, the total of wins dropped three percent. It's as if, without Langston and Viola, they were playing a shorter schedule.

All the reserve lists do is provide a sponge; they absorb some of the unbought talent, instead of leaving it to waivers or leaving it out there. So the question becomes, What size sponge? Can you ever go deep enough with your reserve lists to absorb everything?

You can't.

Well, you can, but it gets to the point where you're doing just what you're trying to avoid: turning a game of some degree of skill into a game of a greater degree of chance.

The reserve draft of the American Dreams goes through 12 rounds. Here's the complete record for last year, along with the players' Patton $ worth in the majors:

AMERICAN DREAMS RESERVE DRAFT LAST YEAR

1. NOVA	$	2. RESIDUALS	$
VENTURA	0	LEACH	3
QUINTANA	0	HEEP	11
FRASER	10	DOBIE	
LONG	2	JEFFERSON	8
YETT	−6	ROSENBERG	−6
BROOKENS	2	FERNANDEZ, S (NL)	
BERGMAN	8	SKINNER	1
SWIFT	2	MOSES	12
KOMMINSK	10	PETERSON	−4
SCHILLING	−1	PALACIOS	0
ESPINOZA	8	ALLEN	
MARZANO	2	DAVIS, M (NL)	

3. VEECKS	$	4. BB GUNS	$
HALL, DREW	2	DEJESUS, J	−1
GUZMAN, J		BROWN, K	14
CAMPBELL	−4	THURMOND	4
SOLANO	0	BELL, JUAN	0
ARNSBERG	1	ALOMAR, S (NL)	
KASIAN		LUECKEN	2
MCCARTHY	1	WILKINSON	
HUISMAN	0	KAISER	−1
MEULENS	−1	BELL, E	
SCHU	3	WOODARD	
PERAZA		BEARSE	
MCLAUGHLIN		YOUNG, MATT	−8

5. BAGS	$	6. AMAROS	$
BUHNER	9	FARRELL	9
BLANKENSHIP	2	HINZO	−1
KNUDSON	12	HICKEY	6
OTTO	0	ORSULAK	14
DE LOS SANTOS	0	MOORE, D	
SHIELDS		PENA, H	
SOSA	6	DAVIS, STEVE	
CLUTTERBUCK	1	FILER	5
FREEMAN	0	MELENDEZ	0
KRAWCZYK		NICHOLS	−1
LUSADER	2	GALVEZ	
BITTIGER		SORRENTO	0

7. NATTERING NABOBS	s		8. PALUKAS	s
MCLEMORE	4		APPIER	−7
FELIX	17		NIEVES	
ROGERS	5		RATHERS	
EISENREICH	27		LOVELACE	0
GUIDRY			WARD, G	7
POWELL	−1		VAUGHAN	7
HALL, DARREN			LEWIS	
CORSI	7		DOTSON	−7
CUYLER			PARKS	
NOSEK			ROCHFORD	−1
MESA			BANKS	
GAINEY			HAVENS	−5

9. MOOSE FACTORY	s		10. TOONERS	s
MARTINEZ, T			HARNISCH	−4
JOHNSON, L	11		JONES, J	−3
FINLEY, C	21		SMITH, R	6
NUNEZ, J	2		BALLARD	13
MCDONALD	−1		HAMILTON	
WICKANDER	−1		SCHROEDER	2
AKERFELDS	0		SANCHEZ, A	−6
BUCKNER	1		MARTINEZ, C	11
CABRERA	0		PALL	10
REIMER	0		VASQUEZ	
RICHIE	2		SANCHEZ, I	
SUTCLIFFE (NL)			JENNINGS	0

11. HACKERS	s		12. WSSOX	s
MCCASKILL	20		MURPHY, DALE (NL)	
BEDROSIAN (NL)			HAYES, V (NL)	
WILLIAMSON	19		JOHNSON, H (NL)	
BAILES	3		MCDOWELL, R (NL)	
SKALSKI			BASS (NL)	
WILLIAMS, B			GUERRERO (NL)	
LAMP	15		DYKSTRA (NL)	
PALMER, DEAN	−1		MALDONADO (NL)	
FETTERS	−1		YELDING	
SMITH, MI	−4		NUNEZ, E	−1
NAVARRO	6		STRAWBERRY (NL)	
CERONE	6		pass	

Nova, the fifth-place finisher the year before, had the first pick; the Wssox, winners in 1988, the 12th. So the order of selection reads from left to right in each round, from Robin Ventura as the first player taken to Rick Cerone as the 143rd.

If you look closely, you'll see different kinds of strategies at work, which I'm going to get to, but I wanted to show the whole list like this in order to address the matter of how big is too big.

Cerone earned $6 last year, Ventura nothing, so there would seem to be goodies still out there. Who? Let's think for a second.

Junior Felix? He was quite a player for a while, and he started out in the minors. Did they get him?

Yep. Nabobs. Their second pick, the 19th player taken.

What about Kevin Hickey? Surely no one would bother with that guy, and he had a pretty good streak.

The Amaros' third pick.

How about Jamie Navarro? Ended up in the Brewers rotation, holding his own—

Hackers, 11th round.

Greg Vaughan?

Palukas, sixth.

Sammy Sosa?

Bags, seventh.

For sure, no one took Jim Corsi. Why would you? Relief pitcher in the Oakland system? And yet Corsi pitched 38 lovely innings in September, worth $7, which is more than Navarro was worth.

Those Nattering Nabobs took Corsi.

I'm not trying to thump the chests of the Dreamers; the Hackers picked Mississippi Smith ahead of Navarro, the total value of the Palukas' reserve list was less than zero, and why you would make Kevin Hickey your third pick I'll never know.

I'm just saying that 144 players is a large sponge.

The following chart sizes up the reserve draft both by rounds and teams.

BY ROUNDS			BY TEAMS	$	ORDER OF PICK
round	1	35	HACKERS	63	11
round	2	51	NABOBS	59	7
round	3	79	NOVA	37	1
round	4	69	MOOSE FACTORY	35	9
round	5	−5	BAGS	32	5

BY ROUNDS		BY TEAMS	$	ORDER OF PICK
round 6	11	AMAROS	32	6
round 7	25	TOONERS	29	10
round 8	30	RESIDUALS	25	2
round 9	14	BB GUNS	10	4
round 10	−5	VEECKS	2	3
round 11	18	WSSOX	−1	12
round 12	−5	PALUKAS	−6	8
	317		317	

There's actually a progression of player-value in the first three rounds, and the first round is only the fourth-best round in the entire draft. The fifth round of the draft was as bad as the 12th. Meanwhile, the team with the best success in the reserve draft, the Hackers, had the second-to-last pick.

As you look at the unsorted columns—the dollars earned in each round, the order of pick of each team—there seems to be mass confusion. Are we really just sitting around after the auction, drinking beer and throwing darts?

Yes. But in fact there is a target, and we are aiming. If you go back to the chart of what's still out there after the draft is over (page 166), you'll see what the target is, and isn't.

It's not saves. There are only 55 of them out there to get. In the auction we've already grabbed 90 percent of the saves that are going to be awarded in the American League. Even Lee Guetterman was taken. The American Dreams is so enamored of relievers, and frightened out of its wits by starters, that the best, and really the only, relief goody available in the reserve phase was Mark Williamson.

What's there plenty of? Wins, of course. There are more wins available than any other commodity, except RBIs. It's amazing just how many: over 30 for each team.

In part, there are so many because we have jammed just about every relief pitcher *but* Kevin Hickey onto our teams, and you can't have everything. In part, we don't want everything.

We want Kirk McCaskill. We don't want Rich Dotson. We want Chuck Finley and Jeff Ballard and Kevin Brown, as long as they do what they end up doing, and not what they did the year before. The year before every one of these pitchers had been heaved out of the American Dreams League by July, except Brown, who got heaved in September.

Other Rotisserie leagues aren't quite as gun-shy. South Main Street bought 816 wins in the draft; Tucson Slug, 796; Cowtown, 826; Sour Grapefruit, 799. The most daring investors of all the leagues I have records for were the Washington Ghost-AL, with 836 wins. Subtract 836 from the amount of games played in the American League every year, and they still have almost 300 wins to shoot for after their auction.

That's why you see pitchers, pitchers, pitchers on these reserve lists. I wouldn't be surprised if they outnumber hitters. Look at the Tooners: They just kept pounding away until they got Ballard, and then they kept pounding away.

The next most attractive item-to-be would appear to be home runs. Almost 20 per team. But where are they? They didn't come from Tino Martinez, Carlos Quintana, or Dean Palmer. Felix was good and Vaughan okay, but they didn't hit 217.

Then, on second inspection, home runs aren't so abundant. Like saves, they've been essentially gobbled up in the draft. These are the percentages of the final AL totals that were bought in the American Dreams draft last year:

Home runs	.87
RBIs	.83
Stolen bases	.89
Saves	.90
Wins	.68

Pitchers, pitchers, pitchers.

However, another curious thing that I see in the reserve lists is that hitters can have just as big an up side as pitchers. Little guys, every bit as innocuous as Williamson: Eisenreich, Orsulak, Heep. Others—Bergman, Leach, Cerone—are definitely worth drafting; just a matter of how high.

Cerone yes, Leach no.

Ultimately, there is a hierarchy, a graduating scale of value that we can see when we step back far enough. The first four rounds are worth $234. The middle four rounds are worth $61. The last four: $22.

After a hundred players, we've shot our bolt. Joey Belle's still out there, but he's going to be there after 200 players, and he wasn't *that* great.

There's a good explanation for the relative fizzle in the first round, too. Most people are looking for a serious jolt. They remember the jolts of yore, from the time Ellis Burks didn't quite make the Red Sox, to the half-year that Oddibe McDowell spent at Oklahoma City after the Olympics, all the way back to Salome Barojas.

Jose DeJesus, Tino Martinez—they have their precedents; they may not be chasing ghosts, but we are.

Finally, we shouldn't leave this part without a nod to those daft Wssox. What's with them? They win the pennant the year before, so this year they're going to try to win in the National League?

The Wssox had a terrible season, believe me, but in fact I like their reserve list. They were chasing Serious Jolts the way the Tooners went after pitchers. No reason to go at it half-assed, and they didn't really miss by all that much. Dykstra and McDowell *were* traded, Murphy should have been, both Hojo and Fernandez were offered for Langston—don't listen to those lying Mets.

I'll admit that I was so impressed with the strategy, getting more and more nervous with each pick, that I copied them in the last round.

Must be why they passed.

Trades

Jerry Heath sends out something called "high fives"—the five most competitive leagues as judged by the average point gap, the top five home run teams in all his leagues, the top five saves leaders, and so on. People must take it seriously, because this year he sent out a revised version that incorporated a couple of teams he had overlooked.

So let's look at some of it.

NL

SB		HOW THEY FINISHED
252	PVBLIPS	2
248	BLACK HILLS BISONS	1
245	NINJA TURTLES	1
243	THE BASES POINTS	4
242	SNYDER'S DUKES	1
BA		
.281	REPTILES	7
.280	GHOST RIDERS	7
.277	ROCK-CHALKERS	9
.277	ROSEN BOMBERS	2
.275	LUCKY LINDIES	1

AL

SB		HOW THEY FINISHED
197	SAY IT AIN'T SO'S	2
195	ARIZONA GROANERS	1
194	9-0 SILKS	2
194	LAZY SUZANS	2
191	TOENAIL CLIPPERS	9
BA		
.283	JIMENEZ'S MENACES	2
.281	JOHN'S OX	1
.281	MATTADORS	8
.281	HILLY'S COMETS	5
.280	FTC'S	5

You're wondering the same thing. How come they didn't trade this stuff? They didn't all finish first. Not even a third did.

What are the Toenail Clippers doing in ninth place with 191 steals? They must have a *few* other needs. I want to know how far behind the Reptiles the next team was in batting average. Ten points?

This list of Heath's is definitely one you don't want to be on at the end of the season. That's the whole point of trades, to shuffle your assets. If you have a lot of something, somebody else has a little, and you get together. You try to make a fair trade.

A depressing idea to many people, I realize. The whole thrill of this game is to stick it to their buddies. I know people who almost enjoy coming out of the draft with junk. They never lose hope. Right up until the trade deadline, they're on the phone. *Are you sure you don't want Ken Williams? Four-category player—all he needs is a little playing time. They're going to fire Torborg any day now.*

For my part, I love getting these hustles. I'd much rather hear from these scoundrels in my league than from—well, the people I don't ever hear from. I settle back in my chair with a big grin on my face, ready for a good time.

In eight years I've yet to see a team trade its way out of its draft-day woes. If you don't have anything to give, other people know it better than you do, because they don't even like your team. We traded 76 players in the American Dreams last year, and Heath runs up a trade summary, so it's very easy to see who did what.

For example, the BB Guns gave up five players and gained nine (reserves are often a key ingredient). On the hitting side, they gained 11 home runs and lost 10 stolen bases. In pitching, they gained one win and eight saves, but the pitchers they gave up had a better ERA.

You see some strange lines. The net in hitting for the Bags reads: 454 AB, 198 hits, −11 HR, 27 RBI, −15 SB . . . a .436 batting average.

Who the heck did they trade for? Rogers Hornsby?

The explanation is that they were last in batting average as the trade deadline approached and swapped Incaviglia and Chili Davis for Greenwell and Puckett—not straight up; they had to throw in the likes of Guillen and Montgomery—and so they not only gained good average hitters, they got rid of bad ones.

Overall, just in hitting, how did the Bags do? Clearly they improved themselves in two categories, batting average and RBIs, and declined in two. What's the net? We can figure that out by treating the statistics like any other hitter and throwing them into the Patton $ formula, minuses and all. This weird hitter earns $11, so the Bags improved themselves in hitting.

Pitching? A glance at that line (-116 IP, -9 earned runs, -113 hits and walks, -7 wins, -17 saves) and we know they gave up a lot of pitching. How much? Again, throw this really bizarre fellow into the Patton $ formula . . . minus $44.

The trading for each team in the league can be evaluated like this. This is how it works out.

BAGS	$	NABOBS	$	AMAROS	$
hitters	11	hitters	-12	hitters	-22
pitchers	-44	pitchers	59	pitchers	17
BB GUNS	**$**	**NOVA**	**$**	**TOONERS**	**$**
hitters	-6	hitters	-19	hitters	1
pitchers	13	pitchers	15	pitchers	15
HACKERS	**$**	**PALUKAS**	**$**	**VEECKS**	**$**
hitters	25	hitters	2	hitters	-1
pitchers	-48	pitchers	-4	pitchers	-33
MOOSE	**$**	**RESIDUALS**	**$**	**WSSOX**	**$**
hitters	0	hitters	-6	hitters	23
pitchers	-36	pitchers	36	pitchers	-15

Whereas Heath's summary always adds up to zero—every steal that one team loses in a trade, some other team gains—mine don't quite. I wish I knew why. It's discussed in the masochist notes. I'm some $30 off, which is not too bad for the volume of trading. This is an accurate measurement of a league's trades. How should it be interpreted?

First, there's just a tremendous amount of shuffling of assets; you're only looking at the net here. The worth of all hitting statistics after hitters were traded works out to $812; pitchers, $398. Over $1200 flung around—dwarfing the value of the entire reserve draft ($317).

Second, just because we're trying—most of us—to make a fair trade doesn't mean it will be. We're not on a treadmill; some teams are gaining through trades. The Tooners, as usual, traded well, and they improved themselves in the standings; according to Heath's hypothetical final standings, two places.

But, third, no one's showing a huge gain or loss. Most teams show a gain *and* a loss; to get something, they gave something up.

The impression I get from looking over leagues is that more teams hurt themselves and take big nosedives through trading than bring about miracle cures. How else do we account for the fourth-place finish of the Generals in the Legal Baseball League?

Let's define "should" as "according to Heath's hypothetical final standings," and browse through this stuff.

The Brewmeisters of the Big D should have finished second, traded 10 players, and finished fourth.

The Outasights of Cliche should have finished third, traded 15 players, and finished sixth.

The Venetian Blinds of All in the Family should have finished first, traded 22 players, and fell to third.

The Hoods of Out of Their League should have finished second, traded 35 players, and fell to eighth.

Selective evidence? Of course. The biggest rise is also in Out of Their League, where the Beer Heres should have finished sixth, traded 21 players, and finished first.

Lots of teams that should have finished second finished first. Even more that should have finished first finished first. Of these, quite a few made no trades at all. Burghers in Washington Ghost AL. John's Ox in Tucson Slug. Alibi in Cowtown. Sheisters in Pauma Valley.

Now *that* is depressing. They don't know how to play.

Let's say you did in fact have a week to study between the auction and the reserve draft: What would you study? (On second thought, this may not be such a good idea, because, like on the bio exam your junior year, you'll do anything—cheat, bribe, even memorize—to get a good grade.)

It's too late to pop down to Florida and too early to hang out in Utica. You're pretty much stuck with the pile of magazines and newspapers that you've just *barely* stopped your wife, who reasoned that you had had your draft, from recycling. In a way she's done you a favor, since you're forced to make sense of the mess.

Some of the yearbooks, the ones that came out in January, you don't even bother to separate from *Vogue* and *National Geographic.* Others, like *Street and Smith,* cover the minors pretty well, but so boringly that you'll only read them again out of desperation. They come inside and get stacked in the corner. You settle in with the old faithfuls, *Baseball America* and *Mazeroski,* and a newcomer, *Baseball Today.*

All three are great, and in a week you'll pore over each of them. But suppose you had to choose? Imagine yourself racing to the recycling center—you won't have a coronary if *one* of them is left. Which would it be?

Last year which should it have been?

This will be difficult and probably in the end subjective, because all three sources are so comprehensive, but I'm going to try to evaluate how they did last year. I'm going to pretend it's not subjective by grading them—how else?—in Patton $.

Baseball America lists the top 10 prospects for each minor league; this is how the Triple A players were ranked going into 1989, along with their earnings, if any, in the majors:

IL	$	AA	$	PCL	$
SMOLTZ	16	HARKEY	dnp	S.ALOMAR	1
SEARCY	−3	SHEFFIELD	9	R.MARTINEZ	6
WEST	−10	R.JOHNSON	−8	JU.BELL	−1
S.FINLEY	11	B.HOLMAN	2	DREW	dnp
JEFFERIES	21	PAREDES	dnp	BRENNAN	dnp
JORDAN	21	CARPENTER	1	GW HARRIS	16
WORTHINGTON	13	SNIDER	0	DEVEREAUX	19
BLAUSER	15	FERMIN	2	JE.CLARK	1
BERROA	2	DE LOS SANTOS	0	L.JOHNSON	11
YELDING	5	PRINCE	−1	MA.WILLIAMS	11
TOTAL	91	TOTAL	5	TOTAL	64

One thing we see immediately is that the International League contributed more talent than the other two leagues combined. (Hitting talent as well as pitching. This is the league, some of you are bound to recall, that I said was "indisputably inferior" to the American Association, based on interleague play.) The 30 players combined contributed $160 worth of performance, more than $5 per player.

Not bad, *Baseball America*.

Mazeroski, after extensive analysis of each major league franchise's farm system, sums up the rookies in two "Gold Lists"—the immediate and less immediate prospects. There are 25 on the first list, so I've borrowed the first five from the second list to add up to 30, and arranged them in groups of 10.

1	$	2	$	3	$
JEFFERIES	21	R.JOHNSON	−8	E.MARTINEZ	3
SHEFFIELD	9	CARPENTER	1	MCCARTHY	0
R.MARTINEZ	6	SEARCY	−3	MEDINA	1
GORDON	14	S.FINLEY	11	MUNOZ	−3
HARKEY	dnp	LILLIQUIST	−3	S.WILSON	2
HANSON	11	COOK	4	GRIFFEY	22

1	s	**2**	s	**3**	s
MILACKI	10	DEJESUS	−1	VENTURA	0
OLSON	34	HARNISCH	−5	K.BROWN	14
WALTON	22	L.HARRIS	8	WEST	−10
ALOMAR	1	KREUTER	−1	GRIFFIN	dnp
TOTAL	128	TOTAL	3	TOTAL	29

How much is all this worth?
Is it possible? $160.
Are these the same players, rearranged?

Tracy Ringolsby, who compiles the Gold Lists, also writes for *Baseball America,* so it's quite possible; however, as we start looking for the differences, we find them. Most conspicuously, Ringolsby has Gregg Olson, Tom Gordon, and Ken Griffey Jr. He doesn't have John Smoltz, Ricky Jordan, and Mike Devereaux.

Ringolsby is culling players from all levels of the minors. *Baseball America,* of course, heeds the lower minors, too, as well as college, and all three of these players get ample attention. (Gordon was named minor league player of the year). Ringolsby, for his part, probably omitted Smoltz and Jordan on the grounds that neither still qualified as a rookie.

So it's a fluke that they come out in a dead tie. But considering the different criteria for selection, it's surprising how similar the lists are. Is there anything fundamental that separates them?

Yes, I think so. The top 15 *Baseball America* prospects (the top five from each Triple A league) add up to $44. The bottom 15 add up to $116. The top 15 *Mazeroski* picks work out to $126; the bottom 15, $34. Clearly, if you're just going to throw darts in order in the reserve draft, better to throw *Mazeroski* darts.

Nice work, Ringolsby.

The new guy in this game is someone named Art Springsteen, writing for *Baseball Today.* The magazine is at least as thorough as the other publications about examining the prospects on each team, but it's left to Springsteen to size up the rookie crop overall, which he does with grades that range from A+ to D−. He knows his audience and groups them by National and American Leagues. Here are the 30 rookies who were given the highest grades.

NL	s	**AL**	s	**both (AL*)**	s
JEFFERIES A +	21	SHEFFIELD A −	9	CARPENTER B	1
HARKEY A	dnp	OLSON A −	34	ZEILE B	1

NL	$	AL	$	both (AL*)	$
R.MARTINEZ A	6	HANSON A −	11	GREGG B	6
R.JOHNSON A −	−8	LEITER A −	−4	DREW B	dnp
S.ALOMAR A −	1	E.MARTINEZ A −	3	GW HARRIS B −	16
WEST A −	−10	GORDON B +	14	DUCEY* B −	1
KEITH BROWN B +	dnp	MEDINA B +	1	R.JONES C +	2
SMOLTZ B +	16	SEARCY B +	−3	B.MEYER C	−1
LILLIQUIST B +	−3	G.GONZALES B +	0	HARNISCH* C	−5
DIBBLE B	18	MILACKI B −	10	PARKS* C	0
TOTAL	41	TOTAL	75	TOTAL	21

These players add up to $137; Springsteen isn't quite in a class with Ringolsby and the *Baseball America* editors. It may be because he's a bigger risk-taker. Keith Brown? Never heard of him. Luis Medina? Yikes; should have listened to those minor league managers that *Baseball America* polls.

Yet, by not being in the fraternity (Ringolsby *is* heavily influenced by *Baseball America*) Springsteen comes up with Rob Dibble. Furthermore, his comments not only cover his butt, they're by far the most lively; sometimes wonderfully prescient. Keith Brown is "a sleeper." Olson is a C − if he starts. Gordon is an A for talent, B − for management's threatening to make him a reliever. Van Snider (a D +, points for identifying this bum) was "given to the Reds for practically nothing (at least the Reds thought so at the time)." I become curious when I read this; I look up who the Reds gave up for him, and it's Jeff Montgomery!

The advantage of Springsteen's grading system is that it cools our jets: These are the top prospects, fine, but are they any good? He tries to warn Sparky, for instance, about Torey Lovullo (C −): "Give me Jim Walewander." Then again, by not always saying nice things, he can put his foot far into his mouth. Mike Devereaux is a "C − at best" for being "a defensive liability."

The grades overall would indicate he expected much better things from the National League crop; my grading system informs him he was wrong.

What about grading me with my grading system?

Last year, in an attempt to shed at least a different light on the subject, I assessed all Triple and Double A players as if there were minor league Rotisserie leagues; that is, in the hitting-happy Pacific Coast League a home run wasn't nearly as valuable as in the hitting-famished Eastern League. Hitters and pitchers were ranked by their earnings, if projected to the same playing time, for the year before.

The result wasn't compelling, frankly. Somehow I managed to contrive lists that were at once bizarre and bland. Ruppert Jones and Dave Meier side by side. But I went with it, and here's my equivalent to the Baseball America rankings, the top 10 players, according to Patton $, in each Triple A league the year before, and what they ended up earning in the big leagues:

PATTON'S TOP 30 PLAYERS IN 1988 IN TRIPLE A

IL	$	AA	$	PCL	$
R.KELLY	30	SHEFFIELD	9	HARPER	17
STOTTLEMYRE	2	V.PALACIOS	dnp	RABB	dnp
CLAY	dnp	MONTGOMERY	33	MACK	dnp
L.SMITH	37	GORDON	14	DEVEREAUX	19
ROMINE	4	J.COSTELLO	8	J.GONZALES	8
BOEVER	17	O.NIXON	14	SCHATZEDER	-3
HARNISCH	-5	HUDLER	10	B.ROBERTS	17
T.BROWN	dnp	STEPHENSON	1	R.MARTINEZ	6
RO.JONES	2	G.RIVERA	dnp	POLONIA	21
BAIR	6	PAREDES	dnp	WOJNA	-1
TOTAL	93	TOTAL	89	TOTAL	84

You add it up—$266—you better run back to that recycling center where you left my book!

I know, I know—I've got all sorts of ringers; some of these players are closer to their pensions than rookie status. Nevertheless, the total lack of any assumptions at all in this mechanical method does prove to have its merits. The fact is, Lonnie Smith *was* a better International League prospect than Jefferies; yet compare their market prices in Chapter 1. Montgomery, Harper—even Hudler and Nixon, even Polonia—made profits last year, meaning that they were underestimated despite (or because of) substantial big league playing time the year before. But they were gangbusters in the minors.

The method is too stupid to give up on Bip Roberts.

There are also seven "dnp's" sticking out, far more than anyone else has. The mechanical method doesn't know Ken Clay and Shane

Mack are stiffs, which the scouts know; it hasn't heard of Tony Brown—doesn't know where he came from or where he went—and lists him anyway.

Throw darts from these tables? Why not? The top five players on each list earned $185; the bottom five, $85.

As I thumb through all the minor league tables in last year's book, I see gem after gem (Guetterman, Smoltz, Eisenreich, Roomes, Dwight Smith, Biggio, Ken Howell, Hibbard, Walton, Felix, Wetteland); trouble is, I also draw blank after blank after blank. There are darts here that even Ultra devotees would never dream of throwing.

Therefore, the projections are being done in exactly the same way this year, except that they are being boiled down to one page for each league—10 starting pitchers, five relievers, 20 hitters—which forces me to make decisions.

If I really want Jose DeJesus as one of my American Association starting pitchers (for he blew people away when they made him a starter again), I tack him on at the bottom (with apologies to Bob Patterson). If I really want Scott Scudder in there, to suggest his hard knocks with Cincinnati may not be the story, I leave him in (squeezing out Chris Hammond, which will probably haunt me).

In the Southern League, I could not do without Laddie Renfro. Not just his name. He saved 15 games, and won 19. He would easily have rated ahead of Steve Wapnick were it not for the sad fact that he pitched in 78 games. Projecting him to 60 games does not help his cause. I don't imagine 78 games (out of his team's 143) did; how can he have an arm left? I should have deleted him.

With hitters I have more room, so I'll indulge myself by not deleting Matt Williams or Jay Buhner if they brighten up the page. I will delete Greg Briley (who projects to $77), because (a) I don't have unlimited room, and (b) in comparison to Williams and Buhner, it seems to me he clouds the page.

So, to be sure, does Luis Lopez, who batted even less than Briley, but—it's so hard to be consistent. If Luis Lopez hadn't gone 0-for-1 in his last game (I'm speculating), he would have batted .500. Really, there ought to be *some* continuity with last year and the glorious tradition of Mitch Lyden.

Some other, possibly more pertinent thoughts about the minor leagues.

Baseball America has pointed out that there's little distinction these days between the Double A and Triple A levels. Many pitchers skip the stop in Triple A, and last year hitters started to.

Has it reached the stage where there's no distinction?

No. Again, by my grading system, which I insist is more or less valid when you crank a large enough volume of players through it, we see that there was significantly less talent making the big jump.

BASEBALL AMERICA'S TOP 10 PROSPECTS IN DOUBLE A LAST YEAR

EL	$	SL	$	TL	$
MEULENS	0	HARNISCH	−5	R.MARTINEZ	6
HARKEY	dnp	PARKS	dnp	SHEFFIELD	9
RICHIE	2	A.SANCHEZ	−6	ZEILE	1
VISQUEL	−1	DEJESUS	−1	JU.BELL	0
WALTON	22	DELIMA	dnp	VAUGHAN	7
MALONE	dnp	LEMKE	1	K.BROWN	14
LAMPKIN	dnp	HAMMOND	dnp	MUNOZ	dnp
GIRARDI	3	G.GONZALES	0	TR.WILSON	−1
WICKANDER	−1	DE.JONES	dnp	WETTELAND	6
MCGUIRE	0	CABRERA	0	MANTO	dnp
TOTAL	25	TOTAL	−11	TOTAL	42

It amounts to $56—counting Sheffield and Ramon Martinez, who are also ranked in Triple A. Walton, Vaughan, Kevin Brown, and Wetteland are the only ones who leapfrogged and made sizable contributions. The only other player out of these 30 who will reward Rotisserie owners by being a ''keeper'' (depending on the salary he's assigned), in all likelihood, is Todd Zeile.

Viewed from April of last year, as predictable commodities, these are slim pickings.

Looking back after the season, we see a different picture: a distressing amount of talent that jumped up out of nowhere. To name a few of the suddenly obvious: Sammy Sosa, Eric Anthony, Joey Belle, Marquis Grissom, Mike Stanton . . . They played in *Single* A the year before. Pat Combs wandered into the majors after frittering away the previous year not quite making the Olympics.

Combs is a reminder that very good ballplayers go to college these days (whether they go to class, I'll have to ask a writer I know); but it seems to be getting more difficult to gauge how far along they are. Monty Farriss is obviously struggling. Ty Griffin had problems. Tino for sure did. Ventura? So-so so far. Olson—outstanding.

Finally, there's winter ball. Each year, more gringos go down there, coaches as well as players, and at least a few players come back transformed. Bryan Harvey and Tim Leary two years ago, Lonnie Smith last year.

It doesn't agree with everyone, which is important to notice, too. Van Snider batted .211 in the Puerto Rican League two winters ago. Medina managed four home runs in 184 at-bats in the Dominican Republic. (Small items that I probably would not have noticed anyway, even if I hadn't turned my manuscript in.)

This is the sort of search that shouldn't decently begin before Groundhog Day, but just to see if any pan out, I'll drop a number of obscure names right now, in November; they're culled from the October 25th issue of *Baseball America:* Braulio Castillo, of, Dodgers; Jose Offerman, ss, Dodgers; Phil Plantier, of, Red Sox; Moises Alou, of, Pirates; Steve Avery, p, Braves; Charles Nagy, p, Indians; Kevin Morton, p, Red Sox; Tom Redington, 3b, Braves; Willie Ansley, of, Cardinals. And (a name I wouldn't want to have dropped on me) Andujar Cedeno, ss, Cardinals.

Of the lot, the one who would undoubtedly get the most Patton $ is Plantier. The Carolina League is famous as a pitchers' league, and his stats stand out like Babe Ruth's in the early '20s. He's also small, and strikes out a lot. For that reason, I'd throw my dart at Moises Alou of the hitters listed. The pitcher? Well, everyone's already heard of Steve Avery.

Don't see any Gary Sheffields out there, in case you're wondering.

Ballpark effects clearly have an even bigger impact in the minors than in the majors. (The transition goes something like this: That bum, Sheffield—he played in two of the biggest bombs-away parks in the country in '88, and I was aware of it, and I still fell for his act. Actually, I don't know what Sheffield's problem was, but I don't think it was County Stadium.)

The Denver Zephyrs (Brewers) of the American Association were first in batting average and home runs, last in ERA. The Colorado Springs Sky Sox (Indians) in the PCL batted almost 30 points higher than the next team, hit 30 more home runs, and had the worst ERA by almost a run; i.e., beware of all the Cleveland hitters, not just Paul Zuvella, that you see listed on the PCL page. (Was the Indians management shrewd enough to realize it might be better if Joey Belle skipped this park?) Be extremely impressed by Steve Davis and Steve Olin.

Other teams whose records suggest hitters' parks: Calgary (Mariners) in the PCL, Midland (Angels) and El Paso (Brewers) in the Texas League, and Charlotte (Cubs) in the Southern League.

At the other extreme is Vancouver (White Sox) in the PCL: first in ERA, last in batting average and runs. Tom Drees maybe isn't for real; Lance Johnson, of all people, perhaps is.

Other apparent pitchers' parks: New Britain (Red Sox) and Williamsport (Mariners) in the Eastern League, Greenville (Braves) and Jacksonville (Expos) in the Southern League, and Jackson (Mets) in the Texas League.

The bias of a league as a whole toward hitting or pitching can be seen by glancing at the average pitcher's ERA in the tables. I also give the average hitter's complete stats. You can tell to what extent the running game is emphasized in a league; the more it's emphasized, the more I de-emphasize it with my denominators. I bend the formula to favor those who can hit the ball.

Formulas and denominators are subjects for the next chapter. Here it's enough to know that the average player, who is one-fourteenth of the average team in the league, is worth $13. He has 340 at-bats; projected to 515 at-bats, he's worth $20—if the average player's worth that much, you can see at the start we're giving these bushers whopping "salaries." The "$" in the charts are these projections.

The 515 figure is a slight rise over last year's 500 at-bats, because so many players seem to get slightly over 500 themselves. The other two projections are unchanged: starting pitchers are stretched to 220 innings, relievers to 60 games. At the major league level, 515 AB, 220 IP, and 60 games are roughly equivalent, so all players are inflated about the same.

It's reasonable. That doesn't mean I didn't go through a lengthy struggle before subduing the urge to stretch all relievers to 78 games for the sake of Laddie Renfroe.

INTERNATIONAL LEAGUE (AAA)
Avg. Player: 6 HR, 39 RBI, 8 SB, .252 BA/3.53 ERA, 11.91 Rto

STARTING PITCHERS		W	S	ERA	Rto	IP	H	BB	SO	"$"
PAT COMBS	(PHI)	3	0	0.37	8.25	24	15	7	20	**69**
BRIAN DUBOIS	(DET)	4	0	2.00	9.83	54	41	18	29	**37**

CONTINUED ON NEXT PAGE

STARTING PITCHERS		W	S	ERA	Rto	IP	H	BB	SO	"$"
MARTY CLARY	(ATL)	7	0	2.04	10.15	102	87	28	70	33
MIKE ROCHFORD	(BOS)	9	2	2.37	10.05	163	139	43	76	30
GARY EAVE	(ATL)	13	0	2.80	10.72	141	111	57	93	27
ERIC HETZEL	(BOS)	4	0	2.48	10.91	80	65	32	79	22
ALEX SANCHEZ	(TOR)	13	0	3.13	10.54	170	125	74	141	22
TOM BOLTON	(BOS)	12	1	2.89	11.77	143	140	47	99	21
KENT MERCKER	(ATL)	9	0	3.20	10.76	169	107	95	144	17
TOMMY GREENE	(ATL)	9	0	3.61	11.01	152	136	50	125	13

RELIEF PITCHERS		W	S	ERA	Rto	IP	H	BB	SO	"$"
MARK EICHHORN	(ATL)	1	19	1.32	7.68	41	29	6	33	60
MIKE STANTON	(ATL)	2	8	0.00	8.55	20	6	13	20	60
JULIO MACHADO	(NY N)	1	5	0.62	10.24	29	16	17	37	42
JOSE NUNEZ	(TOR)	11	7	2.21	11.49	134	116	55	122	33
DWAYNE HENRY	(ATL)	11	1	2.44	11.01	85	43	61	101	21

		HR	RBI	SB	BA	AB	BB	SO	"$"
GLENALLEN HILL of	(TOR)	21	72	21	.321	483	34	107	49
HAL MORRIS 1b	(NY A)	17	66	5	.326	417	28	47	43
CARLOS QUINTANA 1b	(BOS)	11	52	6	.287	272	53	39	40
CHICO WALKER of	(TOR)	12	63	37	.239	431	58	61	38
BUTCH DAVIS of	(BAL)	10	64	19	.303	479	28	57	35
KEVIN MAAS of	(NY A)	6	45	2	.320	291	40	73	33
TOM O'MALLEY 3b	(NY N)	15	84	3	.295	492	67	63	33
RICK LANCELLOTTI 1b	(BOS)	17	56	2	.254	350	61	80	32
DAVE JUSTICE of	(ATL)	12	58	12	.261	391	59	66	31
BILLY BEAN of	(DET)	4	29	7	.315	267	27	35	31
FRANCISCO CABRERA c	(ATL)	9	72	4	.300	434	20	72	30
TOM BARRET 2b	(PHI)	0	25	44	.278	443	51	47	30
ROB RICHIE of	(DET)	6	26	3	.293	215	30	40	30
BRIAN DORSETT c	(NY A)	17	62	2	.250	388	31	87	29
TONY BROWN of	(NY N)	11	60	13	.271	454	23	75	28
JOAQ. CONTRERAS of	(NY N)	8	43	11	.287	401	38	92	27
KEITH MILLER of	(PHI)	13	62	8	.264	474	75	101	26
RANDY VELARDE ss	(NY A)	11	53	3	.266	387	38	105	25
LUIS SOHO ss	(TOR)	3	54	9	.276	482	21	42	19
MARK LEMKE 2b	(ATL)	5	61	4	.276	518	66	45	18

AMERICAN ASSOCIATION (AAA)
Avg. Player: 6HR, 40 RBI, 9 SB, .253 BA/3.68 ERA, 12.71 Rto

STARTING PITCHERS		W	S	ERA	Rto	IP	H	BB	SO	"$"
MARK GARDNER	(MON)	12	0	2.37	9.99	163	122	59	175	35
BOB TEWKSBURY	(STL)	13	0	2.43	9.71	189	170	34	72	35
RICH THOMPSON	(MON)	9	0	2.06	10.23	161	146	37	73	34
TOM FILER	(MIL)	5	0	2.80	9.75	84	77	14	34	32
JACK ARMSTRONG	(CIN)	13	0	2.91	9.93	183	144	58	152	31
DORN TAYLOR	(PIT)	10	0	2.58	10.32	171	145	51	103	30
SCOTT SCUDDER	(CIN)	6	0	2.68	11.33	81	54	48	64	27
MORRIS MADDEN	(PIT)	12	1	3.39	12.46	130	117	63	94	20
BOB BUCHANAN	(KC)	8	0	3.29	10.92	164	150	49	104	20
JOSE DEJESUS	(KC)	8	1	3.78	13.03	145	112	98	158	7

RELIEF PITCHERS		W	S	ERA	Rto	IP	H	BB	SO	"$"
STAN BELINDA	(PIT)	2	9	0.95	8.36	28	13	13	28	49
JAY BALLER	(MON)	1	34	2.02	10.02	62	49	20	53	,37
RICK LUECKEN	(KC)	4	16	2.31	10.53	47	33	22	39	36
PAUL WILMET	(TEX)	7	13	2.33	9.99	100	71	40	94	30
BRETT GIDEON	(MON)	7	5	2.26	8.00	72	41	23	71	28

		HR	RBI	SB	BA	AB	BB	SO	"$"
PHIL STEPHENSON 1b	(SD)	13	62	28	.300	290	58	41	59
GREG VAUGHAN of	(MIL)	26	92	20	.276	387	62	94	56
JOEY MEYER dh	(MIL)	9	37	1	.281	146	16	42	47
LARRY WALKER of	(MON)	12	59	36	.270	385	50	87	44
LEON DURHAM 1b	(STL)	10	30	0	.287	178	20	38	39
JAY BELL ss	(PIT)	10	54	12	.285	298	38	55	39
ALBERT HALL of	(PIT)	4	33	31	.304	345	28	53	37
CHRIS BROWN 3b	(PIT)	4	32	0	.343	181	19	19	37
TODD ZEILE c	(STL)	19	85	0	.289	453	45	78	35
JEFF HUSON ss	(MON)	3	35	30	.304	378	50	26	34
MARQUIS GRISSOM of	(MON)	2	21	16	.278	187	14	23	33
JUNIOR NOBOA 2b	(MON)	2	62	14	.340	467	21	34	32
ALEX COLE of	(STL)	2	29	47	.281	455	71	78	31

CONTINUED ON NEXT PAGE

		HR	RBI	SB	BA	AB	BB	SO	"$"
NICK CAPRA of	(KC)	7	44	31	.290	500	70	67	30
DOUG DASCENZO of	(CHI N)	4	33	34	.281	431	51	41	29
SKEETER BARNES of	(CIN)	6	55	15	.303	472	32	59	28
STEVE CARTER of	(PIT)	1	43	17	.295	356	27	62	26
JOE OLIVER c	(CIN)	6	31	0	.292	233	13	35	26
SCOTT COOLBAUGH 3b	(TEX)	18	74	1	.260	527	57	93	24
LUIS DE LOS SANTOS 1b	(KC)	3	62	1	.297	387	29	53	23

PACIFIC COAST LEAGUE (AAA)
Avg. Player: 6 HR, 42 RBI, 7 SB, .269 BA/4.26 ERA, 12.93 Rto

STARTING PITCHERS		W	S	ERA	Rto	IP	H	BB	SO	"$"
JEFF BITTIGER	(CHI A)	9	0	2.12	9.73	123	93	40	122	46
KEVIN TAPANI	(MIN)	4	0	2.20	10.98	41	38	12	30	45
STEVE DAVIS	(CLE)	12	0	2.45	11.38	121	113	40	75	39
RAMON MARTINEZ	(LA)	10	0	2.79	11.31	113	92	50	127	35
ADAM PETERSON	(CHI A)	14	0	2.72	11.09	172	141	71	116	34
ED WOJNA	(CLE)	9	0	2.87	11.21	122	116	36	81	32
JOSE CANO	(HOU)	5	0	2.84	10.80	95	87	27	57	32
ROGER MASON	(HOU)	7	0	3.54	9.93	155	125	46	105	28
TOM DREES	(CHI A)	12	0	3.37	11.46	168	142	72	66	26
MIKE FETTERS	(CAL)	12	0	3.80	12.43	168	160	72	144	18

RELIEF PITCHERS		W	S	ERA	Rto	IP	H	BB	SO	"$"
STEVE OLIN	(CLE)	4	24	3.22	8.82	50	34	15	46	44
ERNIE CAMACHO	(SF)	3	13	1.47	8.02	55	33	16	59	39
KEITH COMSTOCK	(SEA)	9	10	2.93	10.80	55	45	21	64	38
MIKE HARTLEY	(LA)	7	18	2.79	10.17	77	53	34	76	31
JOHN DAVIS	(CHI A)	4	11	2.37	12.12	49	33	33	57	29

		HR	RBI	SB	BA	AB	BB	SO	"S"
LUIS LOPEZ 3b	(LA)	2	16	1	.493	75	6	7	69
MATT WILLIAMS 3b	(SF)	26	61	9	.320	284	32	51	62
JAY BUHNER of	(SEA)	11	45	4	.311	196	44	56	47
JIM WILSON dh	(SEA)	26	133	8	.314	519	54	102	46
MIKE HUFF of	(LA)	10	78	32	.318	471	38	75	43
DAVE HENGEL of	(CLE)	18	82	1	.316	354	35	56	42
JERALD CLARK of	(SD)	22	83	5	.313	419	38	81	41
MIKE BROWN of	(CAL)	13	70	6	.340	373	40	64	41
DENNY GONZALES 3b	(CLE)	27	76	4	.288	420	69	92	39
BRUCE FIELDS of	(SEA)	10	48	14	.351	407	44	52	39
BILLY JO ROBIDOUX 1b	(CHI A)	11	42	3	.317	246	38	46	38
MARK HIGGINS 1b	(CLE)	10	34	0	.329	213	16	45	37
PAUL ZUVELLA ss	(CLE)	10	66	8	.331	387	24	27	36
JEFF MANTO 3b	(CAL)	23	67	4	.277	408	91	81	34
FELIX JOSE of	(OAK)	14	62	11	.287	383	41	81	33
THOMAS HOWARD of	(SD)	3	31	22	.300	303	30	56	33
BERNARDO BRITO of	(MIN)	22	74	1	.254	355	31	111	33
CASEY CLOSE of	(SEA)	7	56	3	.330	324	36	42	32
LANCE JOHNSON of	(CHI)	0	28	33	.304	408	46	36	30
SANDY ALOMAR c	(SD)	13	101	3	.306	523	42	58	29

EASTERN LEAGUE (AA)
Avg. Player: 5 HR, 36 RBI, 9 SB, .248 BA/3.53 ERA, 12.00 Rto

STARTING PITCHERS		W	S	ERA	Rto	IP	H	BB	SO	"S"
KEVIN MMAHAT	(NY A)	5	0	1.58	9.53	51	35	19	48	46
STEVE ADKINS	(NY A)	12	0	2.07	9.53	118	67	58	132	41
RODNEY IMES	(NY A)	17	0	2.73	9.63	172	143	41	128	34
BRIAN DUBOIS	(DET)	6	0	2.49	8.92	112	93	18	82	33
MIKE YORK	(PIT)	11	0	2.31	10.79	121	105	40	106	31
MIKE LINSKEY	(BAL)	10	0	2.81	10.05	128	108	35	90	28
BILL SAMPEN	(PIT)	11	0	3.21	10.19	166	148	40	134	22
GLENN SPAGNOLA	(SEA)	8	0	3.06	10.56	127	113	36	69	21
PAT COMBS	(PHI)	8	0	3.38	10.37	125	104	40	77	20
JASON GRIMSLEY	(PHI)	11	0	2.98	12.03	172	121	109	134	14

CONTINUED ON NEXT PAGE

RELIEF PITCHERS		W	S	ERA	Rto	IP	H	BB	SO	"$"
TIM LAYANA	(NY A)	7	17	1.73	8.87	68	52	15	48	45
DARYL IRVINE	(BOS)	4	16	1.30	9.70	90	74	23	50	33
CHUCK MCELROY	(PHI)	3	12	2.68	10.15	47	39	14	39	31
KEITH HELTON	(SEA)	3	14	1.47	11.51	61	54	24	42	29
STAN BELINDA	(PIT)	1	13	2.33	13.15	39	32	25	33	24

		HR	RBI	SB	BA	AB	BB	SO	"$"
JOEY BELLE of	(CLE)	20	69	8	.282	312	32	82	56
WES CHAMBERLAIN of	(PIT)	21	87	11	.306	471	32	82	48
TROY NEEL of	(CLE)	21	73	5	.292	404	51	87	47
BEAU ALFRED of	(CLE)	14	75	16	.303	412	56	88	46
ROB SEPANEK 1b	(NY A)	22	77	1	.264	367	55	99	46
BERNIE WILLIAMS of	(NY A)	11	42	26	.252	314	60	72	42
JASON MAAS of	(NY A)	5	74	24	.296	382	61	74	41
DEION SANDERS of	(NY A)	1	6	17	.286	119	11	20	41
JIM LEYRITZ c	(NY A)	10	66	2	.315	375	65	51	38
LEO GOMEZ 3b	(BAL)	16	78	2	.281	448	89	102	36
MAURICE VAUGHAN 1b	(BOS)	8	38	1	.278	245	25	47	32
FRANK BELLINO dh	(PHI)	10	77	2	.285	453	57	59	30
TOMMY SHIELDS 3b	(PIT)	5	47	16	.288	417	25	62	28
HENSLEY MEULENS 3b	(NY A)	11	45	3	.257	335	61	108	28
JEFF BANNISTER c	(PIT)	12	48	2	.241	336	30	57	27
PHIL CLARK c	(DET)	8	42	2	.290	373	31	49	26
TINO MARTINEZ 1b	(SEA)	13	64	7	.257	509	59	54	25
VICTOR HITHE of	(BAL)	0	44	29	.277	451	36	83	25
TRAVIS FRYMAN ss	(DET)	9	56	5	.265	426	19	78	25
KEVIN BURDICK 2b	(PIT)	7	34	5	.285	369	23	23	24

SOUTHERN LEAGUE (AA)
Avg. Player: 6 HR, 42 RBI, 10 SB, .248 BA/3.78 ERA, 12.53 Rto

STARTING PITCHERS		W	S	ERA	Rto	IP	H	BB	SO	"$"
HOWARD FARMER	(MON)	12	0	2.20	8.41	184	122	50	151	43
BOB WISHNEVSKI	(TOR)	6	0	2.31	10.36	66	50	26	36	39

STARTING PITCHERS

		W	S	ERA	Rto	IP	H	BB	SO	"$"
MARK GUTHRIE	(MIN)	8	0	1.97	10.59	96	75	38	103	**39**
DARRYL KILE	(HOU)	11	0	2.58	10.14	126	74	68	108	**36**
LEE UPSHAW	(ATL)	8	0	2.75	10.23	95	78	30	72	**34**
PAUL MARAK	(ATL)	8	5	3.11	10.99	122	102	47	83	**32**
JIM LEMASTERS	(ATL)	7	0	2.19	10.52	148	137	36	107	**30**
STEVE AVERY	(ATL)	6	0	2.77	11.04	84	69	34	73	**28**
TONY MENENDEZ	(CHI A)	10	1	3.19	11.00	144	123	53	115	**25**
WAYNE EDWARDS	(CHI A)	10	1	3.19	11.16	158	131	65	122	**23**

RELIEF PITCHERS

		W	S	ERA	Rto	IP	H	BB	SO	"$"
MEL STOTTLEMYRE JR.	(KC)	3	6	1.59	9.39	23	15	9	18	**42**
JOE KLINK	(ATL)	4	26	2.82	10.18	61	46	23	59	**33**
MIKE STANTON	(ATL)	4	19	1.58	11.12	51	32	31	54	**33**
STEVE WAPNICK	(TOR)	1	2	0.49	9.50	18	12	7	20	**31**
LADDIE RENFROE	(CHI N)	19	15	3.14	10.98	132	127	34	85	**27**

		HR	RBI	SB	BA	AB	BB	SO	"$"
BOB HAMELIN 1b	(KC)	16	47	3	.308	211	52	52	**55**
ERIC ANTHONY of	(HOU)	28	79	14	.300	403	35	127	**53**
MIKE SIMMS 1b	(HOU)	20	81	12	.257	378	66	110	**40**
RICHIE AMARAL 2b	(CHI A)	4	48	57	.285	432	88	66	**40**
DANN HOWITT 1b	(OAK)	26	111	2	.281	509	68	109	**39**
ERIK PAPPAS c	(CHI N)	16	49	7	.299	354	66	50	**38**
DELINO DESHIELDS ss	(MON)	3	35	37	.270	307	76	80	**36**
PAUL SORRENTO 1b	(MIN)	27	112	1	.255	509	84	119	**35**
GREG SMITH 2b	(CHI N)	5	64	38	.296	467	42	54	**35**
MARQUIS GRISSOM of	(MON)	3	31	24	.299	278	24	31	**35**
ERIC FOX of	(OAK)	15	51	49	.251	498	72	85	**35**
CHITO MARTINEZ of	(KC)	23	62	3	.243	399	63	137	**31**
SCOTT HEMOND 3b	(OAK)	5	62	45	.265	490	62	77	**31**
REGGIE JEFFERSON 1b	(CIN)	17	80	2	.287	487	43	73	**31**
DERRICK MAY of	(CHI N)	9	70	19	.295	491	34	77	**31**
HARVEY PULLIAM of	(KC)	10	67	5	.290	417	44	65	**29**
BRIAN LANE 3b	(CIN)	12	90	6	.254	465	47	95	**25**
TERRY JORGENSEN 3b	(MIN)	13	101	1	.263	514	76	78	**25**
DEREK BELL of	(TOR)	16	75	15	.242	513	26	92	**25**
SCOTT LEIUS ss	(MIN)	4	45	3	.303	346	38	74	**24**

TEXAS LEAGUE (AA)
Avg. Player: 6 HR, 41 RBI, 8 SB, .260 BA/4.08 ERA, 12.86 Rto

STARTING PITCHERS		W	S	ERA	Rto	IP	H	BB	SO	"S"
PAUL MCCLELLAN	(SF)	8	0	2.24	9.75	84	56	35	56	47
ANDY BENES	(SD)	8	0	2.16	9.83	108	79	39	115	43
KIP GROSS	(NY N)	6	0	2.49	8.76	112	96	13	60	43
ERIC GUNDERSON	(SF)	8	0	2.72	11.22	73	68	23	61	38
JULIO VALERA	(NY N)	10	0	2.49	10.45	137	123	36	107	37
JAIME NAVARRO	(MIL)	5	0	2.47	11.22	77	61	35	78	33
JOHN HOOVER	(TEX)	9	1	3.38	11.02	125	116	37	77	28
DAVE OSTEEN	(STL)	15	0	3.49	11.56	165	179	33	72	26
DENNIS SPRINGER	(LA)	6	0	3.15	11.19	140	128	46	89	23
OMAR OLIVARES	(SD)	12	0	3.39	11.42	186	175	61	79	23

RELIEF PITCHERS		W	S	ERA	Rto	IP	H	BB	SO	"S"
JEFF RICHARDSON	(CAL)	1	10	1.59	5.48	23	9	5	12	51
MIKE PEREZ	(STL)	4	33	3.64	11.69	77	68	32	74	37
GARY BUCKELS	(CAL)	2	12	1.47	9.24	37	24	14	32	36
DAVE LYNCH	(TEX)	8	7	0.87	10.90	52	39	24	53	32
DOUG ROBERTSON	(SF)	4	25	3.00	12.57	63	50	38	50	32

		HR	RBI	SB	BA	AB	BB	SO	"S"
RUBEN AMARO of	(CAL)	3	9	7	.382	110	10	19	50
RAY LANKFORD of	(STL)	11	98	37	.317	498	65	57	46
BOB ROSE 3b	(CAL)	11	73	3	.359	351	50	62	44
WARREN NEWSON of	(SD)	18	70	20	.304	427	103	99	43
MARK LEONARD of	(SF)	10	52	1	.311	219	33	40	42
GERONIMO PENA 2b	(STL)	9	44	14	.296	267	38	68	40
CHRIS CRON 1b	(CAL)	22	103	0	.301	491	39	126	37
RAMON SAMBO of	(MIL)	2	34	47	.322	466	50	99	36
MARK HOWIE 2b	(CAL)	5	51	6	.331	272	35	24	36
BERNARD GILKEY of	(STL)	6	57	53	.278	500	70	54	36
TIM MCINTOSH c	(MIL)	17	93	5	.300	463	29	72	36
JOSE OFFERMAN ss	(LA)	2	22	32	.288	278	40	39	35
DEAN PALMER 3b	(TEX)	25	90	15	.251	498	41	152	35

		HR	RBI	SB	BA	AB	BB	SO	"s"
SAMMY SOSA of	(TEX)	7	31	16	.297	273	15	52	**34**
SHON ASHLEY of	(MIL)	14	65	2	.315	394	36	92	**34**
DAN GRUNHARD of	(CAL)	12	57	8	.304	388	38	60	**32**
JUAN GONZALES of	(TEX)	21	85	1	.293	502	31	98	**32**
JOHNNY MONELL of	(NY N)	6	29	6	.310	232	13	28	**31**
ROY SILVER dh	(STL)	4	44	2	.348	296	21	16	**31**
CARLOS HERNANDEZ c	(LA)	8	41	2	.300	370	12	46	**22**

The most notable aspect of the new formulas is how little they've changed. The average players last year were virtually the same as in 1988. The only thing of even remote curiosity that I saw in the three-year scans on page 42 was the slight rises in ratios but not in hits: The new strike zone was actually smaller?

So I really didn't have to change the denominators at all. But since 1987 was shown in exact relation to 1988 by tinkering with decimals, to be consistent, naturally I had to tinker some more.

Maybe I'll just throw the denominators out and work backwards. That usually scares off most people.

NL & AL pitchers:

$W+ = W/3; S+ = S/2.5$

NL pitchers:

$ERA+ = (3.36 - (392 + ER)/((1050 + IP)/9))/0.05$

$Ratio+ = (11.27 - ((1314 + H + BB)/((1050 + IP)/9)))/0.08$

AL pitchers:

$ERA+ = (3.76 - (439 + ER)/((1050 + IP)/9))/0.05$

$Ratio+ = (11.92 - ((1391 + H + BB)/((1050 + IP)/9)))/0.08$

NL hitters:

HR + = HR/4.2

RBI + = RBI/15.9

SB + = SB/5.4

BA + = (((1207 + H)/(4700 + AB)) − 0.257)/0.0015

AL hitters:

HR + = HR/4.5

RBI + = RBI/17.4

SB + = SB/4.5

BA + = (((1294 + H)/(4900 + AB)) − 0.264)/0.0015

A denominator is what you divide the statistics in any of the eight categories by to figure out what they were worth to you. By far the easiest one to understand is the wins category.

Year after year in all the Rotisserie leagues, every three wins a team gets will be enough for it to pass one other team: Three wins mean a point in the standings. Therefore, divide the number of wins a player gets to see how many points he gained you in that one category alone.

Saves are consistently 50 percent of wins, year after year. That would seem to mean the denominator should be half the wins denominator, or 1.5; unfortunately, the saves category is almost never that close. Far fewer than 50 percent of the pitchers get the saves, and the tendency is for the category to spread out. So I arbitrarily assign the denominator of 2.5. I'm giving each save only slightly more value than each win, even though a save is considerably harder to find.

About to slip off the three-year-scan screen is the oddity in the American League in 1987. Saves dropped to something like 40 percent of wins. They were an endangered species, and I made the saves denominator two, which explains why Tom Henke shows such a large salary that year.

ERA and ratio are found everywhere, but how do you get a grip on them?

Same method. By how much the pitcher's ERA and ratio help—or hurt—in the standings. You take an average Rotisserie team and subtract an average pitcher; you add a specific pitcher. What's your team's new ERA and ratio? Have you gone up or down?

By the way, the ERAs and ratios in the formulas are the average Rotisserie League figures, which are always somewhat better than the major leagues, for obvious reasons.

League differences only affect the pitchers' two qualitative categories (ERA and ratio); the four denominators are the same for each league. The three cumulative denominators in hitting must be different, while both leagues have the same batting average denominator.

To understand them, think whole numbers, not decimals. Between four and five home runs make a difference in the National League; between five and six steals make a difference. Between 15 and 16 RBIs separate National League teams; in the American League it's more like 17 or 18.

These denominators are getting closer; even Rotisserie batting averages last year were more or less the same. If Gibson, Van Slyke, Strawberry, Hernandez, Daniels, McGee, etcetera, etcetera, hadn't crapped out (with few Milt Thompsons rising in their ruins), it's possible that for the first time the National League would have had a better average hitter than the AL.

I give the decimals in the denominators because I need them to make everything come out just right, and some people do seem to like to play with them. I don't give *all* the decimals I use, because it's sort of embarrassing.

"Just right" is making the average hitter and pitcher earn exactly what they're supposed to earn, $13.00 and $8.67. If I don't go to two and even three decimals, I'm going to find the average hitter earning $13.03 or $12.98, and that I will not tolerate.

As for who this average hitter is, I really got slack this year and used only five Rotisserie leagues from each major league. The following chart will tell why:

FIVE NATIONAL LEAGUE ROTISSERIES IN 1989

	AB	HR	RBI	SB	BA
WASHINGTON GHOST	51108	1175	5892	1345	.257
PRO-BALL	50516	1165	5816	1338	.257
PTL CLUBS	51150	1152	5849	1332	.257
OUT OF THEIR LEAGUE	50695	1151	5816	1326	.257
ALL IN THE FAMILY	50820	1156	5841	1305	.258
Average league	50858	1160	5843	1329	.257
Average team	5086	116	584	133	.257
Average player	363	8.3	41.7	9.5	.257

There's not a dime's worth of difference, is there, between these five leagues? I'm absolutely certain that yours falls within these parameters.

These stats are what 140 hitters bought in various drafts produced, and so here's our average hitter—in decimals, since we're eyeballing him more closely now. (Home runs are getting much closer to stolen bases than the round numbers suggest.)

What do we do with him? Why, we set him on top of the denominators—all the other numbers, too—to find the number of points gained.

	HR+	RBI+	SB+	BA+	pts
WASHINGTON GHOST	279.8	370.1	249.1	0.1	899.0
PRO-BALL	277.4	365.3	247.8	0.3	890.8
PTL CLUBS	274.3	367.4	246.7	0.1	888.5
OUT OF THEIR LEAGUE	274.0	365.3	245.6	−0.1	884.8
ALL IN THE FAMILY	275.2	366.9	241.7	0.5	884.3
Average league	282.9	381.9	225.3	0.0	890.0
Average team	28.3	38.2	22.5	0.0	89.0
Average player	2.0	2.7	1.7	0.0	6.355

Hmmm . . .

Each year when I get to this stage, I hear the pitter-patter of feet. I look up, and everybody's heading for the door.

They don't *like* my standings-gain points. I called them SGP and they hated them. Last year I called them simply points, and still they brought yawns.

I admit there are some unpleasant mental contortions to go through: This guy is claiming the WGN league gained 279.8 points in the home runs category last year—would someone please tell him there are only 55? Heath Research, or any other service that's at all accurate, divvies up 440 points among its NL leagues; he's giving them almost 900.

I reply that I start at zero, on the first day of the season. Heath and the others count from the 10th team in each category, at whatever stage.

I cling to my decimals. Isn't it fascinating that the average player doesn't get as much credit for his steals as his home runs, even though both categories count the same?

Nope.

That while I'm often accused of overrating the Vince Colemans of this world, I actually have a prejudice against them?

No. Confusing, yes; fascinating, uh-uh. Just tell me what Coleman is worth, will you?

Yes, it's a society of materialists, and I'm one, damn straight, so points are being trashed this year.

All credit for the solution goes to Les Leopold, Peter Golenbock's new numbers guru. When I heard what he was going to do—break down the categories by dollars—I snorted, That's easy, *I* could do that . . . And then I thought, Bingo.

I used to convert only the total points to dollars. A truly easy formula does the job. If the average hitter gains 6.355 points and earns $13, then—

13 times any hitter's points divided by 6.355 equals his salary; and, for pitchers—

8.67 times any pitcher's points divided by 4.236 equals his salary.

These dinky formulas convert *any* points to dollars, so we apply them to the chart above and get:

DOLLAR WORTH OF THE NLR DRAFT STATISTICS

	$HR	$RBI	$SB	$BA	$TOT
WASHINGTON GHOST	572	757	510	0	1839
PRO-BALL	567	747	507	1	1822
PTL CLUBS	561	752	505	0	1817
OUT OF THEIR LEAGUE	561	747	502	0	1810
ALL IN THE FAMILY	563	751	494	1	1809
Average league	565	751	504	0	1820
Average team	56	75	50	0	182
Average player	4	5	4	0	13.00

Still maybe not riveting, but we're getting there. Here's the American League hitting picture in condensed form.

	AB	HR	RBI	SB	BA	$HR	$RBI	$SB	$BA	$TOT
AVG LG	63146	1502	7682	1334	.264	683	895	606	0	2184
AVG TM	5262	125	640	111	.264	57	74	51	0	182
AVG PL	376	8.9	45.7	7.9	.264	4	5	4	0	13.00

And, even more quickly, the average pitchers.

	IP	W	S	ERA	Rto	$W	$S	$ERA	$Rto	$TOT
NL	130	7.8	4.1	3.36	11.27	5	3	0	0	8.67
AL	130	7.8	4.1	3.76	11.92	5	3	0	0	8.67

Until finally even us masochists get to have some fun.

The next chart breaks down the earnings of five different hitters last year. The first three are American Leaguers, the next two Nationals, and the last I'm not saying, but in the end it can only be one person.

$HR	$RBI	$SB	$BA	$TOT
5	7	35	1	48
10	12	9	8	38
0	0	0	−2	−1
11	14	3	12	40
23	16	1	5	45
1	6	1	10	19

Answers next year.

No, no—just didn't want to make it too easy to cheat. They are (1) Rickey Henderson, which was meant to be like one of those anxiety-reducers at the start of the SAT tests. I mean, I do hope you got it. (2) Robin Yount. (3) Sam Horn, and if you got that, you're in my college. (4) Will Clark. (5) Kevin Mitchell.

(6) Wade Boggs.

Here's another one. (The second pitcher won more games.)

$W	$S	$ERA	$Rto	$TOT
10	0	7	9	25
10	0	−7	−7	−4

(1) Scott Garrelts. (2) Andy Hawkins.

I don't know why, but to see Hawkins losing imaginary money, instead of merely killing you in the standings, has so much more oomph.

Although they're really looking at the very same thing this year in the appendix, I'm pretty sure people are going to be looking at it longer. Great idea, Les.

There's one tiny item on my conscience, before I get to some big items that are on my conscience. Way back in the first chapter I shaved some wins and saves off the teams in the PTL Clubs—so few I doubt many of them spotted it. It was fair, inasmuch as each team lost equally, yet why would I do that?

The only reason I change denominators from year to year is that "amounts"—even in the qualitative categories (BA, ERA, and ratio)—change. The one denominator that should never change is the one for wins, and as long as saves are about half of wins, that denominator shouldn't change either. The three for wins is the rock-solid item that all other denominators are in proportion to.

But wins available in April do change from year to year. Last year in both major leagues, more pitchers than usual stayed the course. The PTL Clubs, if they were cooperating, would have bought 700 wins and 370 saves. But they proceeded to buy 711 wins and 401 saves.

If I didn't have the other years to worry about, I'd let the average pitcher have eight wins and 4.5 saves (rather than 7.8 and 4.1); the average pitcher would gain more points, the points would still be worth $8.67, salaries wouldn't be inflated.

And I could no longer have my hitters in relation to the previous year, for if the average pitcher's points go up, so must the average hitter's; he's always worth 50 percent more. Once you start changing the hitter's points from year to year, the denominators have to change with them—they can no longer be pegged to some other year.

The visible result would be slight indeed; it might be nothing. But the hitters' denominators should change from year to year because of changes *in hitting,* not because of some technical difficulties stemming from the bogus idea that the number of wins has changed. So I shave from the pitchers.

I only bring it up because if you do put your league's draft-day pitching totals onto a spreadsheet, and if you do have appreciably more than 700 wins and 370 saves, you're going to get an exaggerated idea of how well your league did in the draft. Scale it to 700 and 370—840 and 444 in the American League—and you'll get the accurate picture.

Notice my buttering up people with spreadsheets? I need help.

Here's one of the leagues I started to audit, and then had to ditch, because it was just giving me too much trouble.

OUT OF THEIR LEAGUE
statistics bought in the draft

PITCHING	IP	W	S	ERA	Rto	EARNED
BAGEL BOYS	1650	104	6	2.99	10.46	98
HOODS	1253	85	43	3.31	11.01	98
ROBBERS	1350	77	34	3.65	11.17	75
BUMS	1390	89	72	3.02	10.83	134
NOTTA LOTS	1098	67	13	3.41	11.53	52
BEER HERES	970	51	62	3.68	11.96	71
PHAROAHS	985	56	44	3.44	11.54	69
GOLIATHS	1087	51	24	3.59	11.87	42
GRAPHICS	1007	53	79	3.14	11.19	106
TOP CATS	1110	67	26	3.74	12.15	48
TOTAL	11899	700	403	3.37	11.30	793

HITTING	AB	HR	RBI	SB	BA	EARNED
BAGEL BOYS	5416	139	661	117	.265	204
HOODS	6290	121	714	120	.258	199
ROBBERS	5068	147	639	153	.250	207
BUMS	4677	102	552	81	.261	156
NOTTA LOTS	4833	136	591	133	.260	195
BEER HERES	5723	107	615	217	.261	214
PHAROAHS	5535	127	587	132	.239	175
GOLIATHS	4799	109	566	144	.260	182
GRAPHICS	3884	61	371	97	.249	109
TOP CATS	4470	102	520	132	.264	171
TOTAL	50695	1151	5816	1326	.257	1810

OVERALL	EARNED	hfs
BAGEL BOYS	302	62.0
HOODS	297	53.0
ROBBERS	282	52.0
BUMS	290	50.0
NOTTA LOTS	247	45.5
BEER HERES	284	41.5
PHAROAHS	244	38.5
GOLIATHS	224	33.5
GRAPHICS	215	33.0
TOP CATS	218	30.5
TOTAL	2603	

You see the amount that each team earned in Patton $ and then the league total. The hitters earned $1810, according to the chart. If you add each team up on your calculator, you'll get $1812.

No sweat. The spreadsheet is adding fractions, the calculator whole numbers, and if enough round up, a change of two is easy to conceive. (That's why the categories in the appendix often appear not to add up.)

However, suppose I don't add the columns to get the league total. Instead I apply the formula to the totals in the various categories—I look at the league as a player. Out of Their League earned $1811 by that reckoning.

It's closer than the calculator. It's coping with all those decimals, too, so take your pick: either spreadsheet method is more accurate than the clunky old calculator.

Just to be certain, let's do the pitching. Spreadsheet sums the team pitching earnings and gets $793; calculator sums them and gets $793. Luck . . . Spreadsheet applies the formula to the league as a whole and gets—$806.

What the heck's that all about? A two percent discrepancy for an entire league isn't going to alter the salary of any player, but you can rest assured, it drives me crazy. Normally the comparisons are as close as they are with the hitting, but I always check, and when they aren't— I look for someone else's league.

The flaw in the trade analysis (page 175) is about the same size, just a little over two percent.

My hunch is that the trouble occurs in the averages. Lotus occasionally gets fed up with the extended formulas in the qualitative categories. However, I barely know how to use the memory on a calculator, and it would take me until opening day to work out a team's ratio SGP with pencil and paper.

Anyone who takes Out of Their League on as a challenge, thanks in advance. If you write me, I won't be at all offended if you treat me as the village idiot. Actually, I'd prefer it. Sometimes I get letters that I'm simply not qualified to respond to.

The decimals bother me, but to be honest, they're not on my conscience. This is.

Ultimately, a player's value is determined by his exact context. Enough of this blather about the Santa Ana Oxymorons, what did that bozo do for *me* last year? We find this out by taking our own final standings.

The Palukas had Saberhagen in my league last year. Without him on their team, where would they have finished?

	IP	ER	H+BB	W	S	ERA	Rto
PALUKAS	1280	514	1713	83	57	3.62	12.05
SABERHAGEN	262	63	252	23	0	2.16	8.65
−SABERHAGEN	1017	451	1461	60	57	3.99	12.93
POINTS LOST				10	0	8	5

The Palukas drop all the way from second to last in wins. Luckily they still get awarded one point, so they lose 10 points. They drop from second to 10th in ERA and from seventh to last in ratio. Add it up; they drop 23 points. *Twenty-three points.* Amazing.

Now, what about my old points system? For I do sort of miss it. Oh, it's there still—just expressed in dollars—but for the sake of Saberhagen, let's bring back the points. In the format of last year's appendix, under W+ (points he gains in wins) you'd see 7.7; under S+, 0; under ERA+, 6.8; under Ratio +, 8.0. Add it up: 22.5 SGP (standings-gain points).

Half a point off. Awesome! That is, amazingly lucky.

The Hackers had Rickey Henderson.

	AB	H	HR	RBI	SB	BA
HACKERS	5864	1517	155	695	156	.259
R.HENDERSON	541	148	12	57	77	.274
−R.HENDERSON	5323	1369	143	638	79	.257
POINTS LOST			3	4	8	1

Not nearly as many points as Saberhagen, but at least he contributes in four categories! Seriously, how does Henderson come out in standings-gain points?

HR+, 2.7; RBI+, 3.3; SB + 17.1; BA +, .6. Add it up: 23.7 SGP.

So clearly, in the exact context of the American Dreams, Saberhagen was more valuable than Rickey. The formula shows Rickey gaining more points, with the result that Patton $ give the slightly higher earnings to him ($48 vs. $45).

What about the exact context of the league, but if the two players were on someone else's team? Getting a *little* hypothetical, but let's see . . .

Take Henderson away from the Nabobs and they lose only 12 points.

Take Saberhagen away from the Nabobs and they lose—*only four points.*

It's rigged, of course, because the Nabobs were already last in ERA and ratio. (Freedom to claim any pitcher you want on waivers is having nothing left to lose.)

If we ran these two players through league after league after league, who do I think would gain more points?

Saberhagen, without question.

Then how come I give Rickey a bigger salary?

Because I like hitters better, that's why. They're where I want to put my money.

Why? Because any hitter helps me in three categories, any pitcher can hurt me in two. That's simplifying it, but I'm confident the people still reading this chapter need no elaboration.

Let's approach this from the other end. Overall, pitching counts as much as hitting, so let's make pitchers worth as much as hitters. (Another questionable assumption, since there are nine pitchers and 14 hitters.) This is what would happen.

The SGP of the average hitter and average pitcher would have to be the same: They are helping the team equally. It's easy to do by simply fiddling with the denominators. Enlarge the hitting denominator to bring the hitter's SGP down. Instead of dividing home runs by 4.5, divide by 5; divide RBIs by 20 instead of 17.4, stolen bases by 5 instead of 4.5. Basically the same profile of the hitter, but now he gains 5.645 SGP rather than 6.356.

Now we have to make the pitcher earn 5.645.

He used to get 4.237. It's not all that hard, conceptually, to say the pitcher gains between five and six points in the standings instead of a little over four; I mean, what the hell.

There are only two denominators to squeeze, though. (No point in changing the average pitcher's ERA and ratio denominators, even if we wanted to, since he's worth zero in those.)

I claim to be wedded to my wins denominator of three, but in fact I have no problem dropping it to two. Again, what the hell. (The wins denominator for Saberhagen, in the exact context of the Palukas, is 2.3—his wins divided by 10.) In the ever-tough center of the wins pack, two is a quite credible denominator.

Now, to make the pitcher worth exactly what the hitter's worth, we'll float the saves denominator. Something has to float. Might as well be those perplexing saves . . . Comes out to a little over two: 2.341 does the trick.

Once more, a perfectly legitimate assertion. The saves category invariably *is* more spread out than wins.

We have the average player's points (he's become unisex, which is another advantage); we know what he's worth ($11.30); we're ready to run with it. Who shall we do first?

Pitchers, this time, since we're dying to know what the mighty Mr. Saberhagen is *really* worth.

	W+	S+	ERA+	Rto+	SGP	$
SABERHAGEN	11.5	0.0	6.4	8.2	26.1	52
RUSSELL	3.0	16.2	2.3	2.8	24.3	49
HAWKINS	7.5	0.0	−3.4	−3.3	0.7	1

Over $50! *Much* more like it. Russell goes up, too, but you don't need a spreadsheet anymore to see that Saberhagen's better. Look at Hawkins . . . *He's* in the black. You feel a little better about taking all that abuse from him, waiting for him to catch a win.

Time for the hitters. Sorry, Rickey, but somebody's got to pay for Bret.

	HR+	RBI+	SB+	BA+	SGP	$
R.HENDERSON	2.4	2.9	15.4	0.6	21.3	43
SIERRA	5.8	6.0	1.6	3.2	16.6	33
MCGWIRE	6.6	4.8	0.2	−2.0	9.5	19
BOGGS	0.6	2.7	0.4	5.0	8.7	17

Well? So? It's not just Rickey, but okay. Sierra drops $5; he's still in the 30s. McGwire killed you in batting average. All Boggs has got is batting average. These are good, fair prices.

They may be.

But they're useless.

Name me an auction in this wide country of ours where, this April, $19 fetches Mark McGwire? $33 for Sierra? $43 for Rickey? You're living on another planet. I topped Boggs last year at $28, and have no complaints.

The reality test does not make Patton $ run for cover.

The theoretical explanation, in fact, is right in front of us, smack-dab in the points.

	W+	S+	ERA+	RTO+	SGP	$
AVG AL PITCHER	3.9	1.8	0.0	0.0	5.645	11.30

	HR+	RBI+	SB+	BA+	SGP	$
AVG AL HITTER	1.8	2.3	1.6	0.0	5.645	11.30

With the assumption that the pitcher is worth as much as the hitter, the single category that becomes hugely favored—far and away the teacher's pet—is the wins category. The weight of 3.9 is almost twice the weight of the next category, RBIs. Does anybody believe that?

We multiply the average player out (108 × pitcher, 168 × hitter) to determine the points for leagues as a whole, convert these points to dollars, and supposedly this is how we are spending our money:

AVERAGE AL ROTISSERIE LEAGUE

	$W	$S	$ERA	$RTO	$TOT
PITCHERS	841	380	0	0	1221

	$HR	$RBI	$SB	$BA	$TOT
HITTERS	599	768	531	0	1898

$841 for wins as against $599 for homers?

No one believes that.

Of the eight categories we worry about, in reality, wins might be at the bottom of the list. Precisely because they're not concentrated in any one player, you don't know where to spend for them; you get hurt chasing them.

And finally, what about the still-unequal budgets? Pitchers earn $1560, just like the hitters, don't they? So Saberhagen must be around $60 and Rickey under $40, and that's that.

Hawkins probably earned $5 last year.

But then I go back to the exact context of my league, my team. Without Hawkins, I lose seven places in wins. Good grief, another very squeaky wins denominator. But without him I'd *gain* five places in ERA . . . gain four places in ratio. That son of a gun cost me two points. For that I don't pay $1.

I can't help but ask you, first, if you were able to see the solution to my little problem with decimals?

I'm thinking about it. I'll let you know. Meantime I've been working on this list here—

Do you think it's all in the qualitative categories?

Not sure. I've been—

For all I know, it may not even *be* the decimals—

I don't want to be rude, but aren't there more important things?

Sure.

You said somewhere—I think it was one of the comments—something about "kissing off a category." Why would you do that?

It's the opposite of the sin of excess: The penalty's no greater for being last by a mile than by a whisker, so why not?

You mean, the Bags should have stayed in last in batting average?

It's possible. You saw their trade summary. They did improve themselves in hitting overall, but in the process gave up a ton of pitching. Maybe they should have tried to go up in homers and RBIs, since those are linked categories. Rob Deer comes cheaper than Kirby Puckett. Rob Deer doesn't hurt you if you plan to bat .240.

Can you win if you bag a category?

Yes. Well, the Bags might not have (you don't *look* like Abbott), because the Hackers took off at the end. There has to be no single outstanding team. Obviously, a 12 or a 10 in a category means you won't be one. But there comes a time in the season when that becomes obvious anyway. Due to a misguided trade I made early, I found myself with no real use for Bryan Harvey in June.

One thing I noticed in the trade summary was that the two worst traders were the two so-called experts, you and Golenbock.

Yes. That is interesting.

So you were dead last in—in saves? You?

Not dead last. Eleventh. But the last-place team was dead last, so it was the same thing. I tried to get another reliever, but I just didn't have any fat anywhere, so I couldn't offer much. I wasn't even going to catch the 10th-place team with just Harvey.

The dollar value of a player is set in the context of an abstract Rotisserie league. In my own league, Harvey's value to me had become nil. He'd neither gain nor keep me from losing save points; he was a wash in ERA and ratio; almost any starting pitcher would get more wins.

So who'd you trade him for?

I think we should enlarge the scope of this. I don't want to sound like the RLBA boys.

Ron Kittle.

Kittle! Was this before or after he was in the hospital?

After. I just thought he was on bed rest.

A guy in the hospital was the best you could get for Bryan Harvey?

I could have had Bob Welch—but hold on; before you say anything, you've got to know everything. Welch was on a strong team—Golenbock's, in fact—and the Palukas, who owned Kittle, had too many problems just like Kittle.

Harvey did help them substantially, but the Palukas never got out of the second division. Every time the Palukas passed one of my competitors in saves, instead of wincing, I applauded Harvey. It was like he was still playing for me, only he was accomplishing something.

Great, but why not get a hitter who plays for you, too?

Much better, no question. I was always one hitter shy.

The Palukas convinced you he was just resting?

Huh? Hey, *I* offered the trade. The Palukas probably swallowed the phone, but I thought it up. Like everyone, we have lots of lopsided trades in the league, most of them self-inflicted. The best thing is to blow a lot of smoke and wait for offers.

A couple of other quick anecdotes:

One of the teams I was trying to get a reliever from was the Wssox. They had Candelaria and eight relievers; in other words, an innings problem. I offered them Swindell for Reardon. They said it was just what we both needed, except for one catch.

What's that?

Reardon was worth more Patton $.

Yeah? So?

That's the story. The fact the trade would help his *team* didn't—never mind.

The other story better?

Actually, you'll probably think so. Just the other day I get this phone call from Steve Stoneburn, the Bags' owner. I'm trying to get this book out, and Steve is reading newspapers for me, watching ESPN and all that, keeping me informed. But this isn't a catch-up call. Steve said, "The Veecks just offered me Eckersley ($41) for Greenwell ($37); would you do it?" I said, "In a minute," and went back to what I was doing.

And then I kind of came to. Hell, I had all sorts of players like Greenwell. McGwire $31. Tony Fernandez $30. Instead of "in a minute," I should have said "just a minute" and called the Veecks, who, as you seem to know, is Peter Golenbock.

But isn't there an ethical problem?

What do you mean?

You're right. When I called Peter it was too late.

What do you think of his prices?

You mean Les Leopold's? Haven't seen them.

What are you going to think when you do see them?

That they're either similar to mine, or they're wrong.

The people who drive me crazy—to be more candid than I was in a player comment—are the forecasters. I've seen mechanical models that project everything from at-bats to Alzheimer's disease. One that I checked out was so sure young pitchers would develop and geezers recover that it spun out 85 more wins than there are games in the season. If you see one that has Phil Bradley, Mike Devereaux, Stanley Jefferson, Joe Orsulak, Steve Finley, and Brady Anderson all playing full seasons this year, send in for a refund.

They say that super-computers will soon beat the chess masters. It's not going to happen in baseball. No computer can receive as much input as you do.

What you're saying is, I should sit down now and start figuring out my own prices for 1990?

Correct.

Figure them exact? Like Clemens $27?

You would mention a pitcher. That pitcher. No, rank the pitchers in price ranges, I suggest.

The few really reliable starting pitchers go in the $20–30 range. These are pitchers who have a good chance of winning $30 or more.

Have a large list of starting pitchers who might earn over $20 in the $10–20 range.

Another group between $5 and $10, and a huge list of starters for the crapshoot.

I'm looking at the cover of this thing. It's called a price guide. That's it?

That's it for starters. We've moved from Patton $ to Patton Guesses, and from recent history to possible strategies.

I have three axioms about my pitching staff as I go into the draft:

(1) I need relievers.

(2) I need starters, but I'm not sure which ones, so I'm not picky.

(3) No matter what, I want some pitching openings in the endgame.

For the very best relievers I'm prepared to go into the 40s. The other good ones are going to fall into the wide range between $20 and $40, and I better be in there somewhere. Let me in low and I'll be there more than once.

However, it's unlikely that you'll be tempted by too many good relievers. Temptation comes in the form of the gavel about to sound on a starting pitcher you like. If you've already got a few, just remember the Torts R Us in the Legal Baseball League: "Bobby Ojeda $14. Fourteen dollars for Bobby O! Going once—"

I remember, but what's a few?

Two, maybe three. That's starters that you've risked any money on. Don't worry about the 1,000 innings, not in April.

Here are some teams that didn't buy the minimum innings in last year's drafts, the innings they ended up with, their hypothetical final standings, and their actual final standings:

	IP-H	IP-F	HFS	AFS
BEER HERES	985	1479	6th	1st
TOUGH DOMINICANS	787	1199	4th	2nd
CANAL ZONES	991	1240	5th	2nd
HOLEY MOLARS	838	705		

Oops. The Holey Molars still finished first. Forty-two wins, 73 saves, almost half a run better than the next team in ERA, first by 15 points. Shows why you need the innings rule.

Here are some of the few teams that, at the year's end, had more than 1450 innings, the number normally needed in real baseball.

	IP-H	IP-F	HFS	AFS
AMAROS	1161	1523	7th	9th
SOUTHERN DAGO	1642	1775	2nd	4th
RATS OF KAHN	1238	1541	11th	11th
GERIATRICS	1555	1465	2nd	10th

Wish I had spotted this last team in the South Main Street league when I was talking about people trading their way out of contention. They traded 49 players.

Funny you didn't mention the Beer Heres.

Excuse me?

Oh, yeah—look at them, 1479 final IP. For a moment I was getting thirsty.

Okay, the Beer Heres got a lot of innings and won. They made trades and won. Gee whiz, Moose Factory could have been on both lists (962 hypothetical innings, 1459 total), and we made trades, and we at least finished third. You've gotta be flexible.

We?

Dollar Bill and I.

I haven't mentioned my partner yet? Dollar Bill Berensmann. I lured him out of retirement to count money in the draft, and then of course he stayed on for the entire season. So wherever I said me before, I meant we.

Except Kittle. That was me.

Good idea to have a money counter, is it?

Hell yes. It frees me up to stare at burly Texans like Mark Goodman of the Palukas, who's staring back while his partner, Tony Lucas, is counting the money for them. Money counters are great and Dollar Bill's the best.

He allowed to make bids?

He doesn't. But he pokes me and kicks me, while Lucas is poking and kicking Goodman. Why? Do you have a partner?

Not really. I was just wondering, know what I mean?

I'm not sure what not really means. But if you do have a partner, definitely divide the duties.

These drafts are—well, here, let me read you this, a letter I got from Tom Leone of the Dirty Dozen in Massachusetts:

"Enjoyed the book . . . Didn't go for the starting pitching theory . . ." That's not it. Here it is. ". . .If you would like a videotape of our draft, it's pretty funny. I'm using the tape to study the body language of the other owners to help in next year's draft. It's amazing to see: Some put pens down on their last bid. Some flip through pages. Remove glasses. Cross arms. Whatever, you know when they've made their last bid. Should come in handy next year!"

He's not going to thank you for this.

No, no, here's the next sentence: "Put it in the book if you like: They can't help it!!"

Why the frown?

I was just thinking. I have a camcorder.

You'll have your hands full as it is, don't worry. Deep lists for everything. Obviously more than 90 pitchers for the NL; for the AL more than 108.

How come more than?

The reserve draft.

Also it helps remind you that there are too many pitchers to become fixated on any one.

For the teams above with the low innings, was it clear or just implied that they are fixated on protecting their ratios and ERA? That's the whole key to pitching; in fact, to Rotisserie baseball. Not saves, not steals—not the scarcity items—but these two averages, because they are usually redundant. No matter how good the rest of your team is, the double millstone of bad ratio and ERA will drag you down.

If you could safeguard these categories with money, I'd totally revise my prices. I'd make the average pitcher worth *more* than the average hitter. The theoretical reason I don't has to do with the fact that they are averages, yet experience leads to the same conclusion. We'll ignore Patton $ (for once) and just look at the teams that spent the most money on pitching in their league and where they finished in the hypothetical standings in ERA and ratio.

LEAGUE		TEAM	PITCHING	ERA	RATIO
CNR	(NL)	PORKCHOPPERS	$130	6th	6th
WDL	(NL)	NICE GUYS	$103	4th	10th
MAG	(NL)	OLD SHOES	$96	10th	10th
WGA	(AL)	MATTADORS	$144	12th	8th
SAO	(AL)	JUMBO SHRIMPS	$114	11th	9th
CAR	(AL)	POLY YANKS	$104	12th	12th

Plenty of excellent pitchers, as well as buys, are to be found on these rosters: Mike Moore $19, Joe Magrane $15. Overall, though, it's self-evident that they didn't get what they should have gotten, considering the money they spent. Collectively, these teams devoted almost 45 percent of their budget, and almost $13 per player, to pitching; much more than the competition, so they have to dominate for it to be worthwhile.

How'd they finish?

I'm sure this is going to be carnage . . . 9th, 3rd, 8th, 11th, 12th, 10th.

How did the Nice Guys do so well? Let's look at their offense— O'Neill $2, Grace $10, Jefferies $10.

They had some good keepers. Otherwise, with $157 to spend on hitters, it's very unlikely they could have come out of the draft with an offense. I'm not talking my prices, you understand, I'm talking reality.

I like that. Let's talk more about it.

We'll go through these leagues again and find out who spent the most on hitting and show—what? What would be the equivalent?

Home runs and RBIs maybe?

Oddly enough, yes. They're the two most important categories on offense, since they tend to be redundant also. Might as well include how they finished overall, since you're bound to ask.

LEAGUE		TEAM	HITTING	HR	RBI	FINISHED
CNR	(NL)	RIVER RATS	$191	2nd	2nd	5th
WDL	(NL)	ISLANDERS	$210	7th	7th	2nd
MAG	(NL)	BLESSINGS	$201	1st	1st	5th
WGA	(AL)	CHICKENS	$202	6th	3rd	3rd
SAO	(AL)	SAFE SEX	$203	7th	8th	7th
CAR	(AL)	GIANTS	$199	6th	9th	12th

Not everyone cooperated.

Who did? Most of these teams look like screwups, too.

Would you take it easy? Some of them are going to read this.

In part they didn't cooperate because the first group is the selective evidence; this one's random. When I was thumbing through the rosters, I ignored the few teams that had the highest pitching budgets in their leagues and got away with it. Why encourage bad habits? Whereas if I looked for teams that succeeded with the highest hitting budgets, I'd find plenty.

Even so, as usual, I find support for my thesis even in the anomalies.

What's that mean?

How could the Islanders spend $210 on hitting—much more than even I would—buy such a poor offense, and finish second?

Batting average and stolen bases?

Good point . . .

Nope. This gets weirder and weirder. They finished eighth in batting average and tied for *last* in steals. They got a grand total of 3, 4, 4, 1.5—12.5 hitting points. For $210.

They spent $47 on pitching, good for 35 points in the hypothetical final standings.

Some of the pitchers were obviously frozen: Belcher $1, Mark Davis $10. Others look like good pickups—Dibble $6, Deshaies $7—although I can't be certain without their freeze list.

Anyway, pitching was their strength and they didn't pay much for it.

And the hitters weren't nearly the safe investments you say they are.

No denying that . . . Gibson, Strawberry, McGee, Doran, Schmidt. Ouch.

Maybe I'm just pigheaded, but I still see evidence in the two lists above that your big pitching budget is more likely to buy you the emperor's clothes.

I'm checking my notes—you said the correct budgets are $182 for hitters, $78 for pitchers?

I said that was what they earned for the average team in the league. Your objective as a specific team is to buy value wherever you find it. That's why I'm vague about the prices of the pitchers I buy for next year: I know I don't know what I'm doing.

With hitters, I'm more confident. Everything that could go wrong with the Islanders' offense did go wrong, but I can't let that shake me up. I've got to have faith in *something*.

What's your faith in Strawberry next year?

$37.

Not $36? Not $38?

Right now, it's $37. This April, the day before the draft, I might decide he was going to earn $45 or $15. I'd pencil that down on my list of outfielders. And I'd obey it; that's my highest bid.

Even if he's the last outfielder available?

First of all, he's not going to be. That's going to be Bob Dernier. Second of all, if I had a good freeze list—which you don't—I might pay a few bucks more. Otherwise I obey it. How do I get profits if I pay these turkeys more than they're worth?

You have a bidding point for every single hitter?

Yes. A Patton Guess. I have them listed by position, of course, and they run deeper than there are openings to fill at the position, because some qualify at more than one position and you have the designated hitter to worry about.

Or the utility player.

If you prefer to call him that. You know what I would do, if I were in a National League Rotisserie? I'd insist that one of the nine pitchers' stats count. Imagine if a pennant was decided by a home run from Mitch Williams, who was hitting for you only because he almost never bats.

I'll propose it. Do you bother to see if your Patton Guesses add up in Patton Dollars?

Oh, of course. Or else what good are they?

If I can uncrumple them and see through the hieroglyphics, I've still got my working sheet from last year . . .

We needed to buy 50 outfielders in the draft, meaning 10 were frozen. I rank all 60 anyway, because I want to see if my sense of the strength of position is at all realistic. I pencil in what I think these 60 players are going to earn and total that up. Last year it came out to $1239. I average it. It's $20.65. I look in the appendix of my book last year, see the average of the top 60 outfielders was $18.72.

I'm making realistic predictions, just a little bit on the fat side.

Who were your top 10?

I'll show the top and the bottom 10, because that's important.

1. R. HENDERSON $59 ($64)	51. BOSTON $9
2. PUCKETT $47 ($40)	52. BUSH $9 ($4)
3. BURKS $41	53. F. JOSE $9
4. GREENWELL $41	54. ARMAS $8
5. CARTER $41	55. K. WILLIAMS $8
6. CANSECO $39	56. JAVIER $7
7. B. JACKSON $38	57. JEFFERSON $7
8. SIERRA $35	58. BROWER $7
9. TARTABULL $32	59. COTTO $6
10. G. BELL $31	60. G. WARD $6

The numbers in parentheses are the salaries that the frozen players already have.

Tartabull $32? Felix Jose $9?

You know—I'm getting a little tired of the attitude of a rookie toward us veterans. Every time I try to learn you our experience, you act like we're retarded. Some of us have put our money where your mouth is.

I take it back; Tartabull I can see.

Have to gamble on the rooks. I won't deny I tried to get him at that price, and didn't come close.

As for Tartabull, you're acting like the glass is half-empty when the fact is, it's almost full.

First, remember you're bound to lose money on your highest-priced players. I don't *want* to, and I'm not trying to, but I'm resigned to it.

Second, let's flip to the appendix under AL Outfielders. Of the top 10 earners, I see one, two, three, four, five, six, *seven* that are on my list.

Third, that's nothing to boast about, because they're on everybody's list.

Fourth, for comparison, look at the pitchers in the appendix. Would you have been able to pick seven of those top 10? Ranking starters alone, did anyone in the country have a list that vaguely looked like: Saberhagen, Moore, Blyleven, Ryan, Bosio, Clemens, Finley, Stieb, Stewart, Gubicza?

Vaguely? Why not? The only two that are really out of the blue are Blyleven and Finley. For your top 10 overall, the only two relievers you'd call real big surprises are Olson and Montgomery.

Ryan, Bosio, Stieb in your top 10? You've got this wonderful amnesia, my friend, that lets you kid yourself that you would have ranked those three, last April, ahead of Swindell, Key, Viola, Robinson, Higuera, Langston, Welch—hell, even Leibrandt.

Know what? I agree with you. Just playing the devil's advocate; trying to see if there are any chinks.

Most of these good starters were righties last year and the crap-outs lefties—think there's a pattern there?

I have no idea. Devil's advocate is one thing, but taking potshots at Felix Jose is gratuitous.

What's that mean?

It means, aren't we about done?

Done? Aren't we going to go through a whole draft?

I did that last year. Here. Take a copy of last year's book. They're all the same.

What are you doing? What do I want this for? Here, you take it.

Are they the same? It suddenly occurs to me . . . that something's happened.

So let's do one.

See, before we were sidetracked, I was trying to make a point, and it wasn't how accurate my list of outfielders was. Nor that my prices were so realistic. I was going to describe how the system works: What you're hoping for is that you *don't* get these players.

We're under way in the draft. A player is nominated. I look at my price, I jump in and out of the bidding until it reaches it, and then I sit back and relax. Oh, I might pretend to be still interested, but I keep my mouth shut, and when the player's bought I cross him off *and* put the price down. Dollar Bill is recording all this by teams. As the bidder, I have to know what the fashion is in the marketplace this year. So I put market prices right next to Patton Guesses.

The pretending is to fake out that guy's camcorder?

If possible. Once a player has gone past my price, the key is, how far past? I'm so confident that I'm right (even though, of course, I might be wrong) that from now on I don't feel like I've lost a player; rather, someone else is losing money.

And if you lose all top 10 outfielders?

I'll buy the next five, or the next, or the next; they are going to come to me.

But what happens when I discover that the market prices and my guesses are very much in sync? For example, on this working sheet of mine, I see $36 scrawled next to the $38 I have down for Bo Jackson. Unfortunately, Bo did not become a Moose last year. Why is that?

You tell me.

The $37 next to Greenwell's name is Moose money. On the first-base sheet, I have $33 for the McGwire guess, and $31 for the McGwire price, and that's Moose money. We can't afford Bo. It pains me deeply to pencil that paltry $36 of the Bags' money next to his name.

Before the draft is too old, all the top outfielders are gone. I look at my sheet, and these are the numbers I've penciled in next to my bidding prices (the numbers in parentheses I'm adding now, the amount the market prices are over or under my guesses): Burks $39 (−2), Greenwell $37 (−4), Carter $40 (−1), Canseco $43 (+4), Jackson $36 (−2), Sierra $36 (+1), Tartabull $38 (+6), Bell $33 (+2). Any minuses that aren't mine are bad news.

Other teams are getting good deals?

Precisely. Again, I emphasize it has nothing to do with my predictive powers. What I know is that my prices for all hitters add up; therefore, my prices for individual hitters can be called par; and worst of all, other teams agree with me.

It's bad, but what can I do about it?

I'm trying to think.

At this point in the draft, Dollar Bill and I have already bought Greenwell, McGwire, Tony Fernandez $30, Wade Boggs $28—

Clemens $32.

Clemens $32. It's a nice, solid start. Indeed, the Moose aren't used to such all-stars on their roster, and they like the feeling. Nevertheless, the five have consumed 60 percent of the budget; we've reached our quota of "good deals" at this level. No choice now but to wait for the next. While we're waiting, naturally, we nominate an all-star each time it's our turn.

Why not nominate one of these bottom 10 scrubs that you listed?

Because that's not the next level. If someone else nominates them, I won't even go to the prices listed.

Then why list them?

They're my bidding *limits;* as I said earlier, you're very pleased if a $30 player earns $30, but you don't want to spend $5 for a $5 player.

By the way, the bottom 10 aren't even the true scrubs, who are listed after the 60th outfielder—no prices, just by preference. I'd read last year's if you could contain yourself.

Read 'em; don't be so sensitive.

Felder, Orsulak, Sheridan, Castillo, Devereaux, Bichette, Moses, Leach, and the last two, Eisenreich (shut up), Briley (shut up).

You had them listed; more than some people did, I bet.

I know you didn't get Eisenreich, because I saw him on a reserve list, but, uh—?

Why would we? He was our last choice. Our outfield ended up Greenwell $37, Pasqua $17, Pettis $10, Devereaux $4, Armas $3. Believe me, it looks better now than it did after the draft.

Seventeen dollars for—sorry.

That's just it. Since the league as a whole refused to duke it out over Burks and Greenwell and Bo, we ended up duking it out over Pasqua.

He was what you were waiting for?

We were waiting for the second echelon—Yount, Devon White, Inky, Chili, Dwight Evans—but they all turned out to be much too thick for our blood. We were spectators again, and glad of it.

What was your price for Pasqua? How high were you going to go?

Let me see . . . $16.

Sixteen?

That's what it says.

So you went over your limit.

Looks like it. For the first time ever, Moose Factory was naughty. That's how rough it was.

Hey—I like naughty. I just want to know why.

This is where Bill's job is important. We've waited so long that finally we're rich again, compared to the 11 other teams. It's taken until the 13th round, but we did it. Both of us feel Pasqua's going to have a big year and we want him. It's obvious from Bill's bookkeeping that only one other team can give us any trouble, the Nabobs. And it's obvious that they're going to.

Outfield opening, money left?

Uh-huh. Yet it's no problem for us to rub them out now. We just have to decide when, for how much? The price is currently $17. Every time the Nabobs spend even $2 on someone the rub-out drops a buck. Bill wants to wait. But I know those Nabobs; they're stubborn.

I look across the room at Walter Shapiro, the Nabobs' bidder. My expression says, "Would you do the decent thing and give up? You're not going to get Pasqua, and meantime there are all these other yo-yos going by that we both should be buying." Walter's expression says, "Screw you."

Bill's whispering to me that I can bid $6 on any player, and we still get Pasqua, so I keep bidding $6. But Mike Witt goes for $7, Gantner goes for $7. It's damned annoying. "Wait," Bill whispers.

Walter will have $4 left for four players if he spends $17 on Pasqua. Is he that rash? He'll run me along to about $10, I figure; it's time to get it over with. I nominate Pasqua.

When Walter's bid reaches $15, I have two choices. I can say $16, he'll say $17, and I surprise the hell out of him by letting him have him. Or I can jump to $17, save a buck, and stop this nonsense.

Frankly, it didn't occur to me until today that I exceeded my limit.

You may be the biggest bullshitter I've ever listened to.

Pardon?

When you break one of your rules, you're flexible. When one of us does, it's like we're going to roast in hell.

You haven't even played the game, yet you sound like some of the letters I get.

I'm not breaking rules, I'm breaking *advice.*

The best advice I can give you, frankly, *is* to be flexible. If you find you're in a room that's not spending on starting pitchers, buy them yourself. If Walter Shapiro wants to spend $4 on his last four players, I should have let him. I wasn't flexible enough.

Trouble is, it's hard to be flexible when there's nowhere to go. I keep looking at those prices for the blue-chip outfielders and wondering what I could have done about it. Round after round after round, I look for an opening, and it's just not there.

Pitchers, by the way, were getting very fair prices. On Bill's team records, pitchers are entered not sequentially but according to their importance and function. The Nabobs, for example, had frozen one pitcher, Wes Gardner $3.

Wes Gardner?

Shut up. Gardner's in the middle, with eight spaces above and below. They buy Tanana for $2; he goes right above Gardner. They buy Morris for $16; he goes at the top. They buy Holton for $5; he goes two spaces below Gardner as a scrub reliever. They buy Morris for $21; he goes right under Key. They buy Lee Smith for $29; he goes at the bottom.

It makes it easy for me to see what people are doing with their pitching staffs. This is the view in the 13th round of the top three lines of each roster (frozen players with an asterisk):

SWINDELL*	7	VIOLA	29	GUBICZA*	11	LEIBRANDT	17
CLEMENS	32	RYAN	11	BOSIO	8	CANDIOTTI*	3
MCDOWELL	3	BODDICKER	8	MILACKI	7	S. DAVIS*	3
ROBINSON	16	MORRIS	16	HIGUERA	24	MOORE	12
C. YOUNG	7	KEY	21	HILLEGAS	4	SABERHAGEN	17
M. WITT	7	HANSON	4	WEGMAN*	4	BANNISTER	8

ANDERSON*	15	LANGSTON	16	WELCH	15
BANKHEAD	8	STIEB	20	HOUGH	12
ALEXANDER	6	LEITER	4	ABBOTT	4

See what's happening?

You're all doing the same thing. Except one team, which doesn't have a starter yet.

The Wssox. And even though they've been hogging relievers (Reardon 34, Olson 16, Gordon 10, Hernandez 5, Guante 7), the other 11 teams read like this along the bottom line:

HARVEY*	15	HENNEMAN	31	PLESAC*	37	THIGPEN	27
HENKE	33	L. SMITH	29	D. JONES*	1	SCHOOLER*	15
RIGHETTI	26	FARR*	15	ECKERSLEY	41	REARDON	34

Still doing the same thing.

Maybe it's because you've brainwashed them with your . . .

With my bullshit? Maybe, but in fact one of the big themes of my book last year was *not* to be balanced; or don't worry about it if you're not. Just get value anywhere you can. One team, the Wssox, followed *that* advice.

Maybe it's because if everyone's looking for value, it's hard to find.

I like that.

What?

What you just said. We may not always get along, but I have to tell you: You are light years ahead of that guy who talked to me last year, and he'd been at this for years. He sounded like one of those people who belonged to all sorts of leagues, even mail orders.

You've got something against mail orders?

I think I would if I belonged to one.

You've got something against the guy last year?

Not at all. One thing he did have was a sense of humor.

Anyway. The point of this is, in the 13th round, if not before, I realize there's been a depressing similarity between the way we've all assembled our teams, and it's going to continue. The Battle of Pasqua makes me think back to the early years when, about this time, we'd be getting George Wright and Greg Walker for nothing. Here I am in my eighth draft, and I'm not having any more fun.

It's not going to be like that in a start-up draft?

Ah, you're going to have it easy. Stop worrying about your start-up draft. A bunch of kids will dive in the pool, flail furiously, and not make it to the other side. With these prices, you'll coast up next to them, smile, and keep going. I'm worried about the people in the older leagues.

Not just your league?

No, it's everywhere. That's what all this information that I've gotten from Heath and from other people has been telling me.

Very quickly, I'll run through a draft for you. Make it two drafts, since they take the same space.

Can we make one of them a—

No, we can't! The reason I'm doing this at all is to show that it's by no means just an affliction of the American Dreams.

Let's take the Dirty Dozen—they of the camcorder—and (thanks to Frank Smith, who sent me this information) the Lone Star League. Massachusetts and Texas. Half a continent apart, meeting on the first Sunday after the season started, perhaps at the same hour.

We've already seen their freeze-list summaries (page 162). Even these are similar.

First round:

LONE STARS	PAID	EARNED	NET	DIRTY DOZEN	PAID	EARNED	NET
1 PARRISH	18	11	−7	CARTER	46	31	−15
2 PUCKETT	50	31	−19	MATTINGLY	36	31	−5
3 RYAN	12	25	13	G. BELL	32	27	−5
4 BRETT	31	23	−8	HENKE	38	33	−5
5 EVANS	30	25	−5	FISK	15	17	2
6 WHITT	9	13	4	BOGGS	28	19	−9
7 C. RIPKEN	26	21	−5	KEY	39	14	−25
8 MILACKI	10	10	0	LANSFORD	25	34	9
9 MOLITOR	31	32	1	MCGWIRE	42	22	−20
10 LANGSTON	17	7	−10	LANGSTON	28	7	−21
11 PARKER	12	21	9	TRAMMELL	31	9	−22
12 P. BRADLEY	17	22	5	SWINDELL	35	15	−20
AVERAGE	22	20	−2	AVERAGE	33	22	−11
TOTAL	263	241	−22	TOTAL	395	259	−136

The Dirty Dozen aren't flailing? They've already lost $136.
I know—shut up.

Nope; I'm looking for something in one of my drawers.
Trouble is, which one?

Here. Here's the first three rounds of their draft the year before; 1988, which—this is going to thrill you—was their first year:

1ST ROUND		2ND ROUND		3RD ROUND	
CLEMENS	47	TRAMMELL	45	RICE	20
G. BELL	50	NOKES	38	BOGGS	50
PUCKETT	44	FISK	20	B. JACKSON	25
R. HENDERSON	55	MOSEBY	47	ECKERSLEY	26
DW. EVANS	34	STEINBACH	25	TARTABULL	36
GLADDEN	22	DA. EVANS	23	HURST	22
CLANCY	23	B. RIPKEN	13	STRAKER	13
FERNANDEZ	35	WHITAKER	21	FRANCO	30
WINFIELD	30	MATTINGLY	50	REYNOLDS	36
CARTER	47	SVEUM	26	SURHOFF	25
O'BRIEN	38	WHITE	19	STIEB	21
MCGWIRE	40	JOYNER	41	CANSECO	37
AVERAGE	39	AVERAGE	31	AVERAGE	28

To be sure, their enthusiasm has been compounded by the rabbit ball in '87; they think more hitting makes hitting worth more. Nevertheless, look at the drop in salaries of good players who are being bid on again one year later. Mattingly down $14, Trammell down $14, Bell down $18, Boggs down $22.

The two second rounds last year:

LONE STARS		PAID	EARNED	NET	DIRTY DOZEN	PAID	EARNED	NET
13	P. O'BRIEN	19	13	−6	WORTHINGTON	7	13	6
14	BOGGS	27	19	−8	SABERHAGEN	21	45	24
15	PALMEIRO	19	15	−4	MORRIS	15	−7	−22
16	R. HENDERSON	56	48	−8	R. MURPHY	10	15	5
17	WINFIELD	17	0	−17	SURHOFF	13	13	0
18	LAUDNER	8	4	−4	SAX	25	37	12
19	BAINES	17	21	4	RIGHETTI	18	22	4
20	YETT	2	−7	−9	BLYLEVEN	8	29	21
21	LANSFORD	20	34	14	WHITAKER	16	24	8

LONE STARS		PAID	EARNED	NET	DIRTY DOZEN	PAID	EARNED	NET
22	D. STEWART	21	20	−1	JOYNER	26	21	−5
23	SAX	25	37	12	GRUBER	32	25	7
24	HRBEK	26	23	−3	STIEB	30	20	−10
	AVG	21	19	−2	AVG	18	21	3
	RUNNING TOT	520	468	−52	RUNNING TOT	616	516	−100

Now we see the Dirty Dozen buying Whitaker again, $5 less. Joyner, $14 less.

We see them nominating lesser players, cooling their jets and spending less, and turning a profit—already—in the second round.

The Lone Stars, meanwhile, are still poking along, getting 90 cents on their dollar. That is restraint, this early. They're playing all kinds of games you might be instructed by:

The rookie-pitcher gambit (Milacki): mild interest.

The who-thinks-Langston-*won't*-be-traded? gambit: not many people.

The position-scarcity gambit (Parrish, Laudner).

The batting-average gambit (Boggs).

The New Yankee gambit (Sax).

Somebody even threw Yett out into the room for one dollar.

And was relieved when someone else said $2?

That's one word for it.

Here are rounds three through five:

LONE STARS   DIRTY DOZEN

ROUND 3		PAID	EARNED	NET		PAID	EARNED	NET
25	RAWLEY	5	−10	−15	RICE	19	3	−16
26	C. DAVIS	21	23	2	D. HENDERSON	17	18	1
27	MORRIS	17	−7	−24	PALMEIRO	16	15	−1
28	GUBICZA	19	20	1	WILLIAMSON	5	19	14
29	FRANCO	28	33	5	BALLARD	3	12	9
30	ABBOTT	7	3	−4	GORDON	14	14	0
31	DOWNING	19	16	−3	GRIFFEY	11	22	11
32	WELCH	20	18	−2	BAINES	20	21	1
33	BUECHELE	13	11	−2	MOSEBY	33	16	−17

ROUND 3	PAID	EARNED	NET		PAID	EARNED	NET
34 MATTINGLY	31	31	0	BOYD	5	1	−4
35 KEY	21	14	−7	BLACK	7	16	9
36 WALKER	16	2	−14	REYNOLDS	23	22	−1
AVG	18	13	−5	AVG	14	15	1

ROUND 4	PAID	EARNED	NET		PAID	EARNED	NET
37 OROSCO	13	14	1	FERNANDEZ	13	21	8
38 TRAMMELL	29	9	−20	NOKES	13	8	−5
39 PETRY	1	−3	−4	SNYDER	27	12	−15
40 GORDON	16	14	−2	MOYER	9	−4	−13
41 LEE	10	7	−3	ATHERTON	5	−1	−6
42 RIGHETTI	29	22	−7	BANNISTER	12	−1	−13
43 BROWNE	5	19	14	GLADDEN	28	23	−5
44 LYNN	17	9	−8	WASHINGTON	12	18	6
45 MCCULLERS	7	1	−6	CALDERON	19	23	4
46 YOUNT	31	38	7	GEDMAN	8	0	−8
47 FELDER	1	14	13	ALEXANDER	9	−6	−15
48 MEDINA	18	1	−17	PEREZ	13	−7	−20
AVG	15	12	−3	AVG	14	7	−7

ROUND 5	PAID	EARNED	NET		PAID	EARNED	NET
49 A. DAVIS	30	26	−4	BARFIELD	22	17	−5
50 O. MCDOWELL	22	7	−15	HARPER	3	17	14
51 ESASKY	15	29	14	M. HALL	12	14	2
52 LOVULLO	9	−3	−12	LYNN	18	9	−9
53 JOSE	8	−1	−9	BROOKENS	8	2	−6
54 BARFIELD	21	17	−4	R. SMITH	3	6	3
55 B. JACKSON	32	38	6	P. O'BRIEN	19	13	−6
56 RICE	21	3	−18	SANTANA	1	0	−1
57 BURNS	7	22	15	ESPY	26	25	−1
58 TANANA	9	7	−2	F. WHITE	8	6	−2
59 WEGMAN	7	−9	−16	R. QUINONES	6	−1	−7
60 SABERHAGEN	20	45	25	MCCULLERS	15	1	−14
AVG	17	15	−2	AVG	12	9	−3
RUNNING TOT	1115	948	−167	RUNNING TOT	1098	890	−208

We now have enough players to begin comparing market prices. Saberhagen $21 and $20. Sax $25 and $25. O'Brien $19 and $19. Palmeiro $19 and $16. Morris $17 and $15. Rice $21 and $19. Is this game nasty or what? They paid less for him in Boston.

Key $21 and $39.

He'll be back in the pool. Two pools.

But I could easily have blurted the first figure for him. There's such a big up side. What really was the difference between betting on him and betting on Saberhagen at the start of last season? Whenever you have one of your fits of amnesia, I advise you to check the market prices at the front of the book.

After five rounds, each league has spent a little over $18 per player. The players the Lone Stars have bought will each earn about $16, the Dirty Dozen about $15.

LONE STARS   ## DIRTY DOZEN

ROUND 6		PAID	EARNED	NET		PAID	EARNED	NET
61	PRESLEY	13	7	−6	RYAN	15	25	10
62	SCHOFIELD	10	6	−4	WEISS	10	5	−5
63	M. STANLEY	3	2	−1	PARRISH	10	11	1
64	B. WITT	12	−8	−20	ESASKY	16	29	13
65	GAGNE	10	16	6	PRESLEY	10	7	−3
66	M. WITT	14	−1	−15	BOSIO	14	23	9
67	WHITAKER	17	24	7	WINFIELD	7	0	−7
68	LYONS	7	11	4	MANRIQUE	3	13	10
69	MINTON	5	15	10	CRIM	17	17	0
70	MORELAND	3	11	8	HUBBARD	3	1	−2
71	KELLY	7	30	23	C. FINLEY	5	21	16
72	HOUGH	21	−1	−22	RAWLEY	6	−10	−16
	AVG	10	9	−1	AVG	10	12	2

ROUND 7		PAID	EARNED	NET		PAID	EARNED	NET
73	WEISS	6	5	−1	BACKMAN	8	1	−7
74	LEIBRANDT	23	−11	−34	HAWKINS	9	−4	−13
75	R. MURPHY	10	15	5	STEINBACH	7	10	3

ROUND 7		PAID	EARNED	NET		PAID	EARNED	NET
76	HIGUERA	29	9	−20	WALKER	19	2	−17
77	FREEMAN	1	0	−1	FERMIN	5	2	−3
78	LIRIANO	5	16	11	MILACKI	5	10	5
79	FLETCHER	15	5	−10	COLES	10	12	2
80	COLES	17	12	−5	BICHETTE	5	2	−3
81	MOHORCIC	8	−1	−9	PHELPS	15	5	−10
82	W. WILSON	24	16	−8	BUSH	14	15	1
83	BLYLEVEN	7	28	21	BROWNE	7	19	12
84	BLACK	5	16	11	LAPOINT	8	−12	−20
	AVG	13	9	−3	AVG	9	5	−4

ROUND 8		PAID	EARNED	NET		PAID	EARNED	NET
85	CADARET	8	−3	−11	D. PARKER	17	21	4
86	FLANAGAN	11	3	−8	M. WITT	9	−1	−10
87	BROCK	9	14	5	B. BELL	5	−1	−6
88	DOPSON	3	5	2	P. BRADLEY	16	22	6
89	TRABER	6	3	−3	LOVULLO	7	−3	−10
90	CERUTTI	10	13	3	HILLEGAS	5	−2	−7
91	BERGMAN	1	8	7	G. OLSON	5	34	29
92	R. QUINONES	10	−1	−11	PHILLIPS	1	8	7
93	C. YOUNG	12	0	−12	PALL	13	10	−3
94	BOYD	4	1	−3	K. WILLIAMS	20	6	−14
95	F. WHITE	15	6	−9	GUANTE	13	3	−10
96	BANNISTER	13	−1	−14	HOLTON	9	−3	−12
	AVG	9	4	−5	AVG	10	8	−2
	RUNNING TOT	1489	1218	−271	RUNNING TOT	1446	1188	−258

More similar prices, even though players are spread far and wide by now. Ryan, in the first round of the Lone Stars, $12; in the sixth of the Dirty Dozen, $15. Whitaker in the second of the Dirty Dozen, $16; in the sixth of the Lone Stars, $17. Phil Bradley in the first round of the Lone Stars, $17; in the eighth of the Dirty Dozen, $16.

The average being spent per round is declining, because the quality is declining, but players aren't getting cheaper. If anything, the other way.

LONE STARS   ## DIRTY DOZEN

ROUND 9		PAID	EARNED	NET		PAID	EARNED	NET
97	WORTHINGTON	8	13	5	SHEETS	13	6	−7
98	HILLEGAS	8	−2	−10	DOPSON	3	5	2
99	SEARCY	1	−3	−4	J. MEYER	7	5	−2
100	LEITER	4	−4	−4	BALBONI	5	13	8
101	T. CASTILLO	1	−2	−3	JAVIER	5	8	3
102	HONEYCUTT	4	19	15	ROSENBERG	1	−7	1
103	GALLAGHER	4	8	4	OROSCO	7	14	7
104	GUANTE	4	3	−1	MOHORCIC	9	−1	−10
105	S. FINLEY	3	11	8	FLETCHER	14	5	−10
106	SLAUGHT	12	6	−6	REUSS	6	−4	−9
107	E. MARTINEZ	3	3	0	HANSON	4	11	−10
108	S. BRADLEY	3	7	4	MINTON	6	15	7
	AVG	5	5	0	AVG	7	5	−2

ROUND 10		PAID	EARNED	NET		PAID	EARNED	NET
109	HARPER	4	17	13	SCHMIDT	7	−8	−15
110	E. WILLIAMS	3	4	1	FARRELL	3	9	6
111	HORN	3	−1	−4	LARKIN	14	11	−3
112	SHERIDAN	4	4	0	EISENREICH	1	27	26
113	BACKMAN	10	1	−9	E. MARTINEZ	1	3	2
114	HOFFMAN	1	−1	−2	TRABER	10	3	−7
115	HOLTON	2	−3	−5	BROCK	7	14	7
116	GALLEGO	2	7	5	QUIRK	1	−1	−2
117	DEVEREAUX	3	19	16	KING	2	9	7
118	KREUTER	1	−1	−2	MEDINA	13	1	−12
119	BICHETTE	3	2	−1	MCMURTRY	4	−6	−10
120	PASQUA	3	10	7	YETT	5	−7	−12
	AVG	3	5	2	AVG	6	5	−1

ROUND 11		PAID	EARNED	NET		PAID	EARNED	NET
121	HEATH	1	13	12	NEWMAN	5	15	10
122	BEAN	1	−1	4	LEE	7	7	0
123	PHILLIPS	4	8	4	BERGMAN	3	8	5
124	MILLIGAN	1	15	−2	GALLAGHER	12	8	−4
125	SPIERS	5	9	−6	TANANA	5	7	2
126	CAMPBELL	1	−5	−16	TETTLETON	9	20	11

ROUND 11		PAID	EARNED	NET		PAID	EARNED	NET
127	BRENLY	1	−1	14	SVEUM	2	0	−2
128	K. BROWN	3	14	−2	C. BROWN	1	−1	−2
129	SVEUM	6	0	−5	BURNS	4	22	18
130	PALL	2	10	7	SCHROEDER	1	2	1
131	LAPOINT	4	−12	−2	FELDER	4	14	10
132	R. GONZALES	1	3	2	ORSULAK	10	14	4
	AVG	3	4	2	AVG	5	10	4
	RUNNING TOT	1613	1388	−225	RUNNING TOT	1651	1414	−237

Worthington, in the ninth round of the Lone Stars, $8. Way back in the second round of the Dirty Dozen, $7. It's uncanny. How can two leagues have such identical appraisals of a rookie? No matter when he comes up? Esasky $15 and $16. Just like Rice, just like Palmeiro, no local favoritism. And no wild gambles. And no one forgetting him, either.

Two leagues, meaning all 24 teams. It's like all the loose cannons of the past have rolled overboard.

By the end of round 11, both leagues are spending $5 or less per player, so we're almost to the crapshoot.

And yet there's still money for fierce struggles. Pall $13, Curt Young $12, Sheets $13, Backman $10, Medina $13.

In retrospect, we see terrific buys in these last three rounds: Balboni $5, Honeycutt $4, Hanson $4, Harper $4, Eisenreich $1. However, do you think these teams had that giddy feeling of having aced out as the gavel rang?

What it tells me is that people are working mighty hard at this game. Medina was much more worth fighting over than Brian Harper, and these leagues fought like alley cats ($18 for Medina in the Lone Star fourth round); and, well, it's just not fair.

You still with me?

Huh? Alley cats?

I was saying Rotisserie baseball is not fair anymore.

What do you mean?

I mean, people have gotten so skilled at this game that it's all luck.
    Let's look at the crapshoot.

LONE STARS	PAID	EARNED	NET		DIRTY DOZEN	PAID	EARNED	NET
133 NEWMAN	1	15	14		133 DUCEY	3	1	−2
134 BUCKNER	1	1	0		134 MORELAND	3	11	8
135 C. BROWN	1	1	−2		135 KUNKEL	3	9	6
136 MCLEMORE	3	4	1		136 BAUTISTA	3	−2	−5
137 HARNISCH	1	−5	−6		137 HONEYCUTT	3	19	16
138 MOYER	1	−4	−5		138 CERUTTI	11	13	2
139 ARMAS	1	8	7		139 SUNDBERG	1	−1	−2
140 HAWKINS	6	−4	−10		140 ARMAS	1	8	7
141 SUNDBERG	1	−1	−2		141 D. CLARK	2	5	3
142 MIRABELLA	1	−3	−4		142 MELVIN	2	3	1
143 GUETTERMAN	1	21	20		143 MIRABELLA	1	−3	−4
144 R. SMITH	1	6	5		144 ESPINOZA	1	8	7
145 JAVIER	1	8	7		145 GLEATON	1	−3	−4
146 B. STANLEY	1	−1	−2		146 HOFFMAN	1	−1	−2
147 LONG	1	2	1		147 MONTGOMERY	8	33	25
148 BRUMLEY	1	2	1		148 DEVEREAUX	2	19	17
149 G. WARD	1	7	6		149 S. BRADLEY	2	7	5
150 STOTTLEMYRE	1	2	1		150 BRENLY	1	−1	−2
151 B. RIPKEN	1	2	1		151 MACFARLANE	1	1	0
152 DUCEY	1	1	0		152 LAMP	1	15	14
153 AGUAYO	1	−1	−2		153 BIRKBECK	1	−7	−8
					154 BEAN	1	−1	−2
					155 M.STANLEY	1	2	1
					156 R. GONZALES	1	3	2
					157 LYONS	2	11	9
					158 PATTERSON	1	1	0
					159 BUCKNER	1	1	0
					160 WELLMAN	1	3	2
					161 JOSE	1	−1	−2
AVG	1	3	2		AVG	2	5	3
DRAFT TOT	1641	1447	−194		DRAFT TOT	1712	1567	−145

The most impressive thing in the entire draft has to be the 147th player of the Dirty Dozen. Montgomery $8! Someone else had $7 left. I feel sorry for the guy who bid that much money on the 147th player and didn't get him.

Did you notice the running total going into the crapshoot? Both teams were virtually identical. Inevitably they're getting some of the losses back at the end, but as late as the ninth round the Dirty Dozen lost $17. In the classic scenario, by the ninth round they have no choice but to underspend.

ROUNDS 9-11, DIRTY DOZEN 1988 DRAFT

9TH		10TH		11TH	
CANDELARIA	4	BROOKENS	5	BUECHELE	4
GRUBER	13	OWEN	6	ELLSWORTH	3
BENIQUEZ	3	RAY	5	LYNN	6
HENNEMAN	18	WELCH	24	CERUTTI	9
D. STEWART	20	YOUNT	10	J. DAVIS	3
JE. REED	9	ATHERTON	3	QUISENBERRY	7
LOMBARDOZZI	6	CALDERON	13	CAMPUSANO	5
REDUS	16	PAGLIARULO	13	MURRAY	11
POWER	5	BUICE	9	WILKINSON	7
NIEVES	8	WARD	7	SIERRA	19
TROUT	4	SWINDELL	6	LEITER	10
BLYLEVEN	6	HOUGH	10	LEIBRANDT	10

If he had the money left, Ronald Reagan would have bought Henneman, Ray, Yount, Murray, and Sierra at these prices. Alvin Davis in the 12th round goes for $12; Thigpen in the 13th for $10; Chili Davis in the 15th for $9; Molitor in the 16th for $11.

These are the players on their freeze lists this year. Ironically, they're the reason the Dirty Dozen opens up with guns blazing again in the first round. The freezes more than make up for the money that the auction loses.

So these were tough leagues?

Brutal leagues.

Neither league spends all its money, though, so the overall profits are misleading.

They waited for the Battle of Pasqua until even Pasqua was gone?

Some did. Some, it's more like disgust. Whoever bid $12 on Medina, and didn't get him, probably just couldn't crank it up for the next two players, McMurtry and Yett.

How'd the people finish who used your prices?

I'm not even saying they *used* them!

The ones who sent you stuff.

Oh, yeah. Well, let's see . . . Tom Leone finished second. And Frank Smith . . . second. So that's nice.

How do you finish first, that's what I want to know?

You'll finish first. Not that I'm rooting for you.

How come you're not rooting for me? You don't root for the people you brainwash?

Of course I do, I always do. You're the exception.
  Relax. I was just kidding. I'll root for you.
  But you're getting really hung up on this brainwashing business.

No I'm not.

Yes you are. First, many more people play the game than buy my book, and it's not the sort of book that gets shared.

Hell, no.

Second, you don't need the book to learn from the school of hard knocks. It's most unpleasant to run out of money too soon; do it a couple of times and you vow never again.
  Third, of course I'm trying to brainwash you. That's my job. I as much as said it in so many words in the masochists' notes, which I know you read; when you come right down to it, all these pricing theories are based on b.s.

Maybe there were too many words; I must have missed it.

Listen, Les Leopold tells me that my notion that the pitcher earns less than the hitter gets me booted right there from the ranks of respectable numbers crunchers. He says it's pure luck that my prices work to some extent. Maybe he's right. I've been lucky before in this game.

I've got a confession to make, too.

What's that?

I've played before.

Played . . . Rotisserie baseball before?

Uh-huh.

You've been sandbagging me all this time?

Uh-huh. It was my partner's idea. He said he knew you wouldn't talk to us if you knew.

You have a partner, too? Hold on a second . . .
    Is he—?

Uh-huh.

The guy *last year?* You bastards. Well, I'll be damned.
    What the hell were you lying for? Why waste each other's time, when we could have really gotten into some subtle points.

We missed some subtle points?

Sure did—why, I could write a whole Book for Masochists.

Maybe that's why we fibbed a little. See, basically we agree with you. Your prices don't work in the older leagues.

Did I say that?

Not in so many words, maybe, but the thing is, we think so, too. These older leagues have gotten too tough. So this year we're heading up a couple of new leagues; that part was true.

I'm sure it is.

We just want to see those prices kick in. For once.

Just disinterested curiosity, right? A scientific experiment. You two are too much. You both live right here in the city, don't you? I'll bet you're the ones who kept moving my book to the aerobics shelves. Each day I had to traipse all over town after you.

That wasn't us. At least it wasn't me.
    Aerobics shelves. I like that.

Hey.

Well, so long. Thanks for your time.

You're not welcome.

Um . . . One thing before I leave?

Now what?

I think I know what's happening to your decimals.

You *do?*

Think so. Could be in Lotus. I've had some problems myself in Lotus.

You have?

To be honest, they're more complicated, but if you want me to look around, maybe I can find out what's going on.

Pull up a chair. Rather, you take my chair. Here. This is really nice of you.

Shouldn't take too long. If we find it quick, I'll make a deal with you?

Anything.

I know you don't like to talk about the strike, but it's going to happen.

That's the deal? We have to talk about it?

No. You've got the new Elias figures, I see. The deal is, when we've done with this, we find out what each player earned month by month. What do you think? Good idea?

The dollar columns are rounded to the nearest whole number, but totals are based on sums with decimals. This explains discrepancies like Fitzgerald, below.

NL CATCHERS

	HR	RBI	SB	BA	AB	$HR	$RBI	$SB	$BA	$TOT
BIGGIO	13	60	21	.257	443	6	8	8	0	22
SANTIAGO	16	62	11	.236	462	8	8	4	−3	17
SCIOSCIA	10	44	0	.250	408	5	6	0	−1	10
PENA, T	4	37	5	.259	424	2	5	2	0	9
FITZGERALD	7	42	3	.238	290	3	5	1	−2	8
BERRYHILL	5	41	1	.257	334	2	5	0	0	8
LAVALLIERE	2	23	0	.316	190	1	3	0	3	7
SANTOVENIA	5	31	2	.250	304	2	4	1	−1	7
KENNEDY	5	34	1	.239	355	2	4	0	−2	6
SASSER	1	22	0	.291	182	0	3	0	2	5
OLIVER	3	23	0	.272	151	1	3	0	1	5
DAULTON	8	44	2	.201	368	4	6	1	−6	5
LYONS	3	27	0	.247	235	1	3	0	−1	4
TREVINO	2	16	0	.290	131	1	2	0	1	4
PARENT	7	21	1	.191	141	3	3	0	−3	4
WRONA	2	14	0	.283	92	1	2	0	1	3
GIRARDI	1	14	2	.248	157	0	2	1	0	3
LAKE	2	14	0	.252	155	1	2	0	0	3
REED	3	23	0	.223	287	1	3	0	−3	2
BILARDELLO	2	8	1	.225	80	1	1	0	−1	2
Average, top 20	5	30	3	.248	259	2	4	1	−1	6.64

	HR	RBI	SB	BA	AB	$HR	$RBI	$SB	$BA	$TOT
ORTIZ	1	22	2	.217	230	0	3	1	−3	2
ZEILE	1	8	0	.256	82	0	1	0	0	1
DEMPSEY	4	16	1	.179	151	2	2	0	−3	1
ALOMAR, S	1	6	0	.211	19	0	1	0	0	1
BATHE	0	6	0	.281	32	0	1	0	0	1
LOMBARDI	1	3	0	.229	48	0	0	0	0	0
MANWARING	0	18	2	.210	200	0	2	1	−3	0
MCGRIFF	0	2	0	.273	11	0	0	0	0	0
MIZEROCK	0	2	0	.222	27	0	0	0	0	0
PEVEY	0	3	0	.220	41	0	0	0	0	0
CABRERA (1b)	0	0	0	.214	14	0	0	0	0	0
MANN	0	1	0	.208	24	0	0	0	0	0
CARTER	2	15	0	.183	153	1	2	0	−3	0
DIAZ, B	1	8	0	.205	132	0	1	0	−2	0
RUSSELL	2	9	0	.182	159	1	1	0	−3	−1
DAVIS, J	4	19	0	.169	231	2	2	0	−6	−1
BENEDICT	1	6	0	.194	160	0	1	0	−3	−2
PAGNOZZI	0	3	0	.150	80	0	0	0	−2	−2

NL FIRST BASEMEN

	HR	RBI	SB	BA	AB	$HR	$RBI	$SB	$BA	$TOT
CLARK, W	23	111	8	.333	588	11	14	3	12	40
HAYES, V (of)	26	78	28	.259	540	13	10	11	0	34
GUERRERO	17	117	2	.311	570	8	15	1	8	32
DAVIS, G	34	89	4	.269	581	17	11	2	2	31
GRACE	13	79	14	.314	510	6	10	5	8	29
GALARRAGA	23	85	12	.257	572	11	11	5	0	27
CLARK, JA	26	94	6	.242	455	13	12	2	−2	25
MURRAY	20	88	7	.247	594	10	11	3	−1	22
JORDAN	12	75	4	.285	523	6	10	2	4	21
REDUS	6	33	25	.283	279	3	4	9	2	19
BENZINGER	17	76	3	.245	628	8	10	1	−2	17
MAGADAN (3b)	4	41	1	.286	374	2	5	0	3	11
PERRY	4	21	10	.252	266	2	3	4	0	8
JOHNSON, W	2	17	1	.272	114	1	2	0	0	4
WALLING	1	11	0	.304	79	0	1	0	1	3
Average, top 15	15	68	8	.276	445	7	9	3	2	21.55
HERNANDEZ, K	4	19	0	.233	215	2	2	0	−1	3
DISTEFANO	2	15	1	.247	154	1	2	0	0	3
STEPHENSON	2	2	1	.237	38	1	0	0	0	1
NELSON	3	7	1	.195	82	1	1	0	−1	1
SPILLMAN	0	3	0	.278	36	0	0	0	0	1
RYAL (of)	0	5	0	.242	33	0	1	0	0	1
BREAM	0	4	0	.222	36	0	1	0	0	0

NL THIRD BASEMEN

	HR	RBI	SB	BA	AB	$HR	$RBI	$SB	$BA	$TOT
BONILLA	24	86	8	.281	616	12	11	3	4	30
WALLACH	13	77	3	.277	573	6	10	1	3	20
PENDLETON	13	74	9	.264	613	6	10	3	1	20
ROBERTS (of)	3	25	21	.301	329	1	3	8	4	17
CAMINITI	10	72	4	.255	585	5	9	2	0	15
SABO	6	29	14	.260	304	3	4	5	0	12
SALAZAR	9	34	1	.282	326	4	4	0	2	11
HAMILTON	12	56	0	.245	548	6	7	0	−2	11
HAYES, C	8	43	3	.257	304	4	6	1	0	11
RILES	7	40	0	.278	302	3	5	0	2	10
READY (of)	8	26	4	.264	254	4	3	2	0	9
LAW	7	42	2	.235	408	3	5	1	−2	7
EVANS (1b)	11	39	0	.207	276	5	5	0	−4	7
GANT	9	25	9	.177	260	4	3	3	−6	5
LITTON	4	17	0	.252	143	2	2	0	0	4
Average, top 15	10	46	5	.259	389	5	6	2	0	12.70
OBERKFELL	2	17	0	.269	156	1	2	0	1	4
KING	5	19	4	.195	215	2	2	2	−4	3
WILKERSON	1	10	4	.244	160	0	1	2	−1	3
PAGLIARULO	3	14	2	.196	148	1	2	1	−3	1
FLANNERY	0	8	2	.231	130	0	1	1	−1	1
WHITED	1	4	1	.162	74	0	1	0	−2	−1
MADISON	1	7	0	.173	98	0	1	0	−2	−1

NL SECOND BASEMEN

	HR	RBI	SB	BA	AB	$HR	$RBI	$SB	$BA	$TOT
SANDBERG	30	76	15	.290	606	15	10	6	5	35
ALOMAR, R	7	56	42	.295	623	3	7	16	6	33
JEFFERIES (3b)	12	56	21	.258	508	6	7	8	0	21
THOMPSON, R	13	50	12	.241	547	6	6	5	−2	15
DORAN	8	58	22	.219	507	4	7	8	−5	15
HERR	2	37	10	.287	561	1	5	4	4	14
OQUENDO	1	48	3	.291	556	0	6	1	5	13
TREADWAY	8	40	3	.277	473	4	5	1	3	13
RANDOLPH	2	36	7	.282	549	1	5	3	4	12
QUINONES, L (3b)	12	34	2	.244	340	6	4	1	−1	10
HUDLER (of)	6	13	15	.245	155	3	2	6	−1	10
LIND	2	48	15	.232	578	1	6	6	−4	9
HARRIS, L (3b, of)	3	26	14	.236	335	1	3	5	−2	8
GARCIA, D	3	18	5	.271	203	1	2	2	1	6
FOLEY	7	39	2	.229	375	3	5	1	−3	6
TEUFEL (1b)	2	15	1	.256	219	1	2	0	0	3
Average, top 15	6	38	12	.260	435	3	5	4	0	12.53
MILLER, K	1	7	6	.231	143	0	1	2	−1	3
JONES, TI (ss)	0	7	1	.293	75	0	1	0	1	2
OESTER	1	14	1	.246	305	0	2	0	−1	2
LEMKE	2	10	0	.182	55	1	1	0	−1	1
SHARPERSON	0	5	0	.250	28	0	1	0	0	1
LOMBARDOZZI	1	3	0	.216	37	0	0	0	0	0
BOOKER	0	0	0	.250	8	0	0	0	0	0
MCKNIGHT	0	0	0	.250	12	0	0	0	0	0
BARRETT	0	1	0	.222	27	0	0	0	0	0
NOBOA	0	1	0	.227	44	0	0	0	0	0

NL SHORTSTOPS

	HR	RBI	SB	BA	AB	$HR	$RBI	$SB	$BA	$TOT
JOHNSON, H (3b)	36	101	41	.287	571	18	13	16	4	51
DUNSTON	9	60	19	.278	471	4	8	7	3	22
SMITH, O	2	50	29	.273	593	1	6	11	2	21
THON	15	60	6	.271	435	7	8	2	2	19
LARKIN	4	36	10	.342	325	2	5	4	7	18
BLAUSER	12	46	5	.270	456	6	6	2	2	15
WILLIAMS, M (3b)	18	50	1	.202	292	9	6	0	−4	11
ELSTER	10	55	4	.231	458	5	7	2	−3	10
RAMIREZ	6	54	3	.246	537	3	7	1	−2	9
THOMAS, A	13	57	3	.213	554	6	7	1	−6	8
TEMPLETON	6	40	1	.255	506	3	5	0	0	8
DUNCAN	3	21	9	.248	258	1	3	3	−1	7
OWEN	6	41	3	.233	437	3	5	1	−3	7
BELL, J	2	27	5	.258	271	1	3	2	0	6
GRIFFIN	0	29	10	.247	506	0	4	4	−1	6
Average, top 15	9	48	10	.257	445	5	6	4	0	14.61
JELTZ (2b, 3b)	4	25	4	.243	263	2	3	2	−1	6
YELDING	0	9	11	.233	90	0	1	4	−1	5
RAMOS (2b)	1	19	1	.263	179	0	2	0	0	4
URIBE	1	30	6	.221	453	0	4	2	−4	2
QUINONES, R	3	29	0	.209	225	1	4	0	−3	2
ANDERSON, D	1	14	2	.229	140	0	2	1	−1	2
BELLIARD	0	8	5	.214	154	0	1	2	−2	1
CORA	0	1	1	.316	19	0	0	0	0	1
REYNOLDS, C (2b)	2	14	1	.201	189	1	2	0	−3	0
GREEN	0	0	0	.259	27	0	0	0	0	0
JURAK	0	1	0	.238	42	0	0	0	0	0
VIZCANO	0	0	0	.200	10	0	0	0	0	0
RICHARDSON	2	11	1	.168	125	1	1	0	−3	0

NL OUTFIELDERS

	HR	RBI	SB	BA	AB	SHR	SRBI	SSB	SBA	STOT
MITCHELL	47	125	3	.291	543	23	16	1	5	45
DAVIS, E	34	101	21	.281	462	17	13	8	3	40
GWYNN, T	4	62	40	.336	604	2	8	15	12	37
SMITH, L	21	79	25	.315	482	10	10	9	7	37
RAINES	9	60	41	.286	517	4	8	16	4	32
MCREYNOLDS	22	85	15	.272	545	11	11	6	2	29
COLEMAN	2	28	65	.254	563	1	4	25	0	29
BONDS	19	58	32	.248	580	9	7	12	−1	28
O'NEILL	15	74	20	.276	428	7	10	8	2	27
THOMPSON, M	4	68	27	.290	545	2	9	10	5	26
SAMUEL	11	48	42	.235	532	5	6	16	−3	24
STRAWBERRY	29	77	11	.225	476	14	10	4	−4	24
DAWSON	21	77	8	.252	416	10	10	3	0	23
BUTLER	4	36	31	.283	594	2	5	12	4	22
WALTON	5	46	24	.293	475	2	6	9	4	22
SMITH, D	9	52	9	.324	343	4	7	3	6	21
BRUNANSKY	20	85	5	.239	556	10	11	2	−3	20
BROOKS	14	70	6	.268	542	7	9	2	1	20
REYNOLDS, RJ	6	48	22	.270	363	3	6	8	1	19
MURPHY, DA	20	84	3	.228	574	10	11	1	−4	17
DYKSTRA	7	32	30	.237	511	3	4	11	−3	16
BASS	5	44	11	.300	313	2	6	4	4	16
MCDOWELL	7	24	15	.304	280	3	3	6	4	16
MARTINEZ, DA	3	27	23	.274	361	1	3	9	2	15
MCCLENDON (1b)	12	40	6	.286	259	6	5	2	2	15
WILSON, G	11	64	1	.266	432	5	8	0	1	15
KRUK	8	44	3	.300	357	4	6	1	4	15
VAN SLYKE	9	53	16	.237	476	4	7	6	−2	15
JAMES, C	13	65	5	.243	482	6	8	2	−2	15
YOUNG, G	0	38	34	.233	533	0	5	13	−3	14

	HR	RBI	SB	BA	AB	$HR	$RBI	$SB	$BA	$TOT
HATCHER	4	51	24	.231	481	2	7	9	−3	14
NIXON, O	0	21	37	.217	258	0	3	14	−3	14
ROOMES	7	34	12	.263	315	3	4	5	1	13
MARSHALL	11	42	2	.260	377	5	5	1	0	12
GRIFFEY	8	30	4	.263	236	4	4	2	0	10
GIBSON	9	28	12	.213	253	4	4	5	−3	9
WYNNE	7	39	6	.243	342	3	5	2	−1	9
WEBSTER	3	19	14	.257	272	1	2	5	0	9
PUHL	0	27	9	.271	354	0	3	3	1	8
WINNINGHAM	3	13	14	.251	251	1	2	5	0	8
GONZALES	3	18	9	.268	261	1	2	3	1	8
CARREON	6	16	2	.308	133	3	2	1	2	8
MALDONADO	9	41	4	.217	345	4	5	2	−4	7
DANIELS	4	17	9	.246	171	2	2	3	−1	7
HATCHER, B	2	25	1	.295	224	1	3	0	2	7
DAVIS, M	5	19	6	.249	173	2	2	2	0	7
NIXON, D	1	15	10	.265	166	0	2	4	0	7
MURPHY, DW	9	27	0	.218	156	4	3	0	−2	6
STUBBS	4	15	3	.291	103	2	2	1	1	6
GREGG (1b)	6	23	3	.243	276	3	3	1	−1	6
Average, top 50	10	46	16	.264	386	5	6	6	1	17.39
MCGEE	3	17	8	.236	199	1	2	3	−1	6
MARTINEZ, C (1b)	6	39	0	.221	267	3	5	0	−3	5
CANGELOSI	0	9	11	.219	160	0	1	4	−2	4
JACKSON, D	4	20	1	.218	170	2	3	0	−2	3
MORRIS	2	14	1	.239	117	1	2	0	−1	3

CONTINUED ON NEXT PAGE

	HR	RBI	SB	BA	AB	$HR	$RBI	$SB	$BA	$TOT
FORD	1	13	5	.218	142	0	2	2	−2	3
BERROA	2	9	0	.265	136	1	1	0	0	2
SHERIDAN	3	14	4	.205	161	1	2	2	−2	2
JONES, R	2	4	1	.290	31	1	1	0	0	2
MEADOWS	3	10	1	.176	51	1	1	0	−1	2
YOUNGBLOOD	3	13	0	.212	118	1	2	0	−2	2
ANTHONY	4	7	0	.180	61	2	1	0	−1	2
COLLINS	0	7	3	.236	106	0	1	1	−1	1
JUSTICE	1	3	2	.235	51	0	0	1	0	1
GRISSOM	1	2	1	.257	74	0	0	0	0	1
WETHERBY	1	7	1	.208	48	0	1	0	−1	1
THORNTON	0	1	2	.308	13	0	0	1	0	1
ALDRETE	1	12	1	.221	136	0	2	0	−1	1
GWYNN, C	0	7	1	.235	68	0	1	0	0	1
ABNER	2	14	1	.176	102	1	2	0	−2	1
DASCENZO	1	12	6	.165	139	0	2	2	−4	1
CLARK, JE	1	7	0	.195	41	0	1	0	−1	1
DAVIDSON	1	5	1	.200	65	0	1	0	−1	0
HUFF	1	2	0	.200	25	0	0	0	0	0
BLOCKER	0	1	1	.226	31	0	0	0	0	0
VARSHO	0	6	3	.184	87	0	1	1	−2	0
GROSS	0	4	0	.200	75	0	1	0	−1	−1
DERNIER	1	13	4	.171	187	0	2	2	−4	−1
BEAN	0	3	0	.197	71	0	0	0	−1	−1
SHELBY	1	12	10	.183	345	0	2	4	−7	−1

NL PITCHERS

	W	SV	ERA	RTO	IP	$W	$S	$ERA	$RTO	$TOT
DAVIS, M	4	44	1.85	9.42	93	3	36	5	4	48
HOWELL, J	5	28	1.58	9.26	80	3	23	5	4	35
BURKE	9	28	2.55	9.57	85	6	23	2	3	35
LANDRUM	2	26	1.67	9.78	81	1	21	5	3	31
WILLIAMS, M	4	36	2.76	13.56	82	3	29	2	−4	30
MYERS	7	24	2.35	10.89	84	5	20	3	1	28
FRANCO	4	32	3.12	12.61	81	3	26	1	−2	27
MCDOWELL, R	4	23	1.96	11.45	92	3	19	5	0	26
GARRELTS	14	0	2.28	9.08	193	10	0	7	9	25
SMITH, D	3	25	2.64	10.55	58	2	20	2	1	25
BEDROSIAN	3	23	2.87	10.10	85	2	19	1	2	25
LEFFERTS	2	20	2.69	9.67	107	1	16	3	4	24
SCOTT	20	0	3.10	9.51	229	14	0	2	8	24
DARWIN	11	7	2.36	9.22	122	8	6	4	6	23
WHITSON	16	0	2.66	9.75	227	11	0	5	7	23
DELEON	16	0	3.05	9.31	245	11	0	2	10	23
HERSHISER	15	0	2.31	10.62	257	10	0	8	3	22
FERNANDEZ	14	0	2.83	9.52	219	10	0	4	8	21
HURST	15	0	2.69	10.30	245	10	0	5	5	20
BELCHER	15	1	2.82	10.25	230	10	1	4	5	20
WORRELL	3	20	2.96	11.85	52	2	16	1	−1	19
SMILEY	12	0	2.81	9.77	205	8	0	4	6	18
LANCASTER	4	8	1.36	9.29	73	3	7	5	3	18
DRABEK	14	0	2.80	10.46	244	10	0	4	4	18
DESHAIES	15	0	2.91	10.33	226	10	0	3	4	18
SMITH, B	10	0	2.84	9.64	216	7	0	4	7	18
DIBBLE	10	2	2.09	9.18	99	7	2	4	5	18
REUSCHEL	17	0	2.94	10.76	208	12	0	3	2	17
BOEVER	4	21	3.94	12.24	82	3	17	−2	−2	17
SMOLTZ	12	0	2.94	10.04	208	8	0	3	5	16
MAGRANE	18	0	2.91	11.16	235	12	0	3	1	16
HARRIS, GW	8	6	2.60	10.53	135	5	5	4	2	16
ANDERSEN	4	3	1.54	8.93	88	3	2	6	5	16
MORGAN	8	0	2.54	9.61	153	5	0	4	6	15
MADDUX, G	19	0	2.95	11.48	238	13	0	3	−1	15

CONTINUED ON NEXT PAGE

	W	SV	ERA	RTO	IP	SW	SS	SERA	SRTO	STOT
MARTINEZ, DE	16	0	3.18	10.71	232	11	0	1	3	15
PARRETT	12	6	2.98	11.41	106	8	5	1	0	14
DAYLEY	4	12	2.87	11.11	75	3	10	1	0	14
BIELECKI	18	0	3.14	11.36	212	12	0	2	0	14
PENA	4	5	2.13	9.47	76	3	4	3	3	13
DIPINO	9	0	2.45	9.48	88	6	0	3	4	13
ROBINSON, D	12	0	3.43	10.10	197	8	0	0	5	13
LANGSTON	12	0	2.39	11.77	177	8	0	6	−2	12
CONE	14	0	3.52	10.53	220	10	0	−1	3	12
SUTCLIFFE	16	0	3.66	10.65	229	11	0	−2	3	12
GLAVINE	14	0	3.68	10.26	186	10	0	−2	4	12
BROWNING	15	0	3.39	10.99	250	10	0	0	1	12
PEREZ, P	9	0	3.31	10.12	198	6	0	0	5	11
GOODEN	9	1	2.89	10.65	118	6	1	2	2	11
HOWELL, K	12	0	3.44	10.63	204	8	0	−1	3	10
QUISENBERRY	3	6	2.64	10.57	78	2	5	2	1	10
KIPPER	3	4	2.93	9.54	83	2	3	1	3	10
CHARLTON	8	0	2.93	10.10	95	5	0	1	3	10
GRANT	8	2	3.33	10.60	116	5	2	0	2	9
LACOSS	10	6	3.17	12.45	150	7	5	1	−4	9
PORTUGAL	7	0	2.75	10.67	108	5	0	2	2	9
STANTON	0	7	1.50	9.38	24	0	6	2	1	9
COSTELLO	5	3	3.32	9.82	62	3	2	0	2	8
ACKER	0	2	2.67	9.58	98	0	2	2	4	8
DARLING	14	0	3.52	11.76	217	10	0	−1	−2	6
TERRY	8	2	3.57	11.20	149	5	2	−1	0	6
HEATON	6	0	3.05	11.12	147	4	0	2	1	6
COMBS	4	0	2.10	9.78	39	3	0	2	2	6
BAIR	2	1	2.27	10.69	67	1	1	3	1	6
WETTELAND	5	1	3.77	10.08	103	3	1	−1	3	6
MARTINEZ	6	0	3.19	10.95	99	4	0	1	1	6
OJEDA	13	0	3.47	12.05	192	9	0	−1	−3	5
SCHIRALDI	6	4	3.51	12.15	100	4	3	−1	−2	5
RIJO	7	0	2.84	12.08	111	5	0	2	−2	5
POWER	7	0	3.71	10.86	97	5	0	−1	1	5

	W	SV	ERA	RTO	IP	SW	SS	SERA	SRTO	STOT
VIOLA	5	0	3.38	10.76	85	3	0	0	1	5
PERRY	0	1	1.77	9.84	36	0	1	2	1	4
SANDERSON	11	0	3.94	11.44	146	8	0	−3	0	4
BENES	6	0	3.51	11.07	67	4	0	0	0	4
CLARY	4	0	3.15	11.10	109	3	0	1	1	4
COOK	7	0	3.72	11.01	121	5	0	−2	1	4
ALVAREZ	3	2	2.86	12.16	50	2	2	1	−1	4
PATTERSON	4	1	4.05	10.47	27	3	1	−1	1	4
AGOSTO	4	1	2.93	12.25	83	3	1	1	−2	3
EAVE	2	0	1.31	11.76	21	1	0	2	0	3
ROBINSON, R	5	0	3.35	11.66	83	3	0	0	−1	3
CAMACHO	3	0	2.76	11.57	16	2	0	0	0	2
DRAVECKY	2	0	3.46	8.31	13	1	0	0	1	2
HAMMAKER	6	0	3.76	11.86	77	4	0	−1	−1	2
LEARY	8	0	3.52	11.87	207	5	0	−1	−2	2
ALDRICH	1	0	2.19	9.49	12	1	0	1	1	2
WILSON, S	6	2	4.20	11.98	86	4	2	−3	−1	2
KRUKOW	4	0	3.98	11.51	43	3	0	−1	0	2
SEARAGE	3	0	3.53	11.86	36	2	0	0	0	1
TEWKSBURY	1	0	3.30	10.50	30	1	0	0	1	1
Average, top 90	8.0	4.9	2.98	10.61	127	5	4	2	2	13.22
EASLEY	1	1	4.38	10.95	12	1	1	0	0	1
FROWIRTH	1	0	3.59	10.63	63	1	0	−1	1	1
INNIS	0	0	3.18	10.44	40	0	0	0	1	1
GREENE	1	0	4.11	9.58	26	1	0	−1	1	1
CARPENTER	4	0	3.18	12.71	68	3	0	0	−2	1
CLEMENTS	4	0	3.92	12.46	39	3	0	−1	−1	1
MUSSELMAN	3	0	3.08	14.01	26	2	0	0	−2	1
BLANKENSHIP	0	0	1.69	10.13	5	0	0	0	0	1
RODRIGUEZ	1	0	4.15	12.46	4	1	0	0	0	1
MACHADO	0	0	3.27	9.82	11	0	0	0	1	1

CONTINUED ON NEXT PAGE

	W	SV	ERA	RTO	IP	$W	$S	$ERA	$RTO	$TOT
KRAMER	5	2	3.96	12.21	111	3	2	−2	−2	1
EICHHORN	5	0	4.35	11.72	68	3	0	−2	−1	0
HENRY	0	1	4.27	12.09	13	0	1	0	0	0
LEACH	0	0	4.22	9.70	21	0	0	−1	1	0
TATE	0	0	3.38	10.15	3	0	0	0	0	0
SMITH, Z	1	2	3.49	11.82	147	1	2	−1	−2	0
CANDELARIA	0	0	3.31	11.57	16	0	0	0	0	0
GOTT	0	0	0.00	27.27	1	0	0	0	0	0
MAHLER	9	0	3.83	11.95	221	6	0	−3	−3	0
BIRTSAS	2	1	3.75	12.27	70	1	1	−1	−1	0
VALENZUELA	10	0	3.43	12.95	197	7	0	0	−7	0
ROESLER	0	0	3.96	11.16	25	0	0	−1	0	0
TERRELL	5	0	4.01	11.68	123	3	0	−3	−1	0
AASE	1	2	3.94	12.44	59	1	2	−1	−1	0
WILSON, T	2	0	4.35	11.90	39	1	0	−1	0	−1
BOOKER	0	0	4.26	11.84	19	0	0	−1	0	−1
BRANTLEY	7	0	4.07	12.76	97	5	0	−2	−3	−1
ASSENMACHER	3	0	3.99	11.97	77	2	0	−2	−1	−1
TUDOR	0	0	3.14	14.45	14	0	0	0	−1	−1
PICO	3	2	3.77	12.91	91	2	2	−1	−3	−1
MEDVIN	0	0	5.69	15.64	6	0	0	−1	0	−1
TAYLOR	1	0	5.07	16.04	11	1	0	−1	−1	−1
CANO	1	0	5.09	12.13	23	1	0	−2	0	−1
MEYER	0	1	4.50	14.50	18	0	1	−1	−1	−1
ONTIVEROS	2	0	3.82	14.38	31	1	0	−1	−2	−1
BELINDA	0	0	6.10	13.07	10	0	0	−1	0	−1
SHOW	8	0	4.23	12.87	106	5	0	−3	−4	−1
HESKETH	6	3	5.77	14.90	48	4	2	−4	−4	−2
CREWS	0	1	3.21	13.43	62	0	1	0	−3	−2
PULEO	1	0	4.66	13.03	29	1	0	−1	−1	−2
MCCAMENT	1	0	3.93	13.50	37	1	0	−1	−2	−2
SMITH, W	0	0	3.75	14.25	24	0	0	0	−2	−2
ARMSTRONG	2	0	4.64	12.87	43	1	0	−2	−1	−2
DOWNS	4	0	4.79	11.76	83	3	0	−4	−1	−2
FREY	3	0	5.49	16.88	21	2	0	−2	−3	−2

	W	SV	ERA	RTO	IP	SW	SS	SERA	SRTO	STOT
GARDNER	0	0	5.13	12.65	26	0	0	−2	−1	−2
WALK	13	0	4.41	12.54	196	9	0	−7	−5	−3
SCHATZEDER	4	1	4.45	14.61	57	3	1	−2	−4	−3
MADDEN	2	0	7.07	19.29	14	1	0	−2	−3	−3
LILLIQUIST	8	0	3.97	12.82	166	5	0	−3	−5	−3
SCHULZE	2	0	5.55	16.28	24	1	0	−2	−3	−3
GROSS	11	0	4.38	12.34	201	8	0	−7	−4	−3
MADDUX, M	1	1	5.15	13.61	44	1	1	−3	−2	−4
MCGAFFIGAN	3	2	4.68	13.80	75	2	2	−4	−4	−4
GRIMSLEY	1	0	5.89	18.66	18	1	0	−2	−3	−4
MADRID	1	0	5.47	16.79	25	1	0	−2	−3	−4
RASMUSSEN	10	0	4.26	12.84	184	7	0	−6	−6	−5
HEINKEL	1	0	5.81	16.07	26	1	0	−2	−3	−5
REED	1	0	5.60	12.02	55	1	0	−5	−1	−5
FISHER	0	1	7.94	18.53	17	0	1	−3	−3	−5
HILL	7	0	3.80	13.04	197	5	0	−3	−7	−5
TEKULVE	0	1	5.02	13.67	52	0	1	−3	−3	−5
KILGUS	6	2	4.39	13.16	146	4	2	−5	−6	−5
MCWILLIAMS	2	0	4.10	12.83	121	1	0	−3	−4	−6
ROBINSON, J	7	4	4.59	14.01	141	5	3	−6	−8	−6
SEBRA	2	1	5.21	15.13	55	1	1	−4	−5	−6
SCUDDER	4	0	4.49	13.64	100	3	0	−4	−5	−6
LEIPER	0	0	5.02	18.84	29	0	0	−2	−5	−7
HORTON	0	0	4.85	13.19	72	0	0	−4	−3	−7
RHODEN	2	0	4.28	13.87	97	1	0	−3	−5	−7
YOUMANS	1	0	5.70	15.82	43	1	0	−4	−4	−7
SMITH, P	5	0	4.75	12.74	142	3	0	−7	−4	−8
MULHOLLAND	4	0	4.92	13.50	115	3	0	−6	−5	−9
CLANCY	7	0	5.08	13.53	147	5	0	−9	−7	−11
RUFFIN	6	0	4.44	15.33	126	4	0	−5	−11	−12
JACKSON, D	6	0	5.60	13.93	116	4	0	−9	−7	−12
FORSCH	4	0	5.32	14.87	108	3	0	−7	−8	−13
CARMAN	5	0	5.24	14.34	149	3	0	−10	−10	−16
KNEPPER	7	0	5.13	14.45	165	5	0	−10	−11	−16

AL CATCHERS

	HR	RBI	SB	BA	AB	$HR	$RBI	$SB	$BA	$TOT
TETTLETON	26	65	3	.258	411	12	8	1	−1	20
HARPER	8	57	2	.325	385	4	7	1	6	17
FISK	13	68	1	.293	375	6	8	0	3	17
WHITT	11	53	5	.262	385	5	6	2	0	13
SURHOFF	5	55	14	.248	436	2	6	6	−2	13
HEATH	10	43	7	.263	396	5	5	3	0	13
PARRISH	17	50	1	.238	433	8	6	0	−3	11
STEINBACH	7	42	1	.273	454	3	5	0	1	10
GEREN	9	27	0	.288	205	4	3	0	1	9
NOKES	9	39	1	.250	268	4	5	0	−1	8
BOONE	1	43	3	.274	405	0	5	1	1	8
BRADLEY, S	3	37	1	.274	270	1	4	0	1	7
PETRALLI	4	23	0	.304	184	2	3	0	2	7
SLAUGHT	5	38	1	.251	350	2	4	0	−1	6
CERONE	4	48	0	.243	296	2	6	0	−2	6
O'BRIEN, C	6	35	0	.234	188	3	4	0	−2	5
BORDERS	3	29	2	.257	241	1	3	1	0	5
VALLE	7	34	0	.237	316	3	4	0	−2	5
KARKOVICE	3	24	0	.264	182	1	3	0	0	4
LAUDNER	6	27	1	.222	239	3	3	0	−3	4
MELVIN	1	32	1	.241	278	0	4	0	−2	3
HASSEY	5	23	1	.228	268	2	3	0	−3	3
ALLANSON	3	17	4	.232	323	1	2	2	−3	2
SCHROEDER	6	15	0	.203	138	3	2	0	−2	2
Average, top 24	7	39	2	.259	309	3	5	1	0	8.27

	HR	RBI	SB	BA	AB	SHR	SRBI	SSB	SBA	STOT
MARZANO	1	3	0	.444	18	0	0	0	1	2
STANLEY, M	1	11	1	.246	122	0	1	0	−1	2
MACFARLANE	2	19	0	.223	157	1	2	0	−2	1
DORSETT	0	4	0	.364	22	0	0	0	1	1
SKINNER	1	13	1	.230	178	0	2	0	−2	1
SALAS	2	7	0	.221	77	1	1	0	−1	1
MERULLO	1	8	0	.222	81	0	1	0	−1	0
WEBSTER	0	1	0	.300	20	0	0	0	0	0
PALACIOS	1	8	0	.170	47	0	1	0	−1	0
GEDMAN	4	16	0	.212	260	2	2	0	−4	0
ORTON	0	4	0	.179	39	0	0	0	−1	0
QUIRK	0	10	0	.176	85	0	1	0	−2	−1
KREUTER	5	9	0	.152	158	2	1	0	−5	−1

AL FIRST BASEMEN

	HR	RBI	SB	BA	AB	$HR	$RBI	$SB	$BA	$TOT
MATTINGLY	23	113	3	.303	631	10	13	1	6	31
MCGRIFF	36	92	7	.269	551	16	11	3	1	31
ESASKY	30	108	1	.277	564	14	13	0	2	29
DAVIS, A	21	95	0	.305	498	10	11	0	5	26
HRBEK	25	84	3	.272	375	11	10	1	1	23
BRETT	12	80	14	.282	457	5	9	6	2	23
MCGWIRE	33	95	1	.231	490	15	11	0	—4	22
JOYNER	16	79	3	.282	593	7	9	1	3	21
MILLIGAN	12	45	9	.268	365	5	5	4	0	15
PALMEIRO	8	64	4	.275	559	4	8	2	2	15
BROCK	12	52	6	.265	373	5	6	3	0	14
O'BRIEN, P	12	55	3	.259	555	5	6	1	—1	13
BALBONI	17	59	0	.237	300	8	7	0	—2	13
KITTLE	11	37	0	.302	169	5	4	0	2	11
MORELAND	6	45	3	.278	425	3	5	1	1	11
LARKIN (of)	6	46	5	.267	446	3	5	2	0	11
BERGMAN	7	37	1	.268	385	3	4	0	0	8
WARD (of)	9	30	1	.253	292	4	4	0	—1	7
Average, top 18	16	68	4	.273	446	7	8	2	1	18.01
DAUGHERTY	1	10	2	.302	106	0	1	1	1	4
TRABER	4	26	4	.209	234	2	3	2	—3	3
FRANCONA	3	23	2	.232	233	1	3	1	—2	3
WALKER, G	5	26	0	.210	233	2	3	0	—3	2
MORMAN	0	8	1	.224	58	0	1	0	—1	1
BUCKNER	1	16	1	.216	176	0	2	0	—2	1
DE LOS SANTOS	0	6	0	.253	87	0	1	0	0	0
CANALE	1	3	0	.192	26	0	0	0	—1	0
SORRENTO	0	1	0	.238	21	0	0	0	0	0
ROBIDOUX	0	1	0	.128	39	0	0	0	—1	—1
LOVULLO	1	4	0	.115	87	0	0	0	—4	—3

AL THIRD BASEMEN

	HR	RBI	SB	BA	AB	$HR	$RBI	$SB	$BA	$TOT
LANSFORD	2	52	37	.336	551	1	6	17	10	34
MOLITOR	11	56	27	.315	615	5	7	12	8	32
GRUBER	18	73	10	.290	545	8	9	5	4	25
BOGGS	3	54	2	.330	621	1	6	1	10	19
GAETTI	19	75	6	.251	498	9	9	3	−2	19
SEITZER	4	48	17	.281	597	2	6	8	3	18
JACOBY	13	64	2	.272	519	6	8	1	1	15
WORTHINGTON	15	70	1	.247	497	7	8	0	−2	13
COLES (of)	10	59	5	.252	535	5	7	2	−2	12
MARTINEZ, C (1b)	5	32	4	.300	350	2	4	2	3	11
BUECHELE	16	59	1	.235	486	7	7	0	−4	11
HOWELL	20	52	0	.228	474	9	6	0	−4	11
PRESLEY	12	41	0	.236	390	5	5	0	−3	7
VELARDE	2	11	0	.340	100	1	1	0	2	4
WILLIAMS, E	3	10	1	.274	201	1	1	0	1	4
MARTINEZ, E	2	20	2	.240	171	1	2	1	−1	3
MULLINIKS	3	29	0	.238	273	1	3	0	−2	3
SCHU	7	21	1	.214	266	3	2	0	−3	3
Average, top 18	9	46	6	.274	427	4	5	3	1	13.55
BROOKENS	4	14	1	.226	168	2	2	0	−2	2
COOLBAUGH	2	7	0	.275	51	1	1	0	0	2
STRANGE	1	14	3	.214	196	0	2	1	−3	1
BLOWERS	0	3	0	.263	38	0	0	0	0	0
ROSE	1	3	0	.211	38	0	0	0	−1	0
MEULENS	0	1	1	.179	28	0	0	0	−1	0
VENTURA	0	7	0	.178	45	0	1	0	−1	0
PALMER	0	1	0	.105	19	0	0	0	−1	−1
AGUAYO	1	8	0	.175	97	0	1	0	−2	−1

AL SECOND BASEMEN

	HR	RBI	SB	BA	AB	$HR	$RBI	$SB	$BA	$TOT
SAX	5	63	43	.315	651	2	7	20	8	37
FRANCO	13	92	21	.316	548	6	11	10	7	33
WHITAKER	28	85	6	.251	509	13	10	3	−2	24
REYNOLDS	0	43	25	.300	613	0	5	11	5	22
BROWNE	5	45	14	.299	598	2	5	6	5	19
LIRIANO	5	53	16	.263	418	2	6	7	0	16
RAY	5	62	6	.289	530	2	7	3	3	16
GANTNER	0	34	20	.274	409	0	4	9	1	14
LYONS (1b, 3b, of)	2	50	9	.264	443	1	6	4	0	11
PHILLIPS (3b)	4	47	3	.262	451	2	6	1	0	8
LEE (ss)	3	34	4	.260	300	1	4	2	0	7
WHITE, F	2	36	3	.256	418	1	4	1	−1	6
FLETCHER (ss)	1	43	2	.253	546	0	5	1	−2	5
BARRETT	1	27	4	.256	336	0	3	2	−1	5
HULETT	3	18	0	.278	97	1	2	0	0	4
MCLEMORE	0	14	6	.243	103	0	2	3	−1	4
GONZALES, R	4	11	5	.217	166	2	1	2	−2	3
WELLMAN (ss)	2	12	5	.230	178	1	1	2	−2	3
Average, top 18	5	43	11	.276	406	2	5	5	1	13.19
RIPKEN, B	2	26	1	.239	318	1	3	0	−2	2
BLANKENSHIP (of)	1	4	5	.232	125	0	0	2	−1	2
BRUMLEY (ss)	1	11	8	.198	212	0	1	4	−4	2
HUBBARD	3	12	2	.198	131	1	1	1	−2	1
BACKMAN	1	26	1	.231	299	0	3	0	−3	1
POLIDOR (ss, 3b)	0	14	3	.194	175	0	2	1	−3	0
ROMERO	0	9	0	.209	163	0	1	0	−2	−1

AL SHORTSTOPS

	HR	RBI	SB	BA	AB	$HR	$RBI	$SB	$BA	$TOT
GUILLEN	1	54	36	.253	597	0	6	16	−2	22
FERNANDEZ	11	64	22	.257	573	5	8	10	−1	21
RIPKEN, C	21	93	3	.257	646	10	11	1	−1	21
GAGNE	9	48	11	.272	460	4	6	5	1	16
NEWMAN (2b, 3b)	0	38	25	.253	446	0	4	11	−1	15
STILLWELL	7	54	9	.261	463	3	6	4	0	13
MANRIQUE (2b)	4	52	4	.294	378	2	6	2	3	13
REED (2b)	3	40	4	.288	524	1	5	2	3	11
SPIERS	4	33	10	.255	345	2	4	5	−1	9
TRAMMELL	5	43	10	.243	449	2	5	5	−2	9
SHEFFIELD (3b)	5	32	10	.247	368	2	4	5	−2	9
KUNKEL (of)	8	29	3	.270	293	4	3	1	0	9
ESPINOZA	0	41	3	.282	503	0	5	1	2	8
GALLEGO (2b)	3	30	7	.252	357	1	4	3	−1	7
SCHOFIELD	4	26	9	.228	302	2	3	4	−3	6
RIVERA	5	29	2	.257	323	2	3	1	−1	6
WEISS	3	21	6	.233	236	1	2	3	−2	5
PECOTA	3	5	5	.205	83	1	1	2	−1	3
Average, top 18	5	41	10	.260	408	2	5	5	0	11.27
FERMIN	0	21	6	.238	484	0	2	3	−3	2
ZUVELLA	2	6	0	.276	58	1	1	0	0	2
BAKER	0	9	0	.295	78	0	1	0	1	2
COCHRANE	3	7	0	.235	102	1	1	0	−1	1
ANDERSON, K	0	17	1	.229	223	0	2	0	−2	0
PEDRIQUE (3b)	0	5	0	.203	69	0	1	0	−1	−1
HOFFMAN	1	3	0	.212	104	0	0	0	−1	−1
VISQUEL	1	20	1	.220	387	0	2	0	−4	−1
TOLLESON (3b)	1	9	1	.164	140	0	1	0	−4	−2

AL OUTFIELDERS

	HR	RBI	SB	BA	AB	$HR	$RBI	$SB	$BA	$TOT
HENDERSON, R	12	57	77	.274	541	5	7	35	1	48
YOUNT	21	103	19	.318	614	10	12	9	8	38
JACKSON, B	32	105	26	.256	515	15	12	12	−1	38
SIERRA	29	119	8	.306	634	13	14	4	7	37
CARTER, J	35	105	13	.243	651	16	12	6	−3	31
PUCKETT	9	85	11	.339	635	4	10	5	12	31
KELLY	9	48	35	.302	441	4	6	16	4	30
GREENWELL	14	95	13	.308	578	6	11	6	6	30
WHITE, D	12	56	44	.245	636	5	7	20	−3	29
BELL, G	18	104	4	.297	613	8	12	2	5	27
EISENREICH	9	59	27	.293	475	4	7	12	3	27
BURKS	12	61	21	.303	399	5	7	10	4	26
EVANS, DW	20	100	3	.285	520	9	12	1	3	25
ESPY	3	31	45	.257	475	1	4	20	−1	25
LEONARD	24	93	6	.254	566	11	11	3	−1	23
CALDERON (1b)	14	87	7	.286	622	6	10	3	3	23
GLADDEN	8	46	23	.295	461	4	5	10	4	23
DAVIS, C	22	90	3	.271	560	10	11	1	1	23
BRADLEY, P	11	55	20	.277	545	5	6	9	2	22
GRIFFEY, K JR.	16	61	16	.264	455	7	7	7	0	22
BAINES	16	72	0	.309	505	7	8	0	6	21
PETTIS	1	18	43	.257	444	0	2	20	−1	21
POLONIA	3	46	22	.300	433	1	5	10	4	21
BRAGGS	15	66	17	.247	514	7	8	8	−2	20
DEVEREAUX	8	46	22	.266	391	4	5	10	0	19
INCAVIGLIA	21	81	5	.236	453	10	10	2	−3	18
HENDERSON, D	15	80	8	.250	579	7	9	4	−2	18
WASHINGTON, C	13	42	13	.273	418	6	5	6	1	18
TARTABULL	18	62	4	.268	441	8	7	2	0	18
CANSECO	17	57	6	.269	227	8	7	3	0	17

	HR	RBI	SB	BA	AB	$HR	$RBI	$SB	$BA	$TOT
BRILEY	13	52	11	.266	394	6	6	5	0	17
FELIX	9	46	18	.258	415	4	5	8	−1	17
BARFIELD	23	67	5	.234	521	10	8	2	−4	17
WILSON, W	3	43	24	.253	383	1	5	11	−1	16
MOSEBY	11	43	24	.221	502	5	5	11	−5	16
BUSH (1b)	14	54	5	.263	391	6	6	2	0	15
DEER	26	65	4	.206	466	12	8	2	−7	14
HALL	17	58	0	.260	361	8	7	0	0	14
FELDER	3	23	26	.241	315	1	3	12	−2	14
ORSULAK	7	55	5	.285	390	3	6	2	2	14
COTTO	9	33	10	.264	295	4	4	5	0	13
SNYDER	18	59	6	.215	489	8	7	3	−6	12
MOSES	1	31	14	.281	242	0	4	6	1	12
HEEP	5	49	0	.300	320	2	6	0	3	11
JOHNSON, L	0	16	16	.300	180	0	2	7	2	11
FINLEY, S	2	25	17	.249	217	1	3	8	−1	11
WILSON, M	2	17	12	.298	238	1	2	5	2	11
PASQUA	11	47	1	.248	246	5	6	0	−1	10
KOMMINSK	8	33	8	.237	198	4	4	4	−1	10
BUHNER	9	33	1	.275	204	4	4	0	1	9
LYNN	11	46	1	.241	353	5	5	0	−2	9
CASTILLO, C	8	43	1	.257	218	4	5	0	0	9
GALLAGHER	1	46	5	.266	601	0	5	2	0	8
JAMES, D	4	29	1	.306	245	2	3	0	3	8
ARMAS	11	30	0	.257	202	5	4	0	0	8
JEFFERSON	4	21	10	.245	139	2	2	5	−1	8
JAVIER	1	28	12	.248	310	0	3	5	−1	8
BOSTON	5	23	7	.252	218	2	3	3	−1	7
VAUGHAN	5	23	4	.265	113	2	3	2	0	7
LEMON	7	47	1	.237	414	3	6	0	−3	6
Average, top 60	12	55	14	.269	415	5	6	6	1	18.53

CONTINUED ON NEXT PAGE

	HR	RBI	SB	BA	AB	$HR	$RBI	$SB	$BA	$TOT
THURMAN	0	5	16	.195	87	0	1	7	−2	6
SOSA	4	13	7	.257	183	2	2	3	0	6
BELLE	7	37	2	.225	218	3	4	1	−2	6
ANDERSON, B	1	16	16	.207	266	0	2	7	−4	6
WILLIAMS, K	6	23	9	.205	258	3	3	4	−4	6
TABLER (1b)	2	42	0	.259	390	1	5	0	−1	5
LAWLESS	0	3	12	.229	70	0	0	5	−1	5
JONES, T	3	26	1	.259	158	1	3	0	0	5
LEACH	1	23	2	.272	239	0	3	1	1	5
ROMINE	1	23	1	.274	274	0	3	0	1	4
SHERIDAN	3	15	4	.242	120	1	2	2	−1	4
MAZZILLI	4	11	2	.227	66	2	1	1	−1	3
KUTCHER	2	18	3	.225	160	1	2	1	−2	3
HILL, G	1	7	2	.288	52	0	1	1	0	3
BICHETTE	3	15	3	.210	138	1	2	1	−2	2
LUSADER	1	8	3	.252	103	0	1	1	0	2
BRANTLEY	8	8	2	.157	108	4	1	1	−3	2
BEANE	0	11	3	.241	79	0	1	1	−1	2
BROWER	2	3	3	.232	69	1	0	1	−1	2
BOSLEY	1	9	2	.225	40	0	1	1	0	2
VENABLE	0	4	0	.358	53	0	0	0	1	2
SANDERS	2	7	1	.234	47	1	1	0	0	2
RICHIE	1	10	0	.265	49	0	1	0	0	2
KINGERY	2	6	1	.224	76	1	1	0	−1	1
WINTERS	2	9	0	.234	107	1	1	0	−1	1
STONE	0	6	3	.176	51	0	1	1	−1	1
DUCEY	0	7	2	.211	76	0	1	1	−1	1
GONZALES, D	0	1	0	.294	17	0	0	0	0	0
QUINTANA	0	6	0	.208	77	0	1	0	−1	0
JOSE	0	5	0	.193	57	0	1	0	−1	−1
GONZALES, J	1	7	0	.150	60	0	1	0	−2	−1

DESIGNATED HITTERS

	HR	RBI	SB	BA	AB	$HR	$RBI	$SB	$BA	$TOT
PARKER	22	97	0	.264	553	10	11	0	0	21
DOWNING	14	59	0	.283	544	6	7	0	3	16
SHEETS	7	33	1	.243	304	3	4	0	−2	6
MEYER	7	29	1	.224	147	3	3	0	−2	5
PHELPS	7	29	0	.242	194	3	3	0	−1	5
CLARK, D	8	29	0	.237	253	4	3	0	−2	5
RICE	3	28	1	.234	209	1	3	0	−2	3
MEDINA	4	8	0	.205	83	2	1	0	−1	1
YOUNG	1	5	1	.186	59	0	1	0	−1	0
HAIRSTON	0	0	0	.333	3	0	0	0	0	0
HORN	0	4	0	.148	54	0	0	0	−2	−1
Average of 11	7	29	0	.250	218	3	3	0	−1	5.77

AL PITCHERS

	W	S	ERA	RTO	IP	SW	SS	SERA	SRTO	STOT
SABERHAGEN	23	0	2.16	8.65	262	16	0	13	17	45
RUSSELL	6	38	1.98	8.55	73	4	31	5	6	45
ECKERSLEY	4	33	1.56	5.46	58	3	27	5	9	43
JONES, D	7	32	2.34	9.93	81	5	26	4	4	39
PLESAC	3	33	2.35	9.39	61	2	27	3	3	36
OLSON	5	27	1.69	10.91	85	3	22	6	2	34
MONTGOMERY	7	18	1.37	8.90	92	5	15	8	6	33
HENKE	8	20	1.92	9.20	89	5	16	6	5	33
REARDON	5	31	4.07	9.86	73	3	25	−1	3	31
SCHOOLER	1	33	2.81	11.69	77	1	27	3	0	31
THIGPEN	2	34	3.76	11.62	79	1	28	0	0	30
MOORE	19	0	2.61	10.28	242	13	0	9	8	29
BLYLEVEN	17	0	2.73	10.05	241	12	0	8	9	28
SMITH, L	6	25	3.58	11.01	70	4	20	0	1	26
RYAN	16	0	3.20	9.78	239	11	0	4	10	25
BOSIO	15	0	2.95	10.47	235	10	0	6	7	23
BURNS	6	8	2.24	8.78	96	4	7	5	7	22
HARVEY	3	25	3.44	12.60	55	2	20	1	−1	22
RIGHETTI	2	25	3.00	12.91	69	1	20	2	−2	22
CLEMENS	17	0	3.13	10.94	253	12	0	5	5	21
GUETTERMAN	5	13	2.45	10.83	103	3	11	5	2	21
FINLEY	16	0	2.57	11.40	200	11	0	8	2	21
STIEB	17	0	3.35	10.45	207	12	0	3	6	20
STEWART, D	21	0	3.32	11.49	258	14	0	3	2	20
GUBICZA	15	0	3.04	11.12	255	10	0	6	4	20
MCCASKILL	15	0	2.93	11.08	212	10	0	6	4	19
HONEYCUTT	2	12	2.35	9.63	77	1	10	4	4	19
CANDIOTTI	13	0	3.10	10.62	206	9	0	4	5	19
WILLIAMSON	10	9	2.93	11.32	107	7	7	3	1	19
WELCH	17	0	3.00	11.55	210	12	0	5	2	18
BANKHEAD	14	0	3.34	10.70	210	10	0	3	5	17
CRIM	9	7	2.83	11.47	118	6	6	4	1	17
BLACK	12	0	3.36	10.73	222	8	0	3	5	16
SWINDELL	13	0	3.37	10.79	184	9	0	2	4	15
MINTON	4	8	2.20	11.30	90	3	7	5	1	15

	W	SV	ERA	RTO	IP	$W	$S	SERA	$RTO	$TOT
LAMP	4	2	2.32	9.85	112	3	2	6	5	15
WARD	4	15	3.77	11.93	115	3	12	0	0	15
MURPHY	5	9	2.74	11.83	105	3	7	4	0	15
WELLS	7	2	2.40	9.80	86	5	2	4	4	15
GORDON	17	1	3.64	11.48	163	12	1	1	1	14
KEY	13	0	3.88	10.54	216	9	0	−1	6	14
MCCLURE	6	3	1.55	9.29	52	4	2	4	3	14
OROSCO	3	3	2.08	9.23	78	2	2	5	5	14
BROWN	12	0	3.35	11.17	191	8	0	3	3	14
CERUTTI	11	0	3.07	11.70	205	8	0	5	1	13
FARR	2	18	4.12	13.78	63	1	15	−1	−3	12
BALLARD	18	0	3.43	12.41	215	12	0	2	−2	12
KNUDSON	8	0	3.35	10.12	124	5	0	2	5	12
HANSON	9	0	3.18	10.72	113	6	0	2	3	11
HENNEMAN	11	8	3.70	13.50	90	8	7	0	−3	11
PALL	4	6	3.31	11.28	87	3	5	1	1	10
ANDERSON	17	0	3.80	12.22	197	12	0	0	−1	10
MILACKI	14	0	3.74	11.89	243	10	0	0	0	10
JACKSON	4	7	3.17	12.23	99	3	6	2	−1	10
FRASER	4	2	3.24	10.11	92	3	2	2	4	10
CARY	4	0	3.26	9.69	99	3	0	2	5	9
NELSON	3	3	3.26	10.13	80	2	2	1	3	9
BERENGUER	9	3	3.48	12.14	106	6	2	1	−1	9
HERNANDEZ	2	15	5.75	14.94	31	1	12	−2	−2	9
HIGUERA	9	0	3.46	11.51	135	6	0	1	1	9
KING	9	0	3.39	11.75	159	6	0	2	1	9
FARRELL	9	0	3.63	11.55	208	6	0	1	1	8
REED	7	0	3.19	11.69	102	5	0	2	0	7
TANANA	10	0	3.58	12.11	224	7	0	1	−1	7
BODDICKER	15	0	4.00	12.25	212	10	0	−2	−1	7
JEFFCOAT	9	0	3.58	11.85	131	6	0	1	0	7
JONES, B	3	1	2.37	8.90	30	2	1	1	2	6
CORSI	1	0	1.88	8.45	38	1	0	3	3	6
PLUNK	8	1	3.28	12.59	104	5	1	2	−2	6
HIBBARD	6	0	3.21	11.99	137	4	0	2	0	6

CONTINUED ON NEXT PAGE

	W	SV	ERA	RTO	IP	SW	SS	SERA	SRTO	STOT
SMITH, R	10	1	3.92	12.06	172	7	1	−1	−1	6
AQUINO	6	0	3.50	11.65	141	4	0	1	1	6
NAVARRO	7	0	3.12	12.39	110	5	0	2	−1	6
AGUILERA	3	0	3.21	10.47	76	2	0	1	2	6
HICKEY	2	2	2.92	11.13	49	1	2	1	1	5
HOLMAN, B	8	0	3.44	12.51	160	5	0	2	−2	5
ROGERS	3	2	2.93	12.46	74	2	2	2	−1	5
FILER	7	0	3.61	12.07	72	5	0	0	0	5
DOPSON	12	0	3.99	12.49	169	8	0	−1	−2	5
CRAWFORD	3	0	2.83	11.17	54	2	0	2	1	5
WAYNE	3	1	3.30	11.54	71	2	1	1	1	5
THURMOND	2	4	3.90	11.90	90	1	3	−1	0	4
PARKER, C	4	0	3.68	11.55	120	3	0	0	1	4
ACKER	2	0	1.59	11.44	28	1	0	2	0	4
DUBOIS	0	1	1.75	11.50	36	0	1	3	0	4
DAVIS, STORM	19	0	4.36	13.55	169	13	0	−4	−6	4
FLANAGAN	8	0	3.93	12.22	172	5	0	−1	−1	3
KRUEGER	3	3	3.84	12.40	94	2	2	0	−1	3
TIBBS	5	0	2.82	13.58	54	3	0	2	−2	3
GUANTE	6	2	3.91	13.30	69	4	2	0	−2	3
FOSSAS	2	1	3.54	11.66	61	1	1	0	0	3
HARRIS	2	0	2.57	11.57	28	1	0	1	0	3
ABBOTT	12	0	3.92	13.10	181	8	0	−1	−5	3
BAILES	5	0	4.28	11.48	114	3	0	−2	1	2
MONTELEONE	2	0	3.18	11.80	40	1	0	1	0	2
WILLS	3	0	3.66	11.99	71	2	0	0	0	2
LONG	5	1	3.92	12.59	99	3	1	−1	−2	2
HALL	2	0	3.70	11.57	58	1	0	0	0	2
STOTTLEMYRE	7	0	3.88	12.76	128	5	0	−1	−2	2
GOSSAGE	1	1	3.77	10.68	14	1	1	0	0	2
MCWILLIAMS	2	0	4.13	10.75	33	1	0	−1	1	2
CUMMINGS	2	0	3.00	12.43	21	1	0	0	0	2
TAPANI	2	0	3.86	11.57	33	1	0	0	0	1
LUECKEN	2	1	3.42	13.69	24	1	1	0	−1	1
SWIFT	7	1	4.43	12.32	130	5	1	−3	−1	1

	W	SV	ERA	RTO	IP	SW	SS	SERA	SRTO	STOT
NUNEZ, J	0	0	2.53	8.44	11	0	0	0	1	1
JOHNSON, D	4	0	4.23	11.89	89	3	0	−2	0	1
OLIN	1	1	3.75	12.25	36	1	1	0	0	1
Average, top 108	7.4	5.1	3.25	11.27	118.	5	4	2	2	12.79
PATTERSON	6	0	4.52	12.61	66	4	0	−2	−1	1
MCCULLERS	4	3	4.57	12.76	85	3	2	−3	−2	1
BOYD	3	0	4.42	11.59	59	2	0	−2	0	1
GOZZO	4	0	4.83	12.51	32	3	0	−1	−1	1
ALDRICH	1	1	3.81	12.81	26	1	1	0	−1	1
DAVIS, J	0	1	4.50	10.50	6	0	1	0	0	1
ARNSBERG	2	1	4.13	12.56	48	1	1	−1	−1	1
MCCARTHY	1	0	3.51	12.42	67	1	0	0	−1	0
CLUTTERBUCK	2	0	4.14	11.90	67	1	0	−1	0	0
OTTO	0	0	2.70	10.81	7	0	0	0	0	0
ST. CLAIRE	1	1	5.24	11.69	22	1	1	−1	0	0
CANDELARIA	3	0	5.14	11.20	49	2	0	−3	1	0
DRUMMOND	0	1	3.86	13.23	16	0	1	0	−1	0
YOUNG, C	5	0	3.73	13.30	111	3	0	0	−3	0
HUISMANN	0	1	6.35	10.33	11	0	1	−1	0	0
GONZALES, G	3	0	4.66	13.34	29	2	0	−1	−1	0
MIELKE	1	1	3.26	13.95	50	1	1	1	−2	0
SCHULZE	1	0	4.09	13.91	11	1	0	0	−1	0
WESTON	1	1	5.54	13.85	13	1	1	−1	−1	0
SOLANO	0	0	5.59	9.32	10	0	0	−1	1	0
AKERFELDS	0	0	3.27	13.09	11	0	0	0	0	0
STODDARD	0	0	2.95	13.50	21	0	0	1	−1	0
OLIVERAS	3	0	4.53	12.77	56	2	0	−2	−1	−1
WOJNA	0	0	4.09	12.27	33	0	0	−1	0	−1
NUNEZ	3	1	4.17	14.17	54	2	1	−1	−3	−1
BANNISTER	4	0	4.66	12.54	75	3	0	−3	−1	−1
CLARK	0	0	4.91	13.09	11	0	0	−1	0	−1
HERNANDEZ, X	1	0	4.77	13.11	23	1	0	−1	−1	−1
HOUGH	10	0	4.35	13.01	182	7	0	−4	−4	−1
ATHERTON	0	2	4.15	14.08	39	0	2	−1	−2	−1

CONTINUED ON NEXT PAGE

	W	SV	ERA	RTO	IP	$W	$S	$ERA	$RTO	$TOT
FETTERS	0	0	8.11	16.22	3	0	0	−1	0	−1
JOHNSON, R	7	0	4.40	12.92	131	5	0	−3	−3	−1
WITT, M	9	0	4.54	12.27	220	6	0	−6	−2	−1
NICHOLS	4	0	4.40	13.19	72	3	0	−2	−2	−1
MOHORCIC	2	2	4.99	12.96	58	1	2	−3	−1	−1
LEACH	5	0	4.15	13.93	74	3	0	−1	−3	−1
PETEREK	0	0	4.02	12.93	31	0	0	0	−1	−1
ROCHFORD	0	0	6.75	18.00	4	0	0	−1	−1	−1
WICKANDER	0	0	3.86	30.90	2	0	0	0	−1	−1
WILLIAMS, F	3	1	3.64	14.57	72	2	1	0	−4	−1
SCHILLING	0	0	6.24	13.51	9	0	0	−1	0	−1
DEJESUS	0	0	4.50	16.88	8	0	0	0	−1	−1
MCDONALD	1	0	8.59	14.73	7	1	0	−1	−1	−1
STANLEY	5	4	4.88	14.52	79	3	3	−3	−5	−1
POWELL	2	2	5.00	14.00	45	1	2	−2	−2	−1
BUICE	1	0	5.82	13.76	17	1	0	−1	−1	−2
BAUTISTA	3	0	5.31	11.42	78	2	0	−4	1	−2
HILLEGAS	7	3	4.74	13.76	120	5	2	−4	−5	−2
PRICE	2	0	4.35	12.92	70	1	0	−2	−2	−2
BARFIELD, J	0	0	6.17	14.67	12	0	0	−1	−1	−2
TUNNELL	1	0	6.00	18.00	12	1	0	−1	−2	−2
CASTILLO, T	1	1	6.12	16.82	18	1	1	−2	−2	−2
SMITHSON	7	2	4.95	12.84	144	5	2	−6	−3	−2
GLEATON	0	0	5.65	16.33	14	0	0	−1	−2	−3
HOLTON	5	0	4.02	13.85	116	3	0	−1	−5	−3
GUTHRIE	2	0	4.55	13.66	57	1	0	−2	−2	−3
PETRY	3	0	5.47	13.41	51	2	0	−3	−2	−3
JONES, J	2	0	5.25	13.50	48	1	0	−3	−2	−3
RITZ	4	0	4.38	14.47	74	3	0	−2	−4	−3
SEARCY	1	0	6.05	15.72	22	1	0	−2	−2	−3
MIRABELLA	0	0	7.63	14.68	15	0	0	−2	−1	−3
CADARET	5	0	4.05	14.03	120	3	0	−1	−6	−3
GIBSON	4	0	4.64	12.68	132	3	0	−4	−2	−4
DYER	4	0	4.82	14.07	71	3	0	−3	−4	−4
TERRELL	6	0	5.20	13.66	83	4	0	−4	−3	−4

	W	SV	ERA	RTO	IP	SW	SS	SERA	SRTO	STOT
COOK	0	0	5.14	16.71	21	0	0	−1	−2	−4
MOYER	4	0	4.86	13.86	76	3	0	−3	−3	−4
HAWKINS	15	0	4.80	13.57	208	10	0	−7	−7	−4
PENA	0	0	6.00	17.00	18	0	0	−2	−2	−4
ROBINSON	4	0	4.73	14.08	78	3	0	−3	−4	−4
LEITER	1	0	5.67	14.85	33	1	0	−3	−2	−4
REUSS	9	0	5.13	13.15	140	6	0	−7	−4	−4
ZAVARAS	1	0	5.19	13.67	52	1	0	−3	−2	−4
SMITH (MI)	2	0	7.65	17.55	20	1	0	−3	−3	−4
CAMPBELL	1	0	7.29	16.29	21	1	0	−3	−2	−5
EILAND	1	0	5.77	14.94	34	1	0	−3	−3	−5
TRUJILLO	1	0	5.96	16.84	26	1	0	−2	−3	−5
HARNISCH	5	0	4.62	14.02	103	3	0	−3	−5	−5
BOLTON	0	0	8.31	16.10	17	0	0	−3	−2	−5
TROUT	4	0	6.60	18.00	30	3	0	−3	−4	−5
WEST	3	0	6.41	15.33	39	2	0	−4	−3	−5
SHIELDS	0	0	7.79	17.66	17	0	0	−3	−2	−5
MMAHAT	0	0	12.92	24.67	8	0	0	−3	−2	−5
HAVENS	1	0	5.00	16.75	36	1	0	−2	−4	−5
ALEXANDER	6	0	4.44	12.96	223	4	0	−5	−5	−6
PALMER	0	0	7.79	18.70	17	0	0	−3	−3	−6
SCHWABE	2	0	6.05	14.91	45	1	0	−4	−3	−6
MCMURTRY	0	0	7.43	16.43	23	0	0	−3	−3	−6
HARRIS, GENE	1	1	6.48	16.74	33	1	1	−4	−4	−6
MUSSELMAN	0	0	10.64	22.91	11	0	0	−3	−3	−6
SANCHEZ	0	0	10.03	23.16	12	0	0	−3	−3	−6
YETT	5	0	5.00	14.36	99	3	0	−4	−5	−7
MORRIS	6	0	4.86	13.10	170	4	0	−6	−4	−7
PEREZ, M	11	0	5.01	13.60	183	8	0	−8	−6	−7
ROSENBERG	4	0	4.94	13.06	142	3	0	−6	−4	−7
NIEDENFUER	0	0	6.69	15.11	36	0	0	−4	−3	−7
BIRKBECK	0	0	5.44	15.92	45	0	0	−3	−4	−7
TOLIVER	1	0	7.76	16.76	29	1	0	−5	−3	−7
APPIER	1	0	9.14	19.11	22	1	0	−5	−4	−8
DOTSON	5	0	4.46	14.21	151	3	0	−4	−7	−8

CONTINUED ON NEXT PAGE

	W	SV	ERA	RTO	IP	SW	SS	SERA	SRTO	STOT
WITT, B	12	0	5.14	13.71	194	8	0	−9	−7	−8
AUGUST	12	0	5.31	14.73	142	8	0	−8	−9	−8
HETZEL	2	0	6.26	15.91	50	1	0	−5	−5	−8
SCHMIDT	10	0	5.69	13.33	157	7	0	−10	−5	−8
JOHN	2	0	5.80	15.41	64	1	0	−5	−5	−9
YOUNG, M	1	0	6.75	17.60	37	1	0	−4	−5	−9
WEGMAN	2	0	6.71	15.88	51	1	0	−6	−5	−9
DUNNE	2	0	5.27	14.87	85	1	0	−5	−6	−9
HUDSON	1	0	6.35	14.31	67	1	0	−6	−4	−9
RAWLEY	5	0	5.19	14.03	146	3	0	−7	−7	−10
GARDNER	3	0	5.97	15.07	86	2	0	−7	−6	−11
LEIBRANDT	5	0	5.14	13.98	161	3	0	−8	−7	−11
LAPOINT	6	0	5.62	15.12	114	4	0	−8	−8	−12

P O S T S C R I P T

Village Consulting (last year's mail drop) consults no more. Please send as much information as you can cram into a manila envelope—freeze list, draft roster, round-by-round record, running commentary—to:

Alex Patton
43 West 13th Street
New York, NY 10011

I'll still depend heavily on Jerry Heath, but I do wish he wouldn't be quite so free with his information. Imitation may be flattery, but repetition is tedious, and I'm going to make a concerted effort to use more of the material that is sent to me. After the season, final standings, trade records, and any further commentary must arrive by the start of the World Series. Player comments, as long as they are reasonably legible and aren't too obscene, may even appear in the book, with credit.

Unless you expressly say that it's not, any material is considered fair game; there's no time for the nicety of getting permission.